Teaching and Learning School Mathematics

A Reader

Edited by David Pimm and Eric Love
at The Open University

Hodder & Stoughton
LONDON SYDNEY AUCKLAND TORONTO
in association with The Open University

This Reader is a component of the Open University course EM236 *Learning and Teaching Mathematics* and the selection is therefore related to other material available to students. Opinions expressed in this Reader are not necessarily those of the course team or of the University.

Details of EM236 *Learning and Teaching Mathematics* and other Open University courses are available from the Central Enquiry Service, The Open University, PO Box 71, Milton Keynes, MK7 6AG. Telephone (0908) 653078.

British Library Cataloguing in Publication Data

A catalogue record for this title is available from the British Library.

ISBN 0 340 56791 0

First published in the United Kingdom 1991

Edited, designed and typeset by The Open University.

Printed in Great Britain for the educational publishing division of Hodder & Stoughton Ltd, Mill Road, Dunton Green, Sevenoaks, Kent by St Edmundsbury Press, Bury St Edmunds.

Contents

Acknowledgements

Grateful acknowledgement is made to the following sources for permission to reproduce material in this Reader:

Text

Chapter 2: courtesy of J. Helen Gardner © 1991; Chapter 4: courtesy of John Crook and Mary Briggs © 1991; Chapter 5: Hoyles, C. (1982), *Mathematics Teaching*, **99**, pp. 54–5, © Celia Hoyles; Chapter 8: Mason, J. H. (1989), *Mathematics Teaching*, **129**, pp. 40–7, © John Mason.

All other material has been specially commissioned for this Reader and is reproduced by permission of The Open University copyright department.

Photographs/Illustrations

p. 109: reproduced by permission of the Trustees of the British Museum; p. 112: title page and page 2 from *The Ground of Artes* by Robert Recorde (Shelfmark = Douce.R.301.) reproduced by permission of the Curators of the Bodleian Library, Oxford; pp. 139, 140, 142, 143, 145: Dowling, P. (1985) *SMP 11–16*, Cambridge University Press; p. 154: Justin Sholk; p. 185: courtesy of Ray Hemmings; p. 228: *L'usage de la parole 1, 1928–9*, René Magritte, © ADAGP, Paris and DACS, London 1991; p. 229: *Les Promenades d'Euclide*, 1955, René Magritte, © ADAGP, Paris and DACS, London, 1991; p. 232 (left): *Le Modèle Rouge*, 1937, René Magritte, © ADAGP, Paris and DACS, London 1991; p. 232 (right): *L'Explication*, 1952, René Magritte, © ADAGP, Paris and DACS, London, 1991; p. 237: cover from *The Economist* 27 October–2 November, 1979, courtesy of Derek Cousins.

The editors would like to thank all those who have assisted in the preparation and production of this book, in particular Jenny Chalmers, Tracy Ellis, Sue Glover and Caroline Hailey.

Introduction

We write this introduction against a rather bewildering background of attempted change in the education system in the United Kingdom. The chapters which follow were written in 1990 and early 1991, which seemed initially to be a time when the first spasm of change brought on by the introduction of national curricula had passed. As the book progressed towards press, however, it became ever more clear that 'implementing' the national curricula, particularly in England and Wales, was going to prove highly problematic. In mid 1991, the England and Wales mathematics national curriculum, which was legislated in 1988 and promulgated in 1989, and which many of these chapters took as a given, was considerably amended; at the time of publication, the assessment of this curriculum is still in disarray. What further changes will occur in the near future remain to be seen. This book perforce must have a deadline, and so authors have adapted their chapters in various ways, on occasion referring either to the first or subsequent versions of the mathematics national curriculum for England and Wales as seemed appropriate.

However, the major influences on mathematics in schools are likely to stay constant for some time. Many of the influences we discern are deliberate attempts to affect the teaching of mathematics in schools, but others are side-effects of changes in society not directly inspired by concern with mathematics education. In an attempt to provide a perspective for the reader of this collection, we delineate here themes that we can see across the pieces in this volume; these also may serve as pointers for likely developments in mathematics education in schools for the 1990s. The themes are rarely the main concern of any one chapter, but they occur and re-occur, usually implicitly, in different chapters. If we were to be producing a book in, say, five years' time, these emerging themes are our present best guess about the central foci of such a collection.

The threads we wish to draw readers' attention to are:

- the changing role of the state in education and the effect this has on the very stable institutions of the school system;
- the question of what mathematical knowledge is;
- the twofold effect of new technology: generally, on mathematics in society and, specifically, in schools.

Each of these already shows signs of considerable strain which is likely to become more intense.

The state and institutions

Writing in 1991, the intervention of the state in the detailed specification of the school curriculum is omnipresent. Until now, individual teachers have enjoyed considerable autonomy with respect to what they actually taught, while being part of a network of influences such as school schemes of work, local authority advisers, examination syllabuses, published schemes, professional associations. Any national curriculum stipulates a public version of what a school curriculum *must* consist of. The detail in the curriculum, although formulated by working groups, and commented on by interested parties, is ultimately at the whim of one person – the Secretary for State – and this power has been used openly. In such a situation, we are unlikely to find either assent or enthusiasm from teachers in implementing the changes. What *is* perhaps surprising is the lack of public dissent on the extremely detailed specification of the intended curriculum.[1] It seems that teachers' first reaction after the initial shock is to 'make it work'.

This reaction points to an important aspect of such changes. Although this is a time of apparent disturbance of the entire school curriculum, we foresee that, after a time, the change will be found not to have been as dramatic as was either hoped for or feared (by different groups). For instance, the published mathematics schemes that were already in existence were supplemented by guidance to show how they were compatible with the national curricula; newly proposed schemes are likely to have a huge amount in common with their predecessors. We may be caught up in a large-scale instance of what Stafford Beer (1974) has called a 'systems version' of Le Chatelier's principle – that when a system is imposed upon from outside, it adjusts its practices, assimilating the new demands in such a way that the system as a whole can carry on much as before.

This is not to say that the effects of the disturbance to people within the system will not be great. We already have incontestable evidence that this is so. Teachers have to find out how to cope with the changes in an attempt to continue to function. There is currently a huge amount of anxiety – especially over assessment – and many who feel that they cannot adjust will leave, and indeed are leaving, the profession. The well-known observation of Gaius Petronius, in the first century AD, reflects how many teachers see the changes:

> We trained hard – but it seemed that every time we were beginning to form up into teams, we would be reorganised. I was to learn later in life that we tend to meet any new situation by reorganising and a wonderful method it can be for creating the illusion of progress while producing confusion, inefficiency and demoralisation.

However, Beer's contention is that the *system* as a whole will preserve itself and persevere. We feel sure that in a few years' time there will still be textbooks and schemes of work and children at desks and tables working in familiar ways. What is likely to be a continuing effect is the intervention of of the state in specifying curricula, so that teachers will be constantly faced with the need to interpret such external demands in order to re-establish the practices they think ought to happen, and to find ways of doing so.

What is mathematical knowledge?

One effect of the national curriculum changes has been to question the widespread beliefs about school mathematics – beliefs which were reinforced through the 1980s following the publication of the Cockcroft report and with the advent of GCSE. In so far as the schemes of the national curricula have any theoretical basis, they exhibit a mix of influences from the traditional subject matter of school mathematics, through the post-Cockcroft strand of children's exploration and the stress on understanding. The 'Cockcroft' orthodoxy has come under challenge not only from those who wish a return to the old ways, but also from more radical quarters. The idea that understanding should be a central goal of school mathematics has been questioned, partly through a questioning of what might be meant by 'understanding'. Whereas understanding has come to be conceived of as having insight into knowledge or connections to other knowledge and is contrasted with rote learning, there is a growing series of attempts to re-conceptualize it. These range from, on the one hand, seeing understanding as 'knowing what to do with symbols' to, on the other, asserting that understanding is being embedded in specific contexts and not separable from them.

This latter view underpins a much more radical challenge to received thinking about mathematics that has been gathering strength over the last decade which comes from those who might be described as the 'ethnomathematicians' – although they would reject any such title. Their concern is that the mathematics implicit in everyday practices at work or leisure has been systematically denied while 'official' mathematics as taught in schools and in higher education is elevated as the only true form of mathematics. Moreover, a major effect of school mathematics is to disable people from operating in the informal and semi-formal world of ethnomathematics – both by legitimizing school mathematics as the only real mathematics and, as a result of the way in which it is taught, by undermining the confidence of a large part of the population in their ability to function mathematically. For this reason, those adopting this standpoint challenge the right of mathematicians to decide what counts as mathematics, and would like their view to be no longer especially privileged.

One concern that underlies the arguments of the ethnomathematical critique, but which is shared more widely, is that not knowing mathematics leaves people at the mercy of those who do understand. Hence, one movement is to help empower people for the world they live in. Because our society describes itself as a democracy, the issues of democratic competence and what part mathematics and its teaching might play in that come to the fore. What at first sight might seem a preoccupation of a fringe group can very easily become matter for wide debate when there is an explicit national curriculum and anxiety about the use of technology. In other countries, for example Australia or Denmark, the official curricula are attempting to address such notions (see Skovsmose, 1990); they are likely to become more prominent in this country.

This concern also embraces the issue of disadvantaged groups in our society and what might be done in mathematics education both to help them become more mathematically competent and also to explore the contribution that the teaching of mathematics might make in creating a society in which such groups are less marginalized. The attempts to cope with this range from emphases in the curriculum (incorporating ideas from other cultures or stressing the achievements of women mathematicians) through to radical critiques which suggest that the very ways in which we think about mathematics in school are so value laden that what is required is a restructuring of the ways in which we see the issues themselves.

We would expect these issues to indicate a battleground because they challenge the deeply-embedded role that school mathematics plays in the selection and accreditation of people for higher education and employment.

The effects of new technology

Although the 1980s have been notable in schools, as elsewhere, for the advent of the electronic technology of calculators and computers, it is simultaneously very easy to underestimate the process of change in technology and to overestimate the likely effects. Bill Higginson, writing about Logo in 1981, said:

> The vision that [Papert] expounds is an attractive one, but it is not one which is at all accessible (at least at the time of writing 1981 04). LOGO is a sophisticated system. It requires a fairly large computer system to support it. One hears rumours of 48K Apples, ... but it is as yet extremely difficult for an interested party not located near one of the rare LOGO installations ... to see the system in action.

(Higginson, 1981)

We quote this not to ridicule it but as a sobering comment on the way in which technological change is likely to exceed all expectations. In less than eight years from this being written, almost every primary school in the United Kingdom had a computer that could implement Logo, and it was included in the compulsory national curriculum for England and Wales. It makes plausible the apparently far-fetched notion that we might soon all have laptop computers with the power only found at present in specialist machines of large installations.

The effect of new technology is twofold: firstly, to challenge practices in the classroom, and secondly to challenge our view of mathematics. One form of educational technology that has been in use in mathematics classrooms for centuries is the textbook. Because it is ubiquitous, the textbook has been an invisible technology, but it has profoundly shaped our notion of mathematics and how it might be taught. By its use of the ideas of examples and exercises, in the way it addresses both teacher and learner, in its linear sequence, in its very conception of techniques, results and theorems, the textbook has dominated perceptions of school mathematics.

The contributions that computers and calculators can make to teaching and learning mathematics will be viewed through the lens of the past, which has been formed by the textbook, and will be used in ways which seek to reproduce what was done previously. Additionally, just as working from textbooks, or watching television programmes can be seen as the end rather than a means to an end, so the use of machines (and software), particularly those with sophisticated effects, can encourage a similar loss of perspective.

Computers will only gradually come to be seen to have their own imperatives. We suggest that practices formed by the textbook are very deeply entrenched, that changes will be quite gradual and it is likely to be a very long time before computers in classrooms will have an effect of comparable scale to that of textbooks.

But the deeper challenge is to school mathematics itself. The availability of calculators has created a still-unresolved crisis in the teaching of arithmetic, where positions from almost total ignoring through to a complete rejection of previous methods of teaching arithmetic coexist. That the advent of calculators is seen as a threat, undermining established practices and perhaps even the order of society itself, accounts in part for the direct intervention of Kenneth Baker who, as Secretary of State, personally decreed that traditional paper-and-pencil methods of computation were to remain in the mathematics curriculum. As Gramsci observed in another context, 'The crisis consists precisely in the fact that the old is dying and the new cannot be born; in the interregnum a great many varieties of morbid symptoms appear'. The Calculator-Aware Number (CAN) curriculum (PrIME, 1991) has had its official blessing withdrawn, but the issues raised by it are unlikely to go away. Some of these are: the role for paper-and-pencil methods, the place of standard algorithms, the use of progression in number as a structuring framework for its teaching. Similar issues are to be found in the challenge to some aspects of the secondary curriculum by algebraic and graphical calculators.

A even sharper point has been made by Yves Chevellard (1989): that as society becomes *more* mathematized, the *less* its citizens need to know of mathematics. The technology we use – from calculators and computers to washing machines and video recorders needs extensive mathematics for its development. But this mathematics is all hidden from the users of these devices, who do not need to know it to use them. This is an accelerating process, whereby less and less mathematics is needed by the ordinary person in their work and everyday life. The remaining justifications for school mathematics in terms of usefulness will get progressively less plausible; mathematics will increasingly be taught for other ends – or perhaps taught less.

This Reader is one component of a course in mathematics education for practising teachers of mathematics at primary and secondary levels; to a large extent, this intent has determined the content and focus of the individual chapters within it. The chapters, almost all of which have been specially commissioned, are arranged in four sections. Each section has an introduction to the individual chapters within it. The first section focuses on the practices of teachers and the experiences of learners, the next offers new ways of thinking about how the mathematics taught in schools might be considered. In the third, several writers examine the role of textbooks and schemes and of imposed national curricula. In the final section, we have six pieces which offer reflections on issues which, although not apparently of immediate concern, are always present behind a mathematics teacher's actions.

Note

[1] There have been attacks within the mathematics education world, most notably in the pages of the TES and in a collection of writings from the University of London Institute of Education (Dowling and Noss, 1990), but these are mostly within a limited readership. It is difficult to ascertain the degree of opposition: the only people with any time to devote to these issues are likely to be academics who work in this area. Professionals in schools are so involved in coping with the external demands that they have little time to mount a critique.

References and further reading

Beer, S. (1974) *Platform for Change*, Wiley.

Chevellard, Y. (1989) 'Implicit mathematics: its impact on societal needs and demands' in Malone, J., Burkhardt, H. and Keitel, C. (eds) *The Mathematics Curriculum: Towards the Year 2000*, Science and Mathematics Education Centre, Curtin University of Technology.

Dowling, P. C. and Noss, R. (1990) *Mathematics versus the National Curriculum*, Falmer.

D'Ambrosio, U. (1985) 'Ethnomathematics and its place in the history and pedagogy of mathematics', *For the Learning of Mathematics*, 5(1), pp. 44–8.

Higginson, W. (1981) Review of Papert's *Mindstorms*, *Mathematics Teaching*, **95**, pp. 60–2 .

The PrIME Project (1991) *Calculators, Children and Mathematics*, Simon and Schuster.

Skovsmose, O. (1990) 'Mathematical education and democracy', *Educational Studies in Mathematics*, **21**(2), pp. 109–28.

Walkerdine, V. (1988) *The Mastery of Reason*, Routledge.

Section I
Teachers' practices and learners' experiences

Section introduction

How are the concerns and preoccupations of teachers to be discussed and shared? What are some effective means for sharing explorations of classroom practice? What does it feel like to be a learner of mathematics? Laurinda Brown writes about questioning her practice while teaching investigatively mainstream mathematical content in the secondary school. In particular, she questions the unnecessary and unnatural separation of content and process concerns, visible in much GCSE practice. Helen Gardner reports her experiences introducing elements of the history of mathematics into her junior school classroom. In so doing, she describes opportunities for her children to engage with and make sense of mathematical ideas and motivations of people from the past. Alan Bishop offers his observations and reflections on teaching and working alongside teachers in secondary schools with a sizeable proportion of ethnic minority pupils. The triad of teacher, learner and mathematics provides the frame for his examination of contributing elements – a framework appropriate to any classroom.

We have all experienced learning mathematics in school settings, and our experiences have shaped our views and beliefs as well as our expectations and images, both of teachers and teaching. Just as parents tend to reproduce their own experiences as a child with their own children, so students and novice teachers often replicate their history in intuitive or reflex actions. John Crook and Mary Briggs give an account of their exploratory work with intending and practising primary teachers on documenting the accumulated experiences and affective issues such as confidence and attitudes to mathematics from their personal histories. They adopt a biographical approach as well as eliciting critical (good and bad) incidents recalled from their interviewees' school experiences. Finally, in a piece reprinted from the early 1980s, Celia Hoyles offers four excerpts from long interviews with pupils about their views and recollections of mathematics lessons, together with their feelings about them – views which are still highly relevant today. Both of these last two pieces offer vivid evidence of the intensity of feeling that attempts to learn mathematics can evoke.

1 Stewing in your own juice

Laurinda Brown

When *Mathematics Counts* (commonly known as 'the Cockcroft report', DES, 1982) was published, a lot of attention was focused on the now-famous paragraph 243. Six different teaching styles were listed which 'mathematics teaching at all levels should include opportunities for'. Subsequent work centred on such questions as the following.

- What are investigations?
- How do problem solving and investigation differ?
- How is it possible to promote learning through discussion in mathematics classrooms?
- How can we define practical work?

Consolidation and practice alongside exposition provoked less activity, since, on the whole, these styles were already being used and were within the realm of experience of most teachers.

The ATM pamphlet *Teaching Styles – Cockcroft 243* (Edmonds and Knights, 1987) lists specifications of these six styles, arising from the views of some teachers collected as the result of brainstorming sessions. Here are two of them.

Problem solving is ...

- making mathematics relevant
- encouraging students to believe that they can control their lives
- using the teacher as a resource
- original thought
- looking for a solution
- applying mathematics to different, perhaps everyday, situations
- closed
- interpreting the question
- answering examination questions

Investigational work is ...

- open ended
- finding patterns
- self discovery
- reducing the teacher's role

- not doing real mathematics

- not helpful for examinations

- not worthwhile

- using one's own methods

- being exposed

- limited to the teacher's experience

- not being in control

- divergent

An interesting exercise in trying to get a clearer idea of what you mean by the six styles is to read these lists and pick out:

    (a) any statements which you find to be in opposition to each other;

    (b) any statements with which you disagree.

Then try to formulate any extra statements which you think should be included, but which you find are not covered in the original lists. One issue here is that, in reading paragraph 243, not having access to the deliberations within the Cockcroft committee which led to the inclusion of those six teaching styles, we were left to reinterpret them for ourselves, sometimes with no personal experience on which to draw.

From such published materials as the JMB/Shell Centre pack *Problems with Patterns and Numbers* (Swan, 1984), one common interpretation of the term 'investigation' is what David Wells (1986) has called the data/pattern/ generalization (DPG) model of generating a number pattern from physical situations, often followed by finding the general rule for the sequence. These investigations can then be offered to students at the end of each half-term for, say, a week's work, to be written up and marked in isolation from the rest of the course.

In one such lesson, I observed students tackling the problem of how many squares the diagonal of a rectangle, drawn on a square grid, passes through.

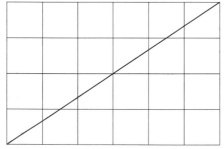

The students had been told that, since this piece of work would contribute to their year 9 examination, they should produce their own work and the activity was to take a week of lessons plus homework. I talked to a number of the students about what they were doing and made the following observations.

- There were many inaccurate drawings leading to wrong results in tables of values from which the students were attempting to find patterns.
- A number of students commented that this sort of maths 'was boring', and one girl stated strongly: 'We don't have to do this sort of work in other subjects. I like humanities where we have to prepare a talk and then discuss it.'
- There was no culture in this classroom of convincing oneself or being sure.
- Some students who were not working particularly hard in the lesson reported that they preferred to do the work at home and would ask the brighter members of the group what rule they had got first.
- Other students reported that this sort of work was unfair because everyone talked about the answer that they should get outside the classroom, so it was possible for some lazy people to get away with not doing very much.

The teacher was convinced that it was important to let the students work without support or comment from her and reported disappointment in finding that doing investigations did not seem to interest the students. I could not see what it was that the students were learning in this process; the structure of the investigation was so tightly laid down that there was little scope for autonomy. The activity had been reduced to one where there were right and wrong answers, with no creativity possible in the method of solution, since this reduced to filling in the gaps in a number sequence.

This example seems to be far away from what the members of the Cockcroft committee might have wished to see happening. They were interested in teaching styles allowing students to learn mathematics more effectively, but here the students were being left to 'stew in their own juice'. Where is the challenge? What are they learning?

Coursework is now a compulsory part of the GCSE examination and such experiences have helped me to cope with articles such as 'Cheating as a course art' by Judith Judd (1990). Comments from that article, such as 'the dividing line between legitimate parental help and breaking the rules is difficult to draw', highlight the same tension that some teachers feel about their own input. The problem seems to lie in the view that coursework is part of an examination and, as such, is not part of the actual learning process. I was, however, pleased to read a letter from John Smith (1990) entitled 'GCSE no cheater's charter', in reply to Judith Judd, which argued that a teacher working with a group of students will come to know them and, in discussing their work with them, will be able to assess whether work has simply been copied or whether the concepts are available for application.

For me, the conflicting impressions reduce to one question: Is coursework part of the learning process for the student? If it is, then it does not matter with whom a student discusses their ideas, be they teacher, parent, guardian or university mathematician, nor what information sources are consulted – texts, library, *Profile* on the electronic network TTNS – as long as there is evidence of learning having taken place.

There is clear guidance from the Midlands Examining Group on this question:

> The assignments are part of the learning process for the candidates, and it is expected that they will receive help and advice from their teachers. The marks awarded will reflect the extent to which the candidates are able to use the advice they receive in the development of the assignments.

and from the Southern Examining Group:

> Coursework submitted for assessment should, wherever possible, arise from the normal activities undertaken during the course.

But, without experience, we are still left with trying to reconcile these statements with practice. What follows is a case study of one attempt to tackle coursework in such a way that content was addressed and the activity was a normal part of the learning process for the students.

I had been invited in to work with a group of year 9 students by their teacher, Jan Denton. The group had previously looked at route matrices, so we decided to try to teach matrices and transformations in an investigative way. We kept notes of the lessons and a write-up was sent as a letter to the examining group concerned, asking whether this was acceptable to them as a way of doing coursework. Consequently, the issues which were raised for us as we worked are recorded as questions.

Matrices and transformations (top set, year 9, Hartcliffe School, Avon)

Lesson 1: A beginning

I took to the lesson felt-tip pens and A2 sheets of cm² grid paper. Given that the square grid board in the classroom was small, I had prepared beforehand a shape to draw and the matrix to use for the transformation.

'There are too many of you for me to learn all your names first! My name's Miss Brown. If you offer any comments then I'll invite you to say your name so that I can start to learn them.'

I walk to the board and start to draw a pair of axes specifying the first quadrant. I would normally always draw four quadrants, but am short of room. I wonder if this will mean that we don't explore negative numbers eventually. I plot the points $(0,0)$, $(0,2)$, $(1,5)$, $(2,2)$, $(5,2)$, $(5,0)$ and join them up, belatedly labelling the axes x and y and filling in the numbers on the axes. This has all been done quite slowly.

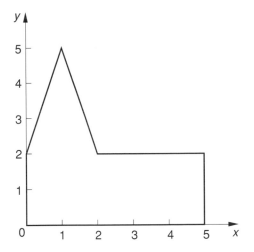

'What does that look like?' I look around expectantly, some hands go up, and I relax!

'A church.'

'Good! That's what I hoped it would look like. I'm going to make the church change shape. The process is quite strange, but you might have met something like it before.'

I write the matrix $\left(\begin{smallmatrix} 2 & 1 \\ 0 & 2 \end{smallmatrix}\right)$ on the board and ask what the coordinates of the origin are by indicating one of the points on the diagram. (0, 0) is offered straight away. I write this information as a column vector to the right of the matrix without explanation.

I go through the rather strange process of multiplying the two matrices, asking for focus on the two elements of the top row pairing with the two elements of the vector, multiply the pairs, then add the results. Change the focus to the two elements of the bottom row and repeat the process. The answer is (0, 0).

'Well, I said that I was going to move the shape, but this point has stayed in the same place.'

I call the original point A and the new point A' for *new* A.

We go through the process for each of the points, with me exploring who can do the process and who can't. At one point, I ask, 'Is there anyone who could not do this one?' No one puts a hand up and, watching carefully, I believe them. If someone had, I would have worked with them. As it was, we finish off the points with me choosing people at random to tell me what to do and we stare at the new, different, church.

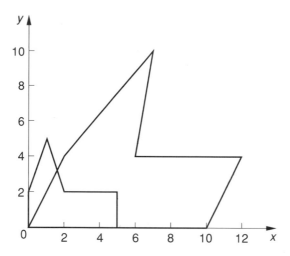

I had to make a decision – do we discuss what this shape looks like or do I offer them a challenge and set up their task? I chose the second option. These students felt like they had sorted out the process and did not need to be held up by me any more. I made a mental note to go round and ask them individually to describe what had happened to their shapes.

'In five lessons' time, I will come in, write any old matrix on the board and expect you to be able to tell me what effect it would have on a shape without actually drawing it out.' There were excited intakes of breath around the room: they felt challenged and were going to engage. I felt relief.

'For a beginning, and to check that each of you can do a basic transformation, I'd like you each to take a piece of this paper, choose your own shape and matrix, and see what happens. When you have finished, we can put them on the display board over there or on the ceiling. Then you will have a collection of a lot of information from which to work.'

One boy said that a square would be the easiest shape to choose. One girl asked if she could put all the vectors in one matrix because it would be easier. I wrote this on the board and suggested that they could use this method if they liked or continue with writing out each vector separately. For the rest of the lesson, Jan and I concentrated on ensuring that each individual was all right with the process. Without sorting this out, the rest of the work would be impossible.

One boy wanted to know whether his original shape was going to transform into a shape that was too big for the piece of paper before he committed himself to a matrix. If the process had been totally in his control, he could have estimated, but at the start of such an activity there is a need for being able to have a go, not worrying about making mistakes. I suggested that he try it and see.

Extremely quickly, a display started to appear, with the students themselves putting up their work. They were offered the choice of doing another display piece while the paper lasted or getting started with their own write-ups using A4 grid paper. Most chose the second option and, as other work went on the walls, they started to collect the information and make rough notes of particular examples. Very few at this stage were 'usual' transformations, although one was a two-way stretch, scale factor 2 in the x-direction and scale factor 3 in the y-direction. The bell seemed to come too quickly. Sharing had happened, but not by reporting back; the display work had done that.

For these sorts of lessons, I find it useful to reflect, after the event, on the sort of questions which might arise next time so that I am prepared in some way.

- Which matrices do the 'usual' transformations for us?
- Is there a link between the matrix and the area change?
- There is a lot of information at the moment which perhaps feels confusing. What about ways of simplifying our task – by getting organized? Simpler shapes? Being organized about which matrices to choose?

The next lesson feels like a continuation, with no formal start.

(The following four lessons are not described in such detail, but concentrate on indicating and exploring the questions which arose for us.)

Lesson 2

How might you cope with absentees?

Four students who had been absent for the first lesson arrived for this one. We had intended just to allow the class to carry on, but, on this hot afternoon, with tutor period to follow, they seemed de-energized. Consequently, the start turned into a recap of the first session with each of the four absentees managing to take a point and work out the image point. This seemed to solve both problems.

Whose work is it?

One group of boys was collecting and processing the information from the display boards effectively, sorting out what the top left and bottom right numbers in the matrix did to the shape. This was annoying to some other students who felt that they were just copying. There seem to be two main issues here.

- Within the group of boys, is it necessary to be able to state explicitly what each individual has contributed?
- When tackling a problem, must I always rely solely on my own ideas? What is wrong with making progress as quickly and easily as possible?

Should you intervene?

One girl discovered the matrix which keeps shapes the same. She wants to use a simpler shape and decides on a kite. Should I talk to her about unit squares?

How much time?

We have set aside five lessons for this piece of work, but is that enough? How much does time pressure affect the entry of students into their own problems? Should an extended piece of work have an arbitrary cut-off point, or should the students be able to continue adding to their coursework over a much longer period?

Even with two teachers present in the room, we still feel that some of the students want more time for discussion with us. Jan arranges to see one group in the lunchtime; some students talk enthusiastically about meeting out of school time to continue ... the others?

Lesson 3

How might you encourage students to share their findings?

We decided to start this lesson by introducing the chalkboard as a place where questions and comments could be written by any of the students at any time. The lesson began with an invitation for anyone who wanted to contribute immediately. A record of the state of the board at the end of the lesson is shown opposite.

I had made a decision to use the board as well, if necessary, and the 'words' section had been written up by me. This was in response to some students being able to describe what was happening for a particular transformation, but not having a word to describe it. As one student needed the word, I wrote it on the board and, if any other student were to ask what a particular word meant, I would send them off to ask the original one.

Discussion vs *write-up?*

I sat with different groups and listened to their conversations. Many grade A ones! It would seem, however, that it is not natural to record such conversations. There was little evidence of them later in the 'final' pieces of work. The energy which characterizes such conversations generates a new path to follow and, having discussed and found such a path, it is natural to address the new question. The fact that this question is an extension of previous work is not necessarily clear in the write-up. Having already been aware of not being able to get around all the students in sufficient depth, I hesitate to suggest that we could annotate the scripts!

What might be possible is to absolve the students from the need for anything else to be given in except, say, one sheet of A4 of succinct observations and justifications, with perhaps some indication of other areas yet to be considered and unresolved questions. This could be submitted before the date of an oral. The only point of the oral would be to ascertain whether the individual student really knew the work and to what depth. It could also provide a vehicle for addressing some problem areas and therefore allow the student to be able to extend their thinking away from the actual lessons. I do not personally mind whether ideas are shared or help is obtained from any source provided the student is learning.

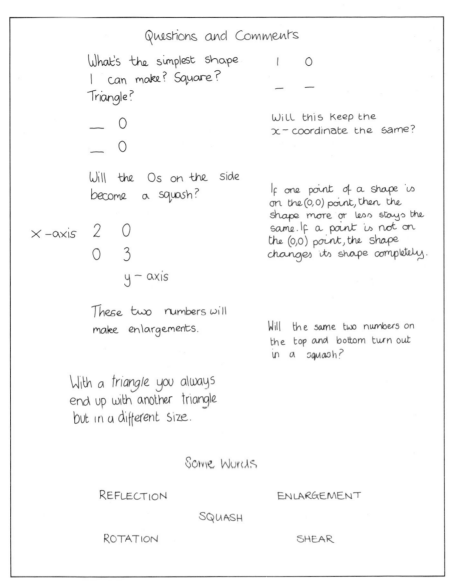

Questions and Comments

What's the simplest shape I can make? Square? Triangle?

| 0

— —

— O

— O

Will the Os on the side become a squash?

x -axis   2 0
          0 3
          y - axis

These two numbers will make enlargements.

With a triangle you always end up with another triangle but in a different size.

Will this keep the x-coordinate the same?

If one point of a shape is on the (0,0) point, then the shape more or less stays the same. If a point is not on the (0,0) point, the shape changes its shape completely.

Will the same two numbers on the top and bottom turn out in a squash?

Some Words

REFLECTION   ENLARGEMENT

              SQUASH

ROTATION   SHEAR

Lesson 4

To tell or not to tell?

At the start of the fourth lesson, we invited the class to share matrices whose effect was known. Pooling the information, we hoped, would have the effect of allowing possible links to be observed and opening up new avenues to explore. Forms for enlargement and stretch matrices were generally appreciated, including the link with the area change.

Many students had examples of matrices which took a shape to a straight line. We collected some examples:

$$\begin{pmatrix} 2 & 2 \\ 1 & 1 \end{pmatrix} \begin{pmatrix} 1 & 1 \\ 2 & 2 \end{pmatrix} \begin{pmatrix} 2 & 0 \\ 1 & 0 \end{pmatrix} \begin{pmatrix} 1 & 1 \\ 1 & 1 \end{pmatrix} \begin{pmatrix} 2 & 3 \\ 2 & 3 \end{pmatrix}$$

'Can I ask you all to make a prediction of a squash matrix?'

How had they arrived at their prediction? What would be the form of a general squash matrix? After the discussion, during which some other transformations were talked about, there were some comments that, after the sharing, it was more difficult to continue on a previous path. However, the form of the general squash matrix proved a popular question, as did following up the area change for more complicated matrices.

Given the fact that they knew that multiplying the numbers on the leading diagonal gave the area change when the two other numbers were zero, a number of groups rapidly came up with various hypotheses for the cases where the other two numbers were non-zero, and worked quickly, checking and refining. What if we take the product of the other two numbers and add or subtract? When this was sorted out, I was aware that these students had, without knowing it, also solved the squash problem.

These two pieces of work were linked in the end, but there remains the question about whether I should have pointed out the link explicitly once *I* had observed it. Surely the teacher is a source of information too? In this case, however, there seemed to be quite a leap to the area change of a squash being zero. There is the risk here that, the teacher's awareness being greater than the student's, sharing too soon could put the students in the position of struggling to understand and possibly failing rather than coming to know. I made the decision to stay silent. But there are times when I would tell, so the issue is not a simple one.

Lesson 5

At the end of this session (which was to be the last I would spend with the group), I offered the challenge of them telling me what the matrix $\begin{pmatrix} 4 & 6 \\ 2 & 3 \end{pmatrix}$ would do.

I made an assumption that this would prove quite difficult, but very quickly two tables had identified what would happen. It was all too fast – my own perception or a more general one? I could not slow the pace down to achieve a more general discussion. We then went to the opposite extreme when four numbers were given to me which gave the matrix $\begin{pmatrix} -2 & 9 \\ 4 & 8 \end{pmatrix}$. We could share some statements, but this one generated more questions than answers!

There were still questions to be answered and the group decided to carry on working on the problem the next lesson and, since the summer holidays were approaching rapidly, hand in their write-ups after the break. There were so many possible extensions that this did not feel like too much time!

- Exploration of all matrices made up of 0, 1 and –1.
- What about three-dimensional transformations?
- Inverse matrices – or what matrix would I use to take the image back to the shape I started with?

The orals

Jan and I decided that we would build in an oral after the pieces of work had been marked. We had decided that the oral should allow each student to show us what they knew and give each one a chance perhaps to go a stage further with a question that was still engaging them. I read through the pieces of work and identified a question or questions which I felt still remained unresolved for them. The first question of every interview was an invitation for them to raise any problem or question that they were still working on. In only one case was a problem raised which had not been apparent to me from their work. I used a contingent questioning style (Ginsburg, 1981) wherein, after the original question from me, further questions or statements were dependent on the responses from the student. Each student, therefore, explored the evidence which led to their problem, and this allowed us to ascertain how secure they were with a range of basic techniques.

For instance, one girl had been trying to generate a general rotation matrix, but had been unsuccessful. I asked her what had led to this question and she demonstrated the results for 90° rotations with ease. As it turned out, her problem was with applying trigonometry to the situation. She had not considered doing so. To allow her the possibility of making further progress on this, I drew a diagram of a right-angled triangle where the length of the hypotenuse was 1 and asked her to find the lengths of the sides. This was fine and she naturally used trigonometry. I suggested that she explore rotating a unit square and applying trigonometry to find the new coordinates – she was keen to go away and work on this. In retrospect, it would be useful to manage a way of building in such focused time to normal practice.

There was no feeling that these students were being left to their own devices – they were not 'stewing in their own juice', but learning. Not only were they learning about matrices and transformations – the content – but also about the processes involved in doing mathematics and, incidentally, about other content areas such as negative numbers or trigonometry as they applied these ideas to new situations. If an individual had a problem with plotting coordinates in the early stages of the investigation, it was soon sorted out because of the frequency of use of the idea. These lessons were all a mixture of exposition, practice, investigation, problem solving, practical work and discussion.

As teachers, we were also learning. The discipline of writing the letter to the examining group had encouraged us to reflect on what was happening in the classroom, and the idea for the orals in the form they eventually took had arisen out of our discussions and been positively received by the students. In the end, we realized that what we had done was more than a possible model for GCSE coursework, it was a possible way of teaching all the time. The challenge that we had set ourselves by experiencing this work was whether it would be possible to address all content in a similar way. In so doing, the 'coursework' would become all the work on the course.

The listing of the six teaching styles in paragraph 243 of the Cockcroft report has led to investigations being seen as a separate and separable part of mathematics teaching and learning by many mathematics teachers. When

I first read the non-statutory guidance (DES, 1989) in the national curriculum for England and Wales, I was struck in section D, 'Using and applying mathematics', by a number of references to this fact.

> **D5 3.1** Many schools have made considerable progress in developing work along these lines since the publication of the Cockcroft report in 1982 ... Much of this work, however, has been undertaken separately from the mainstream of mathematics lessons.

> **D5 3.2** The National Curriculum requires all schools to address this issue, and to develop a teaching and learning approach in which the uses and applications of mathematics permeate and influence all work in mathematics.

> **D1 1.2** Thus acquiring knowledge, skills and understanding and using and applying mathematics are closely related matters:
>
> - Gaining knowledge and developing skills and understanding in mathematics *facilitates and enables* the use and application of mathematics in solving problems.
>
> - Tackling problems, both of the practical, 'real life' sort, and within mathematics itself, *motivates and requires* the learning of further skills and the development of greater understanding.

When I read D1 1.2, I could rehearse again the horns of the dilemma that (a) you need to identify the skills necessary to solve a problem and then teach them before you pose it, and (b) one way of finding out what students know and what they have problems with is to start with a challenge.

Initially, I saw the two statements in D1 1.2 as mutually exclusive, but now I see them as two parts of a cycle and the question of which comes first is the same problem as which comes first, the chicken or the egg! Given that I find I cannot do something, I must learn a further skill or develop my understanding until I can return to the original difficulty. A new question might then present itself or I might be drawn into a different, unrelated problem. Whichever of these is true, I am likely to learn when I find that there is something to resolve.

This is only one interpretation of what I have read, but I find that it gives me a challenge and a possible way of working to explore in classrooms. In the end, no matter if I had sat on the Cockcroft committee itself and been a party to its deliberations, I would still have work to do in re-interpreting the statements from the final report into the action of my own practice.

This is the challenge of such documentation for all of us. Is it possible to find some personal questions within it that we can begin to work on in our own classrooms, which might make the learning of our students more effective? Can we take charge of our own learning – or are *we* just going to stew in our own juice?

Notes

For a discussion of differentiation by outcome through coursework based in the same content area, see Mike Ollerton (1990) 'Seeding', *Mathematics Teaching*, **132**, pp. 32–4.

The work at Hartcliffe School was undertaken as part of a project at the Resources for Learning Development Unit, Sheridan Road, Bristol, Avon. A fuller report of the case study can be found in the RLDU publication *Styles of Coursework* (1990).

References

DES (1982) *Mathematics Counts* (the Cockcroft report), HMSO.

DES (1989) *Mathematics in the National Curriculum: Non-Statutory Guidance*, HMSO.

Barbara Edmonds and George Knights (eds) (1987) *Teaching Styles – Cockcroft 243*, Association of Teachers of Mathematics.

Herbert Ginsburg (1981) 'The clinical interview in psychological research on mathematical thinking: aims, rationales, techniques', *For the Learning of Mathematics*, **1**(3), pp. 4–11.

Judith Judd (1990) 'Cheating as a course art', *The Independent on Sunday*, 13 May 1990.

John Smith (1990) 'GCSE no cheater's charter', *The Independent on Sunday*, 20 May 1990.

Malcolm Swan (ed.) (1984) *Problems with Patterns and Numbers*, JMB/Shell Centre

David Wells (1986) *Problem Solving and Investigations*, Rain Publications.

2 *How fast does the wind travel?* History in the primary mathematics classroom

J. Helen Gardner

There may be a feeling that the use of history in the mathematics classroom is something which only applies to older pupils. Obviously, the greater the mathematical sophistication of children, the more history is available to help consolidate their learning of mathematics. But my experience is that appropriately chosen history is both suitable and valuable for the mathematical education of younger children too.

The school at which I teach is a multi-ethnic primary school in the English Midlands, with many pupils for whom English is a second language; many are insecure, which adds to their language handicap. These are often anxious children who already feel lost in the escalating curriculum. They want strait-jacket directions from their teachers and, when these are not forthcoming, they become even more bewildered.

However, they find story-time relaxing and enjoyable, and by telling stories from mathematical history I believe that the trauma of mathematics lessons can be reduced. This is why my classes are used to me starting them off on a piece of investigation, only to have me stop them after six or seven pencil-chewing or last-night's-television-filled moments with 'Come on, I'll tell you a story'.

This, of course, encourages the idea – already well-established among some of my teaching colleagues – that I don't teach 'proper maths' (as in working section by section through the scheme preferred by the school), but concentrate on what my colleagues call 'play maths'. That is, we work on things like finding out how far it is round a model railway track, how long it takes the train to go a complete circuit and trying to determine its speed; or finding the number of colours needed to decorate the Christmas bells; or partitioning 12; or doing probability experiments; and what they consider to be other irrelevant stuff. In each new topic, I try to include some historical aspect, either a problem as a launch pad, or a brief biography for encouragement and interest, or a story to stimulate discussion or creativity.

Discussion in the staffroom

During a recent planning meeting, I asked a colleague to work with me towards formalizing the use of historical perspectives in mathematics lessons. Readily agreeing, and taking the topic 'Elizabethan Times', she suggested the exercises outlined opposite.

Elizabeth I

1558	Accession of Elizabeth I
1561–1626	Francis Bacon
1564–1616	Shakespeare
1573–1652	Inigo Jones
1577–1580	Drake's voyage round the world
1577–1640	Rubens
1587	Execution of Mary, Queen of Scots
1588	Spanish Armada
1603	Accession of James I

Activities

1   How long did Elizabeth I reign?
2   Draw a barchart to show how long Bacon, Shakespeare, Jones and Rubens lived.
3   Of these, who (a) lived longest, and (b) had the shortest life?
4   How long did Drake's voyage last?
5   Can you name these men?
    (a) He was born 42 years before Elizabeth died: he was a writer.
    (b) He designed scenery for the theatre and lived the longest.
    (c) He was born while Drake sailed: he was a painter.
    (d) He lived less than 60 years and was a playwright.

My colleague's response took me by surprise. My initial request for collaboration between us was evidently ambiguous: what exactly, as far as primary – or any – education is concerned, does 'a historical perspective in mathematics' mean? There are, of course, few true mathematics specialists in a primary school. Most teachers are generalists, which is a good thing on the whole, but can sometimes diminish subject sensitivity. I was not happy with my colleague's suggested teaching material, because I felt there was nothing intrinsically historical about drawing numbers and information out of a list of facts. When I told her I had been thinking, rather, of the history of mathematics, she was somewhat surprised – does mathematics have a history? It just is and always has been! But she tried to humour me by suggesting I could use facts about mathematicians. To humour her, I drew up the following table.

Elizabethan mathematicians

1558	Accession of Elizabeth I	
1550–1617	John Napier	Invented first mechanical calculator, called *Napier's Bones*.
1560–1621	Thomas Harriot	In 1585, went to map the 'New World'.
1564–1642	Galileo Galilei	Tried to determine the speed of light; made telescope.
1574–1660	William Oughtred	Was responsible for the cross (×) for multiplication.
1588–1648	Marin Mersenne	Tried to determine the speed of sound; worked with prime numbers.
1596–1650	René Descartes	Worked with graphs and coordinates.
1603	Accession of James I	

Activities

1   Draw up a barchart to show the length of these mathematicians' lives.

2   List them in order of how long they lived. Start with the man who lived the longest.

3   Find the chapter on Napier's Bones in Nuffield 6, and do it.

4   How old was Thomas Harriot when he sailed for the 'New World'?

5   A *prime* number is one which has no factors other than 1 and itself. For example, these odd numbers 3, 5, 7, 11, 13 are prime numbers; but no even number is prime, except for 2. Why not?

6   Can you find nine prime numbers between 13 and 50?

7   Find the chapter on coordinates in Nuffield 5 and do it.

8   (a) How old was Galileo when Descartes was born?

     (b) How old was Descartes when Galileo died?

     (c) How old was Oughtred when Napier died?

Rather to my surprise, my colleague liked this – but largely because it was hardly any different in concept from her own first idea; it still failed to capture the sense of history which even children of this age are well able to absorb. This is, I am certain, *not* the way to join mathematics and history: it is far too mechanical, lacking the human dimension which is crucial both to history and to (well-taught) mathematics.

If this is not the way, *how* can we, in primary schools, make use of mathematics history? I have previously tried to indicate *why* I use history in my teaching; there follow two examples of how history has contributed to my mathematics lessons.

How fast is the wind travelling?

I was working with a mixed-ability group of pupils from years 3 and 4 (eight- and nine-year-olds) when one of the mobile classrooms had to be evacuated because of storm damage to the roof. The children were excitable, as they always are during high winds, so I decided to work with the wind rather than against it. I challenged the group to 'find out how fast the wind is travelling'.

Now that's difficult! But I agree with the observation that the 'limits on the insight and creativity of children are being set by the materials presented to them and not by the native talent of the children' (Schools Council, 1965, p. 97). As can be imagined, we had all sorts of wild suggestions and guesses, but no real idea how to start. To everyone's relief (including mine), I had a story ready. I outlined the story of how Mersenne measured the speed of sound. Then I caused amusement by saying that two great mathematicians, Descartes and Galileo, had completely opposite views as to the speed of light. ('Did they fight?' inquired one interested soul.)

I briefly described Galileo's experiment as he tried to prove himself right. We improvised across the classroom, and then across the playground. I was reliably informed that he should have videoed it and played it back in slow motion, with half the group amused and the other half nodding in agreement. This led to a discussion on how anyone in 'those times' could measure time accurately if they hadn't invented stop-watches – but that's another lesson.

Finally, we discussed how this might be relevant to the problem we had to solve. Then off we went again in groups, to discuss our problem. This time we had some ideas to try. I was pleased to note that having been led towards a strategy this particular group was keen to repeat their experiment in their own time – the inclusion of a historical story had indeed interested and motivated the children as I had hoped. The report below comes from one of the pupils.

Mohammed Kaleem's report

We were asked to find out how fast the wind travels. We were having guesses and they were all wrong. After that Mrs Gardner told us a story about a man who wanted to find out how fast light travels. He did an experiment with a lantern and a candle. He called his friend and gave him a lantern and the man had a bucket and the man covered the lantern with the bucket. Then the man uncovered his lantern and when his friend saw the light he could work out how fast light travels. Then we had an idea how to find out how fast the wind travels. We decided we wanted to see the wind like we can see light. So we got a piece of paper and put it at one end of the playground and when Jason Binder said 'go', I let go of the paper and the wind blew it and I followed it and we counted the paces. It was 44 paces in 16 seconds. We did it again at playtime, but it was different.

Is it *really* time to go home?

The whole school was studying the topic of Food one term, with years 4 and 5 – my eight- to ten-year-olds – concentrating on Bread. This gave me the opportunity to introduce some work based on problems from the *Rhind Mathematical Papyrus* (Chace, 1929). First we looked at the unit fraction table, representing the divisions $1 \div 10, \ldots, 9 \div 10$, which precedes six problems of dividing loaves. The Egyptians only used 'one over something' fractions and two-thirds.

Table of the results of division of the numbers 1–9 by 10

1 divided by 10 gives $1/10$	6 divided by 10 gives $1/2$ $1/10$
2 divided by 10 gives $1/5$	7 divided by 10 gives $2/3$ $1/30$
3 divided by 10 gives $1/5$ $1/10$	8 divided by 10 gives $2/3$ $1/10$ $1/30$
4 divided by 10 gives $1/3$ $1/15$	9 divided by 10 gives $2/3$ $1/5$ $1/30$
5 divided by 10 gives $1/2$	

Problem I

Example of dividing 1 *loaf among* 10 *men.*
Each man receives $1/10$.
Proof. Multiply $1/10$ by 10.

Do it thus:	1	$1/10$
	\2	$1/5$
	4	$1/3$ $1/15$
	\8	$2/3$ $1/10$ $1/30$

Total 1 loaf, which is correct.

Discussion of the table, of how the first problem was solved, and consequent work on the five very similar problems which followed, proved to be an interesting way in which to introduce work on fractions and other topics from Egyptian mathematics which are still with us today. The Egyptian method of multiplication was not unfamiliar to the children, but they had not met its use with fractions. I assumed from previous experience that these children would not be completely comfortable when working with fractions, an assessment which this work confirmed. However, they enjoyed using the table and checking the calculations in the book.

One day, the class visited Avoncroft, the Museum of Buildings in Warwickshire, to study the buildings connected with bread production. On our return, it seemed a good idea to tackle Rhind problem 44: 'Example of reckoning a granary four-angled, length of it 10, the breadth of it 10, the height of it 10; what is that which goes into it in grain?'

The time available for this lesson was two and a half hours, during which I was to introduce the material and its background, and any concepts or skills needed, and then to assess each child individually as they worked through the problem. Assessment is done on a form which includes the England and Wales national curriculum attainment target levels, and which (in this case) I drew up myself, so as to draw attention to the specific learning targets attained through this experience with the Rhind papyrus. (See Appendix for details.)

In the time that has elapsed since issuing the challenge 'how fast is the wind travelling?', my use of history in the mathematics classroom has indeed become formalized. I was particularly keen to use this problem on the granary, because I felt that it would not only challenge the more-able pupils, but as the correlation with levels shows, there is also the possibility of work at lower levels for those with either mathematical or language problems.

I began the lesson by talking about Egyptian farming methods and the relative importance of bread. Then, we discussed the problem in its original form (Chace, 1929, p. 109, plate 66), picking out hieroglyphic symbols for numbers, symbols which seemed interesting (the beetle, two different birds, etc.).

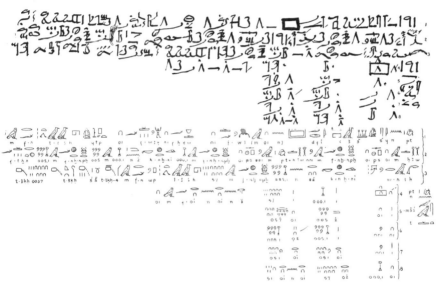

The granary problem from the Rhind Papyrus

We also touched on what made us believe that Egyptians wrote from right to left. We then translated the question into our English, and concentrated on the aspect which I wanted to pursue – the shape of the granary and its volume.

We spent a bit of time on recognizing cubes and cuboids, because this was the level I supposed the majority of the group to be working at, but I also forayed into the concept of using a symbol for an unknown number. The children then worked alone or as a group, as suited them, for about fifteen minutes, recording their decisions about the shape of the granary, with their reasons.

> MARTYN: The granary is a cube because $l = w = h$.
> l = length, w = width and h = height.
> And four angled means 4 corners which are right angles.

LYNDSAY:

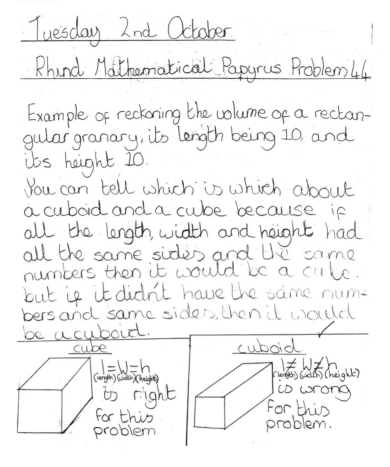

Tuesday 2nd October

Rhind Mathematical Papyrus Problem 44

Example of reckoning the volume of a rectangular granary, its length being 10, and its height 10.

You can tell which is which about a cuboid and a cube because if all the length, width and height had all the same sides and the same numbers then it would be a cube. but if it didn't have the same numbers and same sides, then it would be a cuboid.

cube

$l = W = h$
(length) (width) (height)
is right
for this
problem

cuboid.

$l \neq W \neq h$
(length) (width) (height)
is wrong
for this
problem.

There followed work on area and volume, using cubes and cuboids of different sizes. Dienes base apparatus was perfect for this. Following this, we talked about how the Egyptians had solved the volume problem, but we have no working on our copies to help us. Some of the children assumed they doubled, though others thought perhaps there was a table somewhere, as with the fractions.

However, time was getting on, and I still had my individual assessments to do, so I set the children to work on calculating the volume. Several did this quickly, using the doubling method, though some knew the effect of multiplying by 10 and applied it. Some children could talk to me and their peers about the task and its solution, but just could not record it in writing.

LYNDSAY:

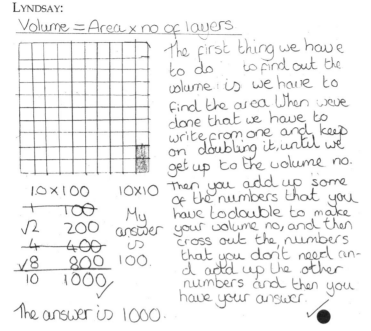

Volume = Area x no of layers

the first thing we have to do to find out the volume is we have to find the area When we've done that we have to write from one and keep on doubling it, until we get up to the volume no.

Then you add up some of the numbers that you have to double to make your volume no, and then cross out the numbers that you don't need and add up the other numbers and then you have your answer.

10 × 100   10X10

√2 200   My answer is
4   400   100.
√8 800
10 1000 ✓

The answer is 1000.

RAHEELA: I just knew that timesing by 10 was 100 and timesing by 10 again was 1000.

Since some children finished quickly, I drew a function machine and suggested that this machine worked out volumes. I gave them several different cubes and cuboids to input and the children enjoyed drawing the machine and working out the outputs from the machine.

Although I didn't manage to chat to every child, nor complete a form for more than five or six of them, I considered the lesson very successful. This belief was reinforced when several of the less-able children commented how enjoyable the afternoon had been: one little lad, not previously noted for his scholastic enthusiasm, said to me plaintively 'Is it *really* time to go home?'

Appendix: Assessment, attainment targets and programmes of study (1991 proposals)

Level	Programmes of study
	AT 1 Using and applying mathematics
1	Using materials for a practical task.
	Talking about own work and asking questions.
	Making predictions based on experience.
2	Selecting the materials and the mathematics to use for a practical task.
	Describing current work, checking results.
3	Selecting the materials and the mathematics to use for a task using alternative approaches to overcome difficulties. Explaining work and recording findings systematically.
	AT 2 Number
2	Reading, writing and ordering numbers to at least 100 and using the knowledge that the tens-digit indicates the number of tens.
3	As 2, but to 1000, and using the knowledge that the position of a digit indicates its value.
	Solving problems involving multiplication or division of whole numbers or money, using a calculator where necessary.
	Knowing and using multiplication facts up to 5×5, and all those in the 2, 5 and 10 multiplication tables.
4	Reading, writing and ordering whole numbers.
	Understanding the effect of multiplying a whole number by 10 or 100.
	Understanding and using the relationship between place values in whole numbers.
	Knowing multiplication facts up to 10×10 and using them in multiplication and division problems.

Level	Programmes of study
	AT 3 Algebra
2	Understanding the use of a symbol to stand for an unknown number.
3	Recognising whole numbers divisible by 2, 5 and 10.
	Dealing with inputs to and outputs from simple function machines.
4	Applying strategies, such as doubling and halving, to explore properties of numbers.
	Understanding and using simple formulae or equations expressed in words.
	Recognising that multiplication and division are inverse operations and using this to check calculations.
	AT 4 Shape and space
1	Using common words such as: *on, inside, above, under, behind, next to*, to describe a position.
2	Recognising squares, rectangles, ..., cubes, cuboids, ..., and describing them.
	Recognising right-angled corners in 2-D and 3-D shapes.
4	Finding areas by counting squares and volumes by counting cubes.

References and further reading

Bunt, L., Jones, P. and Bedient, J. (1988) *The Historical Roots of Elementary Mathematics*, Dover.

Chace, A. B. (1929) *The Rhind Mathematical Papyrus*, Mathematical Association of America.

Fauvel, J. (ed.) (1990) *History in the Mathematics Classroom: the IREM Papers Vol. I*, The Mathematical Association.

Gillings, R. J. (1972) *Mathematics in the Time of the Pharaohs*, Dover.

Schools Council (1965) *Curriculum Bulletin 1:Mathematics in Primary Schools*, HMSO.

3 Teaching mathematics to ethnic minority pupils in secondary schools

Alan J. Bishop

Snapshot 1

It's a Monday morning; a lower-set, year 9 group are working on their booklets. One of the boys always appears restless in the class. He talks a lot with his friends and doesn't do much work.

This seems a familiar situation, doesn't it? What do you do in these situations – keep encouraging him? Try to stop him talking and disrupting the others? Move him to sit by himself? Challenge him with tougher problems? Move him to a lower set? Do you have sets in your school?

He arrived from Bangladesh last year and chats in Bengali to his friends most of the time. His spoken English is rather weak, but he can read some of the text if he wants to. But mostly he guesses what's needed, or copies from his friends. His English writing is poor.

Does that change anything for you? If so, what? Does it bother you if you can't understand what he's saying? Would you try to stop him talking in Bengali and ask him to try to tell it to you in English? Would you sit him next to some native English speakers?

As I go to speak to him, he shows me a sheet of paper with algebraic equations on it, all solved correctly. They are at a high, year 10, level (level 7/8, AT 3). He claims to have done them all himself, but says 'I don't understand'. I ask him where he learned to do them . 'In Bangladesh'. So where have these come from? 'My book at home, my father helped me.' I give him a new equation to solve, like the others, and he 'talks through' the solution and solves it correctly, with a beaming smile. My move?

How familiar is that kind of situation for you? For me, it was very unfamiliar. I have had little experience of teaching young people like Mohammed in this country, and this incident represents the kind of decision-making complexity which was new for me and which is faced by increasing numbers of mathematics teachers in this country. It is a 'snapshot' of an incident which occurred while I was working in Mohammed's school in London recently. I was fortunate to be able to do my 'recent and relevant' school experience work[1] at three interesting secondary schools, which had large numbers of pupils from ethnic minority communities. I look back on my experiences with various mixed feelings – I saw some dedicated but very overworked and stressed teachers at work, some highly motivated youngsters who were a challenging pleasure to teach and some with whom I couldn't even begin to make real contact; some effective materials but other standard texts which were next to useless; some imaginative and flexible teaching approaches but some routine, inflexible and 'English tourist' teaching (say it loudly, slowly and often!). But my lasting impressions of the experiences were that:

(a) teaching ethnic minority pupils was one of the most complex teaching assignments I have ever had;

(b) I had to use all my research experience and knowledge to its fullest in trying to understand what I was seeing and participating in;

(c) few teachers seemed confident that what they were doing was appropriate;

(d) no one from 'outside' really understands or can help, except by being 'in there' and sharing.

If that final point is true, then what can I offer in this chapter? My answer is: reflections on my experiences, shared perceptions and insights, ideas from some wider reading and writing which seem particularly relevant, and perhaps a different way of thinking about familiar situations which can trigger some new actions. My hope is that these offerings will be instructive whether the reader regularly teaches ethnic minority pupils or not.

Personal background

Although I was undertaking this work primarily for the purposes of informing my initial teacher training activities, my personal background is mainly in research, and as far as time will allow, research with real children and real teachers in real classrooms. So, although I was teaching young people for much of the time, I was inevitably also viewing the situation as a researcher: a 'participant observer' is the commonly used term, but it is not the right description here. I was more of an observing (and reflecting) participant. I wasn't doing action research since I didn't know what, if anything, to try to change and evaluate. I was a kind of mathematical anthropologist – a powerful analogy in many ways – visiting what for me were foreign lands (multi-ethnic classrooms), working and 'living' there, sharing in their mathematical activities and trying to unravel some of the complexity I could see. Anthropology often attempts to make the unfamiliar understandable by trying to make the familiar seem rather different.

I emphasize my researcher background, because I found that so often during that period I just didn't understand what was happening in the classrooms. I initially thought I did, from my experiences of many other classrooms and other teaching situations, but then as the unfamiliar became more familiar, I realized that there was much that I was missing. I was misreading language cues, unsure about body language and behavioural movements, and misinterpreting mathematical difficulties. I became uncertain about reading 'messages' and unconfident about the effectiveness of previously practised skills – hence my need to investigate, to experiment and to analyse.

It was also very important for me as a researcher to try not to 'judge' what I saw happening, although of course, as a teacher, one is judging and evaluating all the time. We all have our personal images here, and mine is of another 'me' sitting on my shoulder saying 'Tut, tut! I wouldn't have said that', or 'Try something different, that's not working', or 'If you were that child, how would you feel?' Whenever I was judging or evaluating, I tried to be more objective about it – asking myself 'What criteria am I using? Are they relevant here? What other criteria could I use?' This kind of research is about opening up one's mind by opening one's senses, by documenting what one 'sees' and by reflecting on the documented impressions.

What's the problem?

As mathematics teachers, we find it so easy to slip into the 'problem' language – mathematics problems are usually structured so that they always have solutions. These problems are also de-contextualized and abstract, as are mathematical solutions. Mathematics, as we know it, looks for generalizations and universal applicability.

Mathematics teaching isn't like that, however. There are no generalized solutions, because there are no de-contextualized problems. Mathematics teaching only exists in a context and, tempting though it may be to try to remove it from that context, it is the context which determines to a large degree what actually happens and what counts as a solution. It is an activity whose context involves three essential components – the teacher, the pupils, and the mathematics – and that triad and its relationships constitute the problem field of research on mathematics teaching.

What is particularly inappropriate with the language of 'problem', in this context, is that it is apparently all too easy for some teachers to think of ethnic minority pupils as constituting 'the problem'. For the pupils, of course, it is often the mathematics which is the problem, and in this chapter I have also to point out that for the pupils I worked with and observed, it was sometimes the teacher who was the problem.

So I will *not* continue with the 'problem' metaphor in this chapter – I will use the word 'field' instead. What I was doing for those two terms (the previous one was largely spent visiting and observing in several schools) was a field study, and the particular research site for my observing–participant work was mathematics classrooms containing large numbers of pupils from ethnic minority communities.

To structure my reflections in this chapter, I will use the three components of the triad mentioned earlier, while remembering that they are interacting and not isolated components. In fact, I believe that it is rather more creative to think of them as three different kinds of contributions to the social practice which we call mathematics teaching.

The pupils' contribution

I begin with this component, because it was ethnic minority pupils who defined my field of interest. As might be expected, the initial descriptions which I found myself using, and which are also used in formal documents, were not at all helpful in the classroom. Labels like 'West Indian' or 'Asian' may be important in some contexts, where perhaps one wishes to draw attention to population features, or to overt discriminatory practices, but in the classroom context they came to be far too simplistic, relatively meaningless and often downright prejudicial.

Thus, although initially I was surprised when teachers couldn't easily answer my naive questions about their pupils' ethnic backgrounds, after a while I understood why that was not necessarily useful knowledge for them. When I began to teach the children, the initial unfamiliarity (to me) of ethnically mixed classrooms quickly became merely familiar collections of young people with individual characteristics. Their particular ethnic background, their skin colour, their hairstyles, and their dress, seemed decreasingly important the more I worked with them. My researcher–teacher style made me attend much more to qualities of mind: What was going on inside that head? What's the conceptual block causing that frown? What has suddenly triggered the engrossed working? Why does that child seek my help so frequently? Just as for any teacher in any classroom, my key question was: 'How do I understand what the pupils are thinking and meaning?'

I believe that this is a crucial area for all teachers to reflect on: What do you know about your pupils and how do you know it? And from where do you know it?

Snapshot 2

It was interesting for me to be in one class, which to my ears and eyes was composed entirely of pupils for whom English was at least their second language (E2L), and to be told by the teacher that 'The E2L learners are those three in the corner'.

The meaning of that statement will, I am sure, be clear to all the teachers I met, implying as it does that those pupils were the ones who needed particular language support. They were the pupils who for several teachers constituted their real 'problem' and, as a result, their contribution tended to be seen negatively rather than positively. I noticed that there was a general awareness of the pupils' English language reading proficiency, presumably because a weakness in that skill meant the need not just for language support, but also perhaps for different materials.

At a departmental level, I found some departments were making attempts to document data about their pupils but most didn't, often believing that it was the school's job not theirs. My researcher background leads me to believe that although data and labels need to be treated cautiously, in general it is better to have information than not, although questions always revolve around what information does help in teaching. My impression certainly was that the more successful teachers, and the more successful departments I saw and worked in, did try to know more, rather than less, about their pupils.

However, some school administrations seemed reluctant to make available to their mathematics departments potentially important, and interesting, information on individual pupils' ethnicity, languages, religion, home and family situation, previous school experiences, etc. E2L departments and special needs departments did appear to have this kind of information, but only for 'their' pupils, i.e. the ones referred to them and whom they were supporting in class. The lack of such information seemed to cause significant problems for mathematics departments, who were thereby forced to deal in relatively intuitive ways with whatever situations occurred.

Let us consider one area of departmental decision making where pupils' contributions are potentially of great significance, namely grouping practices and how to allocate pupils to different groups. Here, I wish to focus on the classroom groups themselves, rather than on small groups within classrooms, which I will deal with in a later section. For most departments I experienced, the decision was about whether to set by ability, and then how to allocate pupils to those ability sets. This grouping decision faces every department, but in multi-ethnic schools there are particular considerations to weigh.

Snapshot 3

While I was discussing such issues with one HoD in his office, a third-year girl brought along another girl who had just arrived from Bangladesh. The HoD was expected to determine on the spot which third-year group she should join for that lesson. The new girl had just arrived in school and appeared to be unable to understand much English. Neither was it immediately clear whether she had even been to school before.

Perhaps as a consequence of intuitive decision making at this level, there did seem to be a tendency for some ethnic groups to appear more frequently in the lowest sets, while some bottom sets seemed to be composed entirely of E2L learners. The arguments for and against this arrangement are complex, and are general in so far as setting is concerned, but I felt that the results of such setting practices were even more suspect than usual. For one thing, the fact that in such 'bottom set' classes the only English language 'models' were those of the teacher(s) present made teaching much more difficult. By contrast, in other more mixed-ability classrooms, there were several instances of pupils helping each other over language difficulties, and there were other English language models present also.

What about the pupils like Mohammed, bored and listless by being in a low set because his mathematical aptitude was obscured by his English language weakness? Why should his English language difficulties be the dominant criterion for his placement? Could it be that predominantly mono-lingual teachers find it more difficult to understand the thinking of multilingual learners? How can departments look for and recognize potentially positive language contributions? For example, the fact that E2L learners are becoming bilingual, and may indeed be multilingual already, can be looked at positively. Mathematics is an ideal subject for exploring linguistic representations, symbolic shorthands and language-based relations. But why only attend to the language aspects? Bilingual learners are also bicultural learners, and for mathematics departments, a greater awareness of that cultural dimension may enable a greater range of pupil contributions to be recognized, valued and developed through teaching.

Perhaps, though, the greatest potentially negative effect of such setting concerns, as it always does, the pupils' self-image and self-esteem. I would not wish to suggest that mathematical setting was an overt racist practice in the schools I worked in, but it was clear to me that there was a great risk of stereotyped and racist images becoming institutionalized through the setting practices used.[2] Hence the need, in my view, for more individual pupil information to be made available to aid departmental monitoring and decision making.

As another aspect of this decision area, should mathematics departments have 'induction' procedures for any new pupils? Or is it better to learn to 'know' the pupils in the normal classroom context? Practices in the schools I worked in varied enormously. If one does adopt the induction idea, who should do it and how? Who is likely to have any time to do it? Theoretically, I would argue for an induction procedure, if it can be made a practical possibility. It is feasible to learn to use relatively language-free assessment, and a designated assessor could discover a great deal of relevant information in a short time. In the schools I worked in, for example, there was much interest shown in some experimental language-reduced assessment tasks which I devised and tried out. Of course, this is not the only kind of assessment that needs to be made, and it does seem to me that there is a definite need for more research and sharing of ideas about the assessment of mathematical knowledge without simultaneously presenting the pupils with linguistic and cultural obstacles.

A particularly interesting and different approach to classroom grouping, and to induction, was illustrated by one school, where the 'tutor group' was the mathematics group also – an intentionally mixed-ability group, which was also taught by the form tutor in some cases. A great deal was therefore known by those teachers, and by the mathematics department, about the pupils and their relationships, which was invaluable in improving the quality of pupils' contributions inside the mathematics classrooms. This particular school had created a very friendly social environment which seemed to produce all kinds of benefits – pupils having a lot of responsibility for their mathematical work, very good staff/pupil relations, good school/home relations, plenty of pupils staying on for sixth-form study, etc. Several pupils also wanted to continue working on their mathematics (or other subjects) during the lunch break, and even after school. From my limited experience in such schools, that was both unusual and impressive.

Pupils can contribute to schools and classrooms in so many ways, and frequently the difficulties of not knowing pupils well are related to the extent to which the teachers welcome and value their contributions. How well you know pupils is related to how much you let them inform you about themselves. Are they all just allowed to present their mathematical knowledge in the same routine Euro-centric contexts, or can you create ways for their individuality to be better represented and recognized?

Secondary teachers can learn much from their primary colleagues in this respect. A primary teacher will tend to learn much more about her pupils than a secondary subject specialist, because she will necessarily see her pupils in a greater variety of learning contexts. If the secondary pupil is seen as just another learner of mathematics, then the teacher will not learn much. If the pupils are allowed to demonstrate and represent their individuality, then cultural, linguistic and social backgrounds can become not 'problems' to be 'solved', not handicaps to be avoided or overcome, but productive resources. For a mathematical education in a pluralist society, the multi-ethnic classroom should surely be a powerful potential resource, but that potential will probably only be realized if the pupils are allowed to make a real contribution to the work of the classroom, and as real young people, not as stereotypical versions of some historical, cultural image.

Ethnic minority pupils are not just bilingual or E2L learners, nor are they only Afro-Caribbean, Turkish or Muslim, for example. They are bicultural young people receiving sometimes conflicting messages from the school and their home, but actively reconstructing new meanings for themselves, and appropriating a new culture for themselves. They are also young people living in today's multi-ethnic society, and like young people every-where, they are busy redefining and reconstructing this society. This reconstruction includes contributing to their own mathematical education.

The mathematical contribution

The mathematical contribution in the classrooms I worked in came princi-pally from published teaching materials, as most schools had adopted a departmental scheme for their classroom work – the most common schemes being SMILE, SMP and NMP. SMILE does, of course, make explicit use of other published materials, but most departments had other texts that were used by particular groups from time to time, as well as their own materials. There was a general view that no one scheme was ideal for use with all ethnic minority pupils, a view which I would definitely share.

I became particularly interested in two aspects of the mathematical contri-bution made by the available materials: first, what I will call their 'cultural frame of reference', and second, their relation to mathematical language development.

Regarding the first, I was rather surprised to find that the fact that a school was a multi-ethnic community was no guarantee of any classroom reference to the multicultural nature of mathematical knowledge. I had assumed that schools with high numbers of ethnic minority pupils would use materials which at the very least offered the possibilities of different cultural interpretations and contributions. However, everything seemed to depend on the scheme being used. For example, the SMILE scheme contains several cards which refer to non-European mathematical representations, while SMP and NMP contain relatively little such material. Whether any reference was made to the multicultural nature of mathematics was then largely a matter for the individual initiative and preference of the particular teacher or of the particular department.

Neither was the predominantly Euro-centric nature of the materials available necessarily felt to present a potential obstacle for children from non-European cultures.

Snapshot 4

I was supporting one maths teacher and an E2L teacher in a class with many E2L learners from Bangladesh who were all struggling with the SMP Book G5 exercises on finding one's way around Hereford with the help of photographs, diagrams and a street map. After several explanations about ring roads, 'A' road signs, steeples on churches, camera positions, etc., I did begin to wonder whether the mathematical value of this activity was being negated by the unfamiliar cultural and social context. I could certainly imagine more relevant contexts for dealing with the same mathematical content with these pupils.

I was thus initially surprised to find scant reference being made to Muslim mathematical ideas in those schools which had large numbers of Muslim children, and only a limited reference to various Asian geometrical and numerical ideas in those schools where there were many Asian children. Despite the obvious concern among the teachers about the underachievement of many of their ethnic minority pupils, I saw relatively little evidence of materials being used which could have directly involved the mathematical ideas and practices of their pupils' cultural backgrounds.

However, this issue is a complex one, and my initial expectation was far too simplistic. Let us first of all consider the mathematics curriculum in general. It is clear that as research on ethnomathematics has been developing in recent years, so we are learning much more about the variety of mathematical symbolizations used by different cultures around the world.[3] Furthermore, it seems to me important to demonstrate that variety in *every* pupil's mathematical education, since otherwise the pupils will leave school with a very narrow view of what mathematics is, and a lack of understanding of the whole human and cultural context of mathematics. It seems to be particularly important to do this in teaching situations where one cannot assume that all the pupils share the same European cultural background as the teacher and the curriculum structure.

Now, of course, in state schools in the United Kingdom, we must all currently operate within the framework of the particular national curriculum in mathematics in force, which unfortunately ignores the available research evidence completely. The national curriculum for England and Wales, for instance, contains no references to any historical or cultural background; it mentions only two mathematicians incidentally (Cartesian coordinates and Pythagoras' theorem); there is no other reference to a human being, and it generally encourages a presentation of the subject as culture free. This, however, is a meaningless concept, because mathematical ideas can be traced back to historical origins, and shown to have a cultural history. That is precisely what historians of mathematics spend much of their time doing. European culture's version of mathematics, as embodied in this national curriculum, is a generalized and universally usable mathematics, which is a very important idea but certainly not a culture-free one.

Fortunately, any national curriculum can be given a cultural and human frame of reference. It is possible, and I would argue highly desirable, to include mathematical activities which allow different number symbolizations, a variety of geometric representations, and examples of algorithmic procedures from different cultures to be demonstrated at the very least. It is also very possible, even if not mandatory, to include overt historically based activities from a variety of sources and situations. The journals *Mathematics Teaching* and *Mathematics in Schools* publish many good articles containing examples of several potentially worthwhile activities.[4] I therefore see no inconsistency between following a national curriculum and including in the mathematics classroom activities from different cultural histories which exemplify, contextualize and enrich the items on the curriculum. (See Helen Gardner's chapter in this volume for an account of historical work on mathematics in the primary school.)

Issues remain, of course, about the extent and character of that cultural contextualization, particularly in the face of competing demands for space and time in the curriculum. Too few examples, and one runs the risk of offering a mere token gesture which achieves little; equally, one cannot do justice to all possible cultural histories and peoples in the time available. Choices must be made, and I would argue that some of the decisions should be made at the departmental level, but some are best made by the individual teacher.

The crucial issues, however, revolve around the framing of the curriculum in relation to the particular cultural backgrounds of the pupils. To what extent should this be done? To what extent *could* it be done? How might it be done in practice?

In my view, there is a crucial difference between activities which teach different kinds of mathematics and ones which allow the pupils opportunities to contribute, or to experience, different interpretations from those of other pupils or of the teacher. Take, for example, the different kinds of multiplication algorithm which exist in different cultural contexts.[5] It is surely inappropriate in this society to argue that one should teach Indian pupils only Vedic multiplication and Muslim pupils only Arabic multiplication, if only because of the questionable assumptions which one would be making both about the pupils' backgrounds and about the two cultural histories. Neither is there evidence from the ethnic communities concerned that this is the kind of cultural framing which they desire. On a more practical note, one can ask how such a dubious strategy could be applied in a classroom containing pupils from several different cultures.

On the other hand, it seems much more appropriate to argue that when 'multiplication' is on the classroom agenda, one can decide to include examples of multiplication algorithms from other cultural contexts, rather than ignore them, as tends to happen at present. For example, I could imagine the following teaching sequence:

(a) number-pattern activities based on addition;

(b) calculator multiplication procedures;

(c) alternative algorithms contributed, demonstrated, and

explored;

(d) pre-algebraic pattern-seeking and descriptions.

Activity (c) is where the pupils and the teacher can contribute alternative algorithms, which would enrich the examples so necessary for the pattern-seeking and description activities in (d). I would not argue for pupils learning more than one multiplication algorithm to any high degree of proficiency, although if a group of pupils wished to go further then I would not object, unless in my view the time could be more profitably spent on other activities.

What seems to me to be most important is that the mathematical activities and the materials used in the classroom encourage, and make space for, the pupils and the teacher to contribute alternative mathematical representations and ideas at appropriate moments. This is where the department can help by being selective about whatever scheme should be adopted, because there are great differences among commercial schemes in the extent to which they encourage or allow alternative representations. In addition, the department can act as a communal resource for activities and materials which have been found appropriate for that school's ethnic community.

Within the national curriculum framework then, what I would look for in the mathematical materials and activities used in teaching ethnic minority pupils is an open and accepting multicultural frame of reference. I would look for the awareness of differences, a non-judgemental stance towards what the teacher may think of as non-standard representations, a valuing of contrasts, and space to allow all pupils to make their personal cultural contribution to the mathematical education of the whole classroom group.

The second main area of interest to me, in relation to the mathematical contribution of the materials, concerns language development. Many times I heard the plea from sensitive teachers for more appropriate materials. This meant not only that they should be less obviously 'culturo-centric' – i.e. that they should make fewer monocultural assumptions about British society in general, that there should be more opportunities for multicultural mathematical contributions, and that they should contain more socially aware contexts for their examples and problems – but also that they should exclude unnecessary language, and include far better mathematical language development activities.

The language aspect of the materials was a continual cause for comment among teachers and pupils, largely because most available texts seem to make little concession to the E2L beginner. Consequently, much time was spent by both mathematics and E2L support teachers in explaining what many of the words meant and what one was supposed to do in any particular exercise.

There are two different aspects to this problem, in what I perceived to be the teacher's order of priority: first, to what extent do the materials help with developing the pupils' mathematical English competence; and second, how do they help with developing the pupils' use of mathematical language in general?

Regarding the first, although the teachers were fully aware of the need for their pupils to be able to develop a good understanding of mathematical English, there were few actual materials available to help with this task. In one school, they were using SMILE matrices of cards which were dubbed 'E2L friendly', i.e. they used few words. While removing unnecessary language can certainly help in conveying meaning, it is clear that removing language does not help with long-term language development. Glossaries of important and recurring words did, however, seem useful, as did posters/displays showing mathematical keywords, with their translations into the school's major first languages, and illustrated with pictures and diagrams. Some mathematics departments were developing their own teaching materials, with this problem in mind, just as some E2L departments were. But, in general, teachers were using standard published mathematics textual materials, the majority of which in my view are totally inappropriate for E2L beginners.

Regarding the second point, that of developing pupils' general use of mathematical language, which to my mind ought to be the first priority, I was struck by the reliance by several teachers on textual materials alone. Different mathematical language grows from different kinds of activities, and a quality mathematical language education necessitates a rich variety of activities. However, for many of the pupils I was working with, the standard English texts presented activities in ways which were often barriers rather than facilitators to developing a rich mathematical language.

I therefore became interested in teachers' uses of other non-text materials, like physical apparatus, photographs, etc., and was surprised that these were not present in every classroom – particularly when we were working with E2L learners who were experiencing difficulties with both text and concepts. There were, however, some classrooms where concrete materials were in abundance, and where, for example, it was possible to work effectively with small groups on 'pattern-continuing' activities. In these situations, the cognitive strains for beginning E2L learners were reduced both by the use of such materials, and also by the pupils being able to discuss ideas in their first language if they so chose. For the bilingual learner, the appropriate mathematical language is not necessarily English.

Regarding other materials, most teachers encouraged calculator use, but computer use was surprisingly rare. At least, that was initially surprising to me, until I realized that most available computer materials suffer from exactly the same inadequacies as many published written materials – they make no allowances for pupils who have difficulties with reading English, or who do not necessarily share the same cultural assumptions as the authors.

In some earlier research I was engaged in, with deaf children,[6] we became aware of precisely the same problem, that computer activities have enormous potential for the learning of mathematics, if only the linguistic obstacles created by the program writers can be overcome. For example, with most computer materials, there is either a long 'page' of initial explanation, or a 'Help' command, which is actually of no help because it too produces a long page of explanation. As part of this earlier research, we therefore produced an analysis of the commonly available computer materials in terms of their English language demands, and it was striking to see just how many of them were also inaccessible to E2L beginners.

Choosing appropriate mathematical activities and materials is a routine task for many teachers, but it is a particularly complex one for teachers of ethnic minority pupils when so few materials are at all appropriate. However, the multicultural nature of British society, and the England and Wales national curriculum requirement of a cross-curricular, multicultural dimension, now creates a cultural challenge for all teachers when choosing activities and materials. (It also, of course, creates a challenge for all producers of commercial texts.)

When you next sit down, either as a department or by yourself, to choose some textbooks, booklets, activity sheets, computer programs, videos, slides and whatever else you may use with your pupils, think about issues such as: what cultural images do they present, and what kind of language do they use, and develop? Ask yourself what messages they transmit about the nature of the multicultural society we live in, and how mathematics relates to and informs young people's ideas about that society.

The teacher's contribution

I have left this aspect until last for two reasons: First, because the teacher is the most obvious contributor to any pupil's mathematical education, I wanted to highlight the other two 'contributors' first. Second, the teacher is in a sense the 'orchestrator' of the whole mathematical environment which surrounds the pupil. Teachers have it within their power to choose the materials, activities, seating arrangements, timing of activities, sequences and many other aspects of mathematics classrooms, and thus it seemed sensible to discuss the teacher's special contribution at this stage.

Regarding the general teaching approach used in the classrooms I visited and worked in, it consisted largely of pupils working through card/ booklet/book materials on an individual basis, with support offered by teachers as the pupil requested it. As a visitor who looked like a teacher, I was frequently asked to help, and as a teacher it was easiest for me to adopt that common mode too, although I did on occasions use a whole-class approach, which the older pupils were slightly surprised by and which they could not always handle as well as various small-group methods.

Some younger pupils, and others who had recently arrived in the country, however, appeared to me to find the individual mode of being taught rather strange, and they demanded a lot of attention and teaching 'help' from any 'teachers' in the classroom. In several cases, the support staff (mainly E2L) were not able to be in all the classrooms which needed their help, and life was occasionally very difficult and demanding for the lone mathematics teacher, particularly when teaching some of the lower sets. Any in-class help was clearly welcome, and in some classrooms there were three teachers in the room, the normal mathematics teacher, the E2L support teacher and myself.

Snapshot 5

In one classroom, 22 children had the benefit of six 'teachers' – the normal mathematics teacher, a student teacher on practice, a support mathematics teacher timetabled for that purpose, me, and two sixth-formers who were generally encouraged to help with the younger classes!

How possible it is to produce that level of support on a regular basis is hard to determine, but it did seem to be a very significant and worthwhile attempt to improve the achievement of those pupils.

The issue, of course, is the one which every teacher worries about – is there a 'best' way of teaching – and, in this case, is there a 'best' way of teaching ethnic minority pupils? The evidence that I saw clearly showed that most teachers had opted for an individualized mode – presumably, because it represented the 'best' approach for them to use. As a researcher, I had the luxury of being a little more open and sceptical. It was clear, for example, that the quality of mathematics teaching in the individualized mode was largely determined by the materials used – and as I have already discussed at length, both I and the other teachers recognized many shortcomings. The most appropriate materials seemed to be those in the SMILE system, presumably because they have been developed by teachers responding to this particular need.

One particular teaching approach which I was interested in concerned the use of small-group work. Though mainly using individual materials, pupils were by and large sitting in small groups, and although the most common rationale for such groupings were friendships, these also tended to be along ethnic and gender lines. Special E2L groups were established in some classrooms apparently 'to help the support teacher', but these rarely functioned as genuine groups – it was merely a case of the E2L learners all sitting at the same table. Group teaching with physical apparatus, games or computers, and other shared/joint activities was also a rare occurrence (at least in the classrooms I visited) but was an effective mathematics and language development activity where it did happen. I also saw an intentional mixing of the ethnicity of the pupils on one 'small-group' occasion, something which seemed important to do in view of the tendency for ethnic groups normally to stay closely together.

One classroom I worked in was frequently organized for small-group activities and I was able to prepare and use some experimental tasks in that context. They were particularly aimed at developing mathematical language in both the pupils' first language and in English. These materials were deliberately limited so that they *had* to be shared, choices had to be agreed (this was usually discussed in their first language), and the final results explained in English. One example of a format used was a language game, where cards with geometric words on needed to be matched – though they were not always identical words, e.g. 'angle' could match with 'elbow' if the pupils agreed on the reason for the connection. Another format used cards which together made a mathematical story, and which needed to be put into a sensible sequence. A third format involved sequences of photographs which had to be ordered. In all cases of group work, it seemed important to allow the pupils to discuss the task in whatever language they preferred, but require them to report their conclusions in English to the teacher, or to other groups, or to the whole class. Wall displays of such work also played an important role in the sharing and discussion of mathematical ideas.

Once again, though, it seemed that these possibilities were essentially limited by the lack of appropriate tasks and materials. Small-group teaching is still not a common mode of teaching mathematics anywhere, despite all the arguments raised in its favour. I am convinced that it will only be more widely used when more group-work materials become published, or are developed by individual teachers themselves.

Another developing technique, among the more sensitive teachers with whom I worked, was what I can best call 'non-directive teaching'. Where the text allowed it, it seemed to be very effective practice to clarify the task facing the pupil but not to specify the process of completing the task. Different learners do have different ways of approaching problems, as we know, and it is likely that some of these differences might relate to the pupils' cultural and language backgrounds. Therefore specifying the process of finding a solution could create yet another obstacle for these pupils. An open and non-directive teaching style allows pupils to use any culturally preferred practices or processes, and can also incidentally inform that teacher about other strengths which may contribute to the learning process.

Concluding remarks

Of course, nothing which I have commented on in these three sections need relate just to teachers of ethnic minority pupils. All teachers are aware of particular inadequacies of the materials they are using, everyone needs to explore different ways of grouping pupils in their classrooms because of strong peer-group influences, and despite knowing that there never will be a 'best' way of teaching mathematics, we all have a professional duty to search for improvements. What I hope these sections may have revealed, therefore, are some promising avenues for any mathematics teacher, at any level, to explore.

As a researcher, I found the classroom experiences stimulating. The research field opening up with this style of working is rich, and I believe highly significant because of that. Recent developments in areas like 'situated cognition' demonstrate the importance of socially situated research in mathematics learning.[7] The field cries out for more classroom ethnographic research, both to document the different kinds of practice which are taking place and to elaborate the criteria which teachers believe are important in the classroom situation.

As a teacher educator, I became aware of different needs. In view of the amount of cooperative teaching I saw happening (more than one teacher in the classroom), and the amount of individualized working being used, I wonder how many of our student teachers are prepared in ways that enable them to maximize the possibilities of those modes. For example, it is very easy to leave the pupils to struggle on their own through interminable numbers of booklets and cards. (A similar theme is explored in Laurinda Brown's chapter in this volume entitled 'Stewing in your own juice'.) It is also relatively easy to explain what the texts say, if the pupil has difficulty reading them and asks for help. It is much more difficult, but I would argue infinitely more important, to teach the pupil *through* the materials, and not just teach the materials. The best teaching I saw had the pupil as the focus, and the materials were one medium for communicating mathematical activity. A non-directive teaching style strongly emphasizes this point.

At the teacher in-service level, I would focus on three aspects. First, I would look at the departmental grouping policies, the induction and monitoring of individual progress. I have never been convinced of the long-term value of rigid setting, and I am even less convinced of its supposed benefits for ethnic minority pupils. I saw too many worrying instances, for example, of English language difficulties obscuring mathematical competence, to have much faith in rigid sets. And the bottom sets filled with E2L learners were discouraging learning environments for many of the young people there, and could well have been reinforcing racist interpretations of ability and failure.

Second, I would encourage much more attention to be paid to within-class groupings and the use of more small-group teaching. Peer-group influences are always significant, and in situations where learners feel uncomfortable with the teaching approach, with the materials or with the teacher, they become even more important. The positive benefits of such peer-group influences and contributions need, in my view, to be recognized, welcomed, and encouraged by many more teachers.

Third, I would encourage far more cooperation between mathematics departments and other departments in the schools. I would particularly argue for more contact with the science department (because of similar E2L difficulties in the two departments), the English department (to focus as much attention as possible on mathematical language), the design department (because of the many possibilities for design work related to mathematics in all cultures) and the RE department (because of the importance of a better understanding of world-views as they relate to mathematics and science). Of course, this level of contact is probably impossible to sustain, but through personal discussions and specific projects certain benefits could undoubtedly develop.

Finally, and most importantly, as a teacher, I found my own conceptions challenged and my skills tested, as one would expect in any new teaching situation. Evidence comes all the time in teaching, from what the pupils say and do, from their written work and from other teachers. The difficulty is making sense of it all and knowing how best to act on it. My personal challenges revolved around interpreting the new kinds of evidence I was receiving. Ethnic minority pupils are not a homogeneous group, and certainly not a generic type. I found it both impossible and useless to try to attach specific characteristics to specific ethnic groups. I was teaching young people, not Asians or West Indians, and what I learned was not specific to any ethnic group.

Moreover, I found that I was teaching surprisingly well-motivated young people. I say 'surprisingly' because of the daunting nature of the task many of them face. Learning mathematics is never easy for any learner, but learning mathematics through a second language, with largely inappropriate materials, in a lonely classroom situation, and with teachers who were in the main overworked and highly stressed, is a formidable task.

However, as I began to empathize more with the pupils and teachers I worked with, I realized that I was becoming concerned with something far more fundamental: what should a mathematical education be trying to offer young people today? Not just young people in the ethnic minority communities, but all young people in our society. Given the tremendous investment of energy by both the pupils I saw and the teachers I worked with, I felt very critical of the value of many of the mathematical activities we were all engaged in. They often seemed trite, trivial and tiresome.

Mathematics is felt by most people to be a highly important school subject. It is a highly significant element in the various national curricula of the UK and all parents stress its importance to their children. I, too, think it is important. But why is it that important? And how should our answer to that question affect what and how we teach our pupils?

It is not enough to believe that the national curricula have answered the question for us. The official document in mathematics for England and Wales states rather starkly the mathematical content which a government department has decided is of importance. But, as teachers, we are the ones teaching young people, and we need to remind ourselves constantly of that fact. So, what mathematical education should we be offering young people today? How can the mathematics curriculum be used to create a significant educational experience for all young people of whatever ethnic background? And how can the rest of us who work in the field of mathematics education support those who have the full-time responsibility for actually teaching young people?

Notes

[1] 'Recent and relevant' experience of school teaching is now required of all initial teacher training lecturers by the Council for the Accreditation of Teacher Education.

[2] This is a theme discussed by several authors, see for example, Verma and Bagley (1982) and Foster (1990).

[3] For overviews and fuller literatures, consult Joseph (1991), Bishop (1991) and Ross (1984); more specialist books include Ascher (1991), Ascher and Ascher (1981), Bain (1977), Bell and Cornelius (1988), Ifrah (1987), Lawlor (1982), Ronan (1981), Williams (1984) and Zaslavsky (1973).

[4] For example, see Moncur (1988), Hoare (1990), Antonouris and Sparrow (1989), Jones (1989), and McLeay (1991).

[5] See the different multiplication algorithms in Joseph (1991).

[6] See Barham and Bishop (1991) for a discussion of ideas and an account of the project.

[7] See Saxe (1990) and Walkerdine (1988).

References

Antonouris, G. and Sparrow, L. (1989) 'Primary mathematics in a multicultural society', *Mathematics Teaching*, **127**, pp. 40–44.

Ascher, M. (1991) *Ethnomathematics*, Brooks/Cole.

Ascher, M. and Ascher, R. (1981) *Code of the Quipu*, University of Michigan Press.

Bain, G. (1977) *Celtic Art: the Methods of Construction*, Constable.

Barham, J. and Bishop, A. J. (1991) 'Mathematics and the deaf child' in Durkin, K. and Shire, B. (eds), *Language in Mathematical Education*, Open University Press, pp. 179–87.

Bell, R. and Cornelius, M. (1988) *Board Games Round the World: a Resource Book for Mathematical Investigations*, Cambridge University Press.

Bishop, A. J. (1991) *Mathematical Enculturation – a Cultural Perspective on Mathematics Education*, Kluwer.

Foster, P. (1990) *Policy and Practice in Multicultural and Anti-Racist Education*, Routledge.

Hoare, C. (1990) 'The invisible Japanese calculator', *Mathematics Teaching*, **131**, pp. 12–14.

Ifrah, G. (1987) *From One to Zero: a Universal History of Numbers*, Penguin.

Jones, L. (1989) 'Mathematics and Islamic art', *Mathematics in School*, **18**(4), pp. 32–5.

Joseph, G. G. (1991) *The Crest of the Peacock: the Non European Roots of Mathematics*, I. B. Tauris.

Lawlor, R. (1982) *Sacred Geometry*, Thames and Hudson.

McLeay, H. (1991) 'Mathematics and knots', *Mathematics in School*, **20**(1), pp. 28–31.

Moncur, D. (1988) 'Labyrinthine mathematics', *Mathematics Teaching*, **123**, pp. 8–9.

Ronan, C. A. (1981) *The Shorter Science and Civilization in China: Vol. 2*, Cambridge University Press.

Ross, A. (1984) *The Story of Mathematics*, Black.

Saxe, G. B. (1990) *Culture and Cognitive Development: Studies in Mathematical Understanding*, Lawrence Erlbaum Associates.

Verma, C. K. and Bagley, C. (1982) *Self-Concept, Achievement and Multicultural Education*, Macmillan.

Walkerdine, V. (1988) *The Mastery of Reason*, Routledge.

Williams, K. R. (1984) *Discover Vedic Mathematics*, Dinah Grice.

Zaslavsky, C. (1973) *Africa Counts*, Lawrence Hill.

4 Bags and baggage

John Crook and Mary Briggs

We are both relatively recent recruits from teaching in the primary class-room to teaching mathematics education in a college of higher education. The more we have worked with student teachers, the more we have found ourselves wondering about the accumulated experiences in mathematics which they bring with them to college, and what effects those experiences have on their interaction with their primary B.Ed. mathematics course. The roots of this chapter lie in our perception of a marked lack of confidence in many of these student teachers when studying mathematics education. We have also encountered similar attitudes exhibited both by primary teachers and children. Our intention is to explore some of the mathematical bags and baggage which we all carry with us, by discussing some of our findings from different avenues of research. By way of comparison, we also talked with experienced teachers about their personal turning points in mathematics.

Unpacking personal bags

There is clearly a wide variety of impressions, feelings and ideas about mathematics and mathematics education which we all have, including those which intending teachers bring with them to college. This consider-able amount of experience, from the consumer's viewpoint, contributes to views on: understanding of what mathematics is, reasons for teaching it, ways to teach it, the roles of the teacher and the pupil, disciplinary meas-ures, and the relationship one has with what one understands mathematics to be. We have all also been exposed to a wide variety of cultural influences. These include parental, family and peer attitudes to mathematics, media usage and portrayal of mathematics, and exposure to cultural myths and legends (Tobias, 1978) which abound in society (these include gender stereotypes, and the belief that mathematical ability is innate).

It is worth paying attention to these experiences for a number of obvious reasons. We need to develop shared meanings with each pupil, student or teacher in order to build on strengths, and to work on areas of weakness. It is also important to address the varying views held on the nature of mathematics, on what constitutes content, and on appropriate teaching and learning styles. There appears to be a strong relationship between the conceptions of mathematics held by a teacher and the teaching and learning styles used by that teacher (Thompson, 1984). A well-developed, holistic view of mathematics leads to a different style of teaching and a different approach to learning from one where the view is atomistic (e.g. a large number of statements of attainment to teach to). If learning mathematics is seen as a creative endeavour, it will be approached in a different way from when it is not.

All teachers are almost certain to have and to use a variety of models, concerns, and priorities when working in the classroom. These will relate, among others, to management, to social and emotional factors, and to other areas of the curriculum. As Thompson points out, such conceptions are likely to take precedence over teaching and learning decisions which are specific to mathematics. This suggests the need for us to unpack accumulated ideas carefully, not only in the context of strategies and approaches favourable to mathematics, but also in the context of the overall task of teaching in the primary classroom. For instance, past success in mathematics may lead to new teachers modelling their ideas about good teaching and learning on patterns they have experienced, whether they are appropriate to a primary school environment. Past failure may encourage them to try to avoid or minimize their contact with mathematics. Where they aspire to change a poor pattern, they may lack alternative models. Past experience may provide a driving force, to mirror or to challenge models of teaching/learning, or it may become an altogether more subtle unconscious director of the approaches used.

We do not always mean what we say nor do we always say what we mean. Equally, we do not always understand what others mean to say nor do we always share the meaning of what others do say. Communication of meaning is at the root of learning. In the multi-layered context of education, shades and nuances of meaning abound. Many opportunities exist for mismatch of ideas. The recollection of the common but individual experience of being taught in school is a rich area in which to discover a lack of shared meanings. We all have sharply observed views on a host of aspects of teaching, including: degree of planning, teacher confidence, management of the class, the learning environment, teaching strategies, use of textbooks, use of materials, sharing reasons for the activity, ability to communicate, the range and pace of work, purposeful activity, enthusiasm, flexibility, bias, pressure, attitudes to individuals, and attitudes to mathematics. Attempting to unpack just this one bag proves to be a difficult task. Doing so highlights the variety of starting-points, yet points towards common concerns of the teacher in the classroom.

Conversations

We all carry, as teachers and learners, our own bags and baggage of knowledge, beliefs and attitudes with us into any new situation. So do those we teach or who learn with us. We have approached this notion by inviting students and teachers to recollect personal experiences. All recollections are charged and coloured. They are not to be taken as anything more than part of a story. However, they can be responsible for contributing to our future actions, so we felt them to be one important focus. One of us (John) asked for specific recollections of good and bad experiences, while the other (Mary) collected mathematical biographies from earliest memories to the present day. Each method has strengths and weaknesses. As we share these recollections, we hope you will reflect on your own personal baggage and consider whether scope exists for new insights, ideas and connections.

Emotion expressed

We start this section with the familiar area of expression of feelings about mathematics. This area has been covered by many reports on attitudes to mathematics. In one piece of research work, undertaken for the Cockcroft report (DES, 1982), as many as fifty per cent of people approached to be interviewed about mathematics in everyday life refused. The most striking feature in some of those who were interviewed was the ability of even apparently straightforward problems to induce anxiety.

John: Although I expected to find negative feelings, I was still surprised at the strength of language used to describe bad experiences. A typical selection includes:

> totally devastated, really useless and frustrated, stupid, humiliated, ashamed, inadequate, small, like crying, slow and thick, a failure, an idiot, shattered, depressed, bored.

These seem pretty strong. The sort of responses I got seems very likely to give rise to the kind of anxiety which is commonly associated with mathematics. I have read a great deal about attitudes to mathematics, but it still surprised me hearing it first hand, especially bearing in mind that these are all people who have got an equivalent to GCE O-level in mathematics. Did you find the same sort of thing?

Mary: Yes, I found similar responses, but I wasn't that surprised because I had picked up some of this vehemence when working with, and interviewing, primary teachers about maths and maths teaching, prior to collecting biographies. In addition to many of the words on your list, I found:

> embarrassed, struggling, failing, terrified, demoralized, pressured, frightened, out of my depth, and many more.

Almost all of the biographies contain some negative aspects such as these. They were generally more negative, even from those who went on to study maths at degree level; very few were wholly positive.

John: My results couldn't show any weighting like that, but I could find out quite a bit about positive attitudes. When reporting good experiences, the kind of language used included words like:

> pleased, proud, growing in confidence, interested, happy, over the moon, absolutely delighted, wonderful, relaxed, encouraged, enjoyable, much more confident, involved.

The most extreme responses often referred to an examination result or being able to grasp something:

> I knew what was going on, everything seemed to be better;

> pleased I could understand and explain to others;

proud and pleased, especially as it was not a natural ability.

There seems almost a sense of relief at being able to do something in many of the responses, and certainly there is not a catalogue of soaring confidence which would balance the negative feelings we talked about.

Mary: I'd agree with that. One response which reflects that is where examination success 'was regarded as a miracle'.

There seemed to be two strands in the responses. One, like you found, related to success. The other strand was where a clear reason for studying mathematics became apparent, for example, where someone who was studying biology became aware that her hard-won understanding of statistics actually had a use.

Particular areas of mathematics

Some of the literature (e.g. Bell *et al.*, 1983) points towards key areas of mathematics which cause difficulty. What else has come through clearly in several pieces of research is that where good recollections occur, there is a strong focus on product, and achievement. (A classroom teacher (Liz) contributed to this discussion.)

Mary: I managed to find three areas of mathematics which were frequently associated with some difficulty. They were algebra, fractions and mental arithmetic. For example:

My mental arithmetic has always been, and still is, atrocious: springing perhaps from extreme anxiety over spot tables, around eight years of age.

Many people mentioned algebra, but did not go into any detail. Perhaps the memories were too painful!

John: I found that recollections about specific areas of mathematics were often very general, but what I did find interesting was that there were a relatively large number of responses which referred to success in examination or test results. Not only were these assessments looked upon with pleasure and pride, but also particular marks (such as 89 per cent) were recollected, even from primary school, suggesting that they had a strong impact on the learner. For example:

A good experience happened in my primary school when after having mental arithmetic tests every week, I came top in the whole class. My average was the highest. In fact, it was so important to me that I missed my brother's degree ceremony, and taking of a day off school, just so I could take the mental arithmetic test. It was the last one of the term and it would decide who won over the whole term.

Mary: I found that too. Not only successes, like grades and top of set, but also memories of always being last, such as:

> I remember feeling very inadequate, as I knew I was on one of the lower tables.

This contrasts with recollections such as:

> I took home extra work because I was successful and enjoyed getting 17 to 20 out of 20. I felt as though I had achieved something.

Liz: That's right, there's something terribly satisfying about having a really difficult trigonometry problem, and actually solving it and knowing you had the right answer. That used to give me quite a thrill to do that. Other subjects weren't quite so clear cut.

John: That feature of satisfaction, of getting things right, did come through, and that is certainly one feature of mathematics. Children in school are very often product orientated – getting it right, or focusing on a Logo picture, rather than talking about the processes they have gone through, or even being pleased with an elegant solution. We need to do more in the way of encouraging children to focus on process.

The role of the teacher

This section has profound implications for all of us in mathematics education in school or college. The teacher's role touches each of us first as learner in school. Early items of luggage are acquired here, which help to form the foundation of our attitudes, beliefs, and knowledge about what a teacher is. Students certainly blamed teachers for imposing a high degree of stress, plain bad teaching, and for poor relationships. All this points to the importance of the affective domain in learning, and it is a crucial area to come to grips with if we are to influence the formation of attitudes to maths.

John: For me, the major discovery was the emergence of the educational context as a key factor in recollections of bad experiences. A large number of responses relate to reports of being humiliated by the teacher in front of the class, like being made to stand on a chair, or pointedly being asked difficult questions. Many examples suggest a marked lack of sensitivity to the pupil's needs. These are the sort of things I mean:

> When I was ten, the teacher used to have mathematical competitions. She used to write a question on the board and then give the chalk to two pupils. I always seemed to be given the chalk and everyone was far quicker than me to answer the question. If you beat the other child, you could sit down. I was at the board for absolutely ages.

> Not being able to understand homework ... and after telling the teacher, she picked on me to go through the work in front of [the] class on the board.

> I had several bad experiences in junior school – being put on the spot and feeling a failure when I got the answer wrong.

Mary: I collected a great deal of material like that too. I would say that the role of the teacher was the main feature of the biographical responses. Here are two similar examples:

> … the teacher thought I had cheated by looking up the amounts in the back of the book, because my answers were exactly right. Although she didn't accuse me, she called everyone up and tore all the answers out from our books. I never forgave her for humiliating me like that.

> My study in mathematics involved me in avoiding the subject as much as possible. My primary school teacher was a quick-tempered woman. I found reciting my tables terrifying, and as a result I still don't know them.

Liz: I was saying this morning that I remember wetting my pants because I did not know 7×7, and even if somebody speaks to me sharply today and asks me 7×7, I still do not know it, it's not there in my memory at all.

John: You mean that the question is attached to an emotional reaction?

Liz: Yes, and I still have trouble with the label of 'mental arithmetic', because it meant flashcards to me and the teacher would say, 'You answer, you answer'.

John: Sometimes even 'good' recollections cast the teacher in poor light, e.g.:

> When I was nine years old, I came top of the class in the end of year exam with ninety per cent. The teacher expressed some surprise at the result and did suggest that it really should not have happened.

I would say that the class teacher was either referred to or alluded to in about half of all responses, good and bad.

Mary: There were some positive responses, such as:

> I can't remember ever thinking that maths was something I couldn't do. I now think that being good at maths influenced the way others perceived me, and therefore how I perceived myself.

Most of the biographies refer to the teacher in some way, and although a lot of them have bad things to say, perhaps this student has a clear view:

> We had an excellent teacher who seemed to make everything easy. I would say that the teacher is everything.

The change from primary to secondary school

This area, always of concern, has become even more important in the context of national curricula. Both British and American research (Bell *et al.*, 1983) support the view that this is a critical time for the laying down of attitudes to mathematics. The contributions here emphasize the importance of good teaching on either side of the split rather than reveal general differences. (Judi is a teacher in a primary school.)

> **Mary**: One of the things I think that you didn't actually get, John, with your good and bad experiences, and that a biography did give, is the issue that relates to the transfer between schools at about the age of eleven. There were quite a lot of people who had good experiences at primary school, so perhaps good teaching approaches had actually reached the primary school, but had not infiltrated the secondary schools.

> **Judi**: I experienced the complete reverse. I was the only child in the summer term intake in the infant school, so I was left to my own devices in reading and in maths. I didn't read till I was seven. I remember in my second year sitting on a workcard as somebody was picking it up. I got my hand slapped for tearing it. I remember in the first-year juniors sitting in a desk and someone turning round to me and asking me a question. I then asked the person behind me and got caught. I was sent to the headmaster accused of copying. That is my hate of maths at primary school.

> **Mary**: It's interesting ... that the students have highlighted problems at the secondary stage. At the primary stage, one person actually described the teacher as being domineering and authoritarian. It seems that when they are talking about negative attitudes to mathematics, they describe the teacher in language that reinforces the popular stereotype of the 'maths teacher'.

> **John**: I did not ask the students to be explicit about phase of education, Mary, but I was able to work out that half of all the bad experiences relate to the ten- to thirteen-year-old age band. This connects both with research and with your point about transfer. Good recollections were spread fairly evenly between primary and secondary phases. Quite a few of the secondary school responses related to success or failure in GCE examination results.

Personal failure

This is a well-documented area (e.g. Tobias, 1978; Buxton, 1981), and the results collected, although depressing, provided very little in the way of surprise.

> **Mary**: Sometimes in biographies, specific instances, such as of personal failure, can be masked in favour of a more general 'feel' created over a period of time. You gain in a more reflective and developmental view. Sometimes, you do get an overwhelming negative attitude which pervades. For example:

>> I started to bunk my maths lessons rather than remain with the constantly quickening heartbeat and the sense that I would be found out as a failure ... To be honest, maths for me is still a case of *red alert* and panic stations.

John: I collected a number of statements which expressed help-lessness.

> I felt I was the only one who was bad at mathematics.

> I couldn't keep up with all my friends who could do it.

> I was the only one who never understood.

> Even though I had an understanding and patient teacher, I still couldn't grasp certain mathematical formulae.

This gives some indication of the wretchedness which character-izes many of the responses. Although such responses are common it does make you wonder about which direction the student teacher is going to move in as a result, doesn't it?

Gender

The literature on gender and mathematics tends to suggest that any apparent differences which exist between boys and girls or men and women are not due to differences in ability (Walden and Walkerdine, 1985). They appear to be rooted in teacher perceptions of a relationship between characteristics of mathematical understanding and gender, in ways in which the pupil relates to the teacher, and in pupil and teacher perceptions of mathematics. (Two teachers, Liz and Val, contribute.)

Mary: I have chosen the following examples to illustrate typical responses.

> I enjoyed maths, especially when I got on well in a female teacher's class at O-level. I realized maths was not 'just for boys'.

> ... there were several boys in class who were very quick, therefore I'd only just started to work out the answer when they had supplied it.

> Boys who were generally better at maths intimidated the less able.

> Due to the fact that I thought at the time that girls don't do maths, and it was unusual for a girl to do maths at university, I based my A-level choices on arts and language.

The second group of examples are more to do with student views of their teachers' responses in mathematics lessons or classes.

> ... both my male teachers had seemed to encourage boys more than girls. I think my stubborn nature made me want to do well because of their attitude to 'show them', as it were.

> He preferred helping the boys with their computer studies.

Liz: I've noticed the difference between some of the girls and the boys in my class, but not all of them. The boys, by and large, seem to be better at mental arithmetic and the girls tend to apply themselves more to longer-term problem solving. I've had consciously to mix them up so that they get different experiences.

Val: My daughter was not that good in the junior school. She had to do Peak, and I think she felt intimidated that some people were ahead of her. Now she's in the secondary school and they are doing new maths, investigational maths, and she's doing very well. Suddenly, she's at the top of the top set, and she's enjoying it.

John: Only yesterday I was discussing gender issues with a female graduate in mathematics. She told me that she has learned not to discuss her degree subject in social situations. She found that it was a conversation stopper. Males in particular often suggested to her that it was not a 'female' subject.

Mary: It is interesting that gender is still very much an issue in mathematics education in schools despite so many initiatives. Why is it that so little has changed?

Choice of teaching course

When people were asked to write their mathematics biographies, they were asked to include whether they felt that their attitude to mathematics had influenced the choice of age groups they planned to teach. It looks increasingly likely that one factor in choosing a course which focused on teaching younger children was the decision to avoid older age groups. This raises the question about what 'content' is needed to teach mathematics to any particular age range, and what relationship that has with pedagogic skills.

Mary: The biographies have shown interesting things about student perceptions of mathematics and how that influences the choice of age group that they are going to teach. Most responses were from students who had opted to teach the three to nine age range, and there seemed to be two broad categories of response. First, there was a group who had thought about their negative attitudes to confidence and ability in a positive way.

> Perhaps my experiences have had an influence on the age group I have decided to choose to teach, because it is important at such an age not to make them feel nervous about maths, and to try to make maths fun.

> I feel more at ease teaching infants in that I don't worry they'll shoot up above my low level. I find it fun with them, because it is concrete and it helps me relate it more easily. I feel I can sympathize with those who find it a difficult subject to grasp, because once you get one rule straight, then there's another and it seems to go on for ages. If you find maths hard, it can be discouraging rather than exciting, like it should be.

Although they are being positive, they are using their poor experiences to restrict their choice, with phrases like:

> My experience may have affected my preference for a lower age group, as I have more confidence to teach 'easier' maths.

> I want to teach infants partly because of my lack of confidence in maths. I can't escape the idea that it is only for clever people.

The second category was of those students who had studied mathematics as a main subject. They gave two contrasting views: those who wanted to help young children enjoy mathematics, or those who wanted to pursue their interest and teach at secondary level.

> I get very wound up when I hear of children that do not enjoy maths, so I feel very strongly about this. I want others to enjoy maths as well as understand.

> I enjoy my maths, and it is because of this experience that I hope to teach maths in secondary school. This was a difficult decision to make, because I also realize how important maths is in primary schools, but the style of teaching in primary schools puts me off. Another reason for choosing to teach 'my subject' is that I really enjoy it and feel this is a great bonus. Hopefully, I can transmit this enjoyment to children.

When I started to collect biographies from practising teachers, I found that this aspect remained an issue for some teachers deep into their career, who expressed it in comments such as: 'I wouldn't dare to attempt maths with older children'. Is all mathematical confidence bound by the situation?

Turning points

This final section looks at some of the turning points reported by maths coordinators who agreed to take part in a short discussion on our work. We felt it offered a useful contribution towards understanding the process of learning to be a teacher, and appeared to underline some of the points already bought out in the context of student teachers.

Judi: It was through teaching upper juniors that I became confident in maths. A lot of things I had learned parrot fashion and didn't understand why. In having to teach it, I had to unjumble it and it was a kind of *eureka*.

John: What is it that made you want to unjumble it? Do you know what made you do it?

Judi: I think … it was understanding decimals. I never understood decimals, I'd only learned that $\frac{1}{4}$ is 0.25 and, if I was lucky, 25 per cent. I didn't really understand what a percentage was, I just knew kind of formulas and that was it. I think I got a lot of books and I tried to unscramble it and it also linked with a course

I went on. A two-day course one weekend which Edith Biggs gave was the start of my love of maths really. If I think of my hobbies and how I was trained, I did embroidery, and I've always made my own clothes and done my own tailoring. I've always enjoyed patterning, so I've always done and enjoyed geometric maths. That never was the worry, measures and geometry. It was the number.

Jenny: I was always one of the ones who used to ring up my friends to find out how to do the homework. My parents couldn't do it either. None of us had a clue most of the time how to do it, so a lot of it I didn't understand.

John: So where has your interest in the process come from?

Jenny: I found out that maths wasn't just what I thought it was – writing down numbers and calculations. It was so much more. It's sort of in every aspect of life.

John: Can you put a finger on it, where that happened? Judi mentioned Edith Biggs.

Jenny: Well, I suppose it's because I have always approached teaching from the fun and interest angle. If the children find it fun, then they are going to learn much better. Even before I was maths coordinator, I used to use *Countdown* games from the television. I've always liked approaching it from that angle. I like the investigation and problem solving.

Catherine: That connects for me. As you know, I'm a trained French teacher, and when I first went into a middle school, I certainly thought maths was going to be a problem. I hadn't taught maths before at all. I went to the maths centre and picked up numerous ideas, mainly based on Cockcroft and recent changes in thinking about maths education, and I thought this is a bit like French. It's a language people often don't speak well. If they don't speak it, they are mystified, but if you manage to teach them a language, they can enjoy it … I realize that I can go into these investigations and say: 'I don't know, you don't know, let's see what happens.'

Val: I had no problem with maths at all – it was my favourite subject at college. When I used to have to teach lessons, I remember the lecturer saying: 'You assume that people know too much.' So I had to be very careful with teaching children: not to patronize, or say: 'It's obvious that's that.' I started new methods at college because they used to say: 'Can you calculate how thick a sheet of paper is?', and probability and Pascal's triangle … but it wasn't really happening in schools in those days. I feel sad that any child doesn't like maths. That upsets me, because I enjoyed it. I feel it's a challenge and I want them to feel that they like it too. They are missing something if they don't.

Liz: For me, it's down to personalities. The personality of the teacher, and of whoever perhaps inspired you to get you going. I know who started me on maths, it was dear old Johnny Ball on the television. He's lovely. That's what made me interact with maths. It was my teachers that had dampened it down and made me feel a failure, when it was their teaching that was the failure.

Adding to our luggage

The teacher appears to fare badly in many of the recollections reported here. It is not our intention to point fingers, but rather to look as clearly as we can at some elements of what constitutes memories of mathematics education and contributes to their perpetuation or change. The affective domain undoubtedly is a very potent and important force in the learning process. Most teachers strive for success, often in difficult circumstances, and would present another truth from the memories reported here. Some of the views expressed may focus on a few casualties among many survivors (although we doubt it). It is more likely that most often the teacher was unaware of the depth of feeling, the hurt felt, the hidden contribution to the laying down of attitudes. None the less, we are certain that most readers will have little difficulty in bringing to mind experiences in mathematics classes which led to strong feelings, which in turn played their part in subsequent action. It is clearly important, and in the best interests of mathematics education, that the experiences we provide for learners lead to positive attitudes towards mathematics.

It is unlikely that we can discard easily any item we carry in our own mathematical baggage, but it is important to be aware of what is there, because it will influence how we teach. As teachers, we do need to acknowledge the importance that the affective domain plays in our teaching, and add that to what we carry.

References and further reading

Bell, A. W., Costello, J and Küchemann, D. E. (1983) *A Review of Research in Mathematics Education, Part A*, NFER–Nelson.

Biggs, E. (1983) *Confident Mathematics Teaching 5–13*, NFER–Nelson.

Buxton, L. (1981) *Do You Panic About Mathematics?*, Heinemann.

DES (1982) *Mathematics Counts*, HMSO, paras 16, 20, 21, 24, 34.

Hoyles, C. (1982) 'The pupil's view of mathematics learning', *Educational Studies in Mathematics*, **13**(4), pp. 349–72.

Shuard, H. (1986) *Primary Mathematics Today and Tomorrow*, Longman.

Thomas, B. and Costello, J. (1988) 'Identifying attitudes to mathematics', *Mathematics Teaching*, **122**, pp. 62–4.

Thompson, A. G. (1984) 'The relationship of teachers' conceptions of mathematics and mathematics teaching to instructional practice', *Educational Studies in Mathematics*, **15**(2), pp. 105–27.

Tobias, S. (1978) *Overcoming Math Anxiety*, Norton.

Walden, R. and Walkerdine, V. (1985) *Girls and Mathematics: from Primary to Secondary Schooling*, Bedford Way Papers No. 24, University of London Institute of Education.

5 What the pupils say about it

Celia Hoyles

PUPIL 1:   Well, there is maths. I always find maths hard. That's why I switched from O-level to CSE, because I found O-level too hard. Maths is my weakest subject and I'm useless at it.

INTERVIEWER: Can you think of a time to tell me about which stands out as being particularly bad?

PUPIL 1:   Well, there is maths all this year. I just cannot do it. I can't remember what it was, even, but it should all be easy. I just find it hard and it is all the easy stuff.

INTERVIEWER: What happens exactly?

PUPIL 1:   I'm trying to do my homework, at home like, it's always the same. I keep trying and trying and just nothing comes out. I feel so tight inside, I want to explode. You know, sick and sweating, shaking. The longer I sit there, the worse it gets. I feel I ought to give up, I'm in such a state.

INTERVIEWER: You're in a state?

PUPIL 1:   I just know I'm useless at maths. When I am sitting there I know I will not be able to do it. Once it was straight lines, the gradients and things. It was terrible. I didn't have a clue and I just felt sick with anxiety. But it's always happening. It affects part of my life. I say at home, 'I did badly in maths today and have not learned as much as I should.'

INTERVIEWER: Is there anything more you can tell me?

PUPIL 1:   Not really. I just give up in the end, I suppose. There is nothing else I can do. I get so het up sometimes, it's just not worth it. I think I give up straight away more now and I don't do much worse. But I still feel sick though when I get maths homework.

◊   ◊   ◊

PUPIL 2:   Oh, I know, we once did these triangles.

INTERVIEWER: Now, when was this?

PUPIL 2:   I'm not sure. Yes, I know, it was the third year because we had Mr —. It was in his lesson.

INTERVIEWER: What happened exactly? I want to try to imagine being there, seeing what was going on.

PUPIL 2:   Well, I just seemed to be able to do these triangles. It was amazing, because I'm usually no good at maths and way behind. Every question came along and I just did it OK. It's not like that now, I can't do anything and find it all awful.

INTERVIEWER: Going back to this nice time with triangles, can you remember what you felt like when it happened? What did it mean to you?

PUPIL 2:   I felt I could see what it was all about for a change. It was amazing but I knew I was doing well because I was way ahead of my mates in the book. It was great to feel that you were good at it, you know, expect to get it out.

INTERVIEWER: You expected to get it out, then?

PUPIL 2:   Yes, I was doing it all and getting on instead of just sitting there letting it pass.

INTERVIEWER: Why was that, do you think?

PUPIL 2:   I don't know. It was one of those things. It just clicked, I suppose, and I was doing well.

These 'critical incidents' were related by fourteen-year-olds. Notice that, in both these interviews, the pupils were very absorbed with themselves. They had strong ideas about what they were capable of doing and achieving in mathematics. The mathematical work being undertaken is not described in any detail, merely mentioned or named. This focus on self rather than on the task in hand seems to be a general trend in mathematics learning.

Another trend is the importance pupils place on the way the teacher behaves in the classroom and presents the mathematics.

INTERVIEWER: Now, these lessons with Mr — with all these worksheets …

PUPIL 3:   Sometimes, you know, he used to give us worksheets and when we came into the year, we had these books, SMP books. And then we hadn't finished it and then he gave us another SMP Book D and Mr — said that we must get two SMP books done in a term, I think. But how can we do that when there are all these things in it that you don't even understand and we used to skip through pages. Like one day we'd be on 42 and the next day we'd be up to 50, and something like that.

INTERVIEWER: You said 'all these things in it'. What sort of things do you mean?

PUPIL 3:   In maths. You know in these SMP books, like – um – I don't know. Because when I ask my Mum, you know, sometimes I used to go and ask Mum, 'Can you do this?', 'Help me do this in the book', and she said that she'd never done that at school, so she doesn't know what it's about.

INTERVIEWER: She doesn't know what it is about?

PUPIL 3: That's right. Mum said that when she was small and used to know her times tables, you know, like now some people don't know their times tables. They used to learn it; they used to have to stand up in class and say it and everything like that. What we do now is not important.

INTERVIEWER: How did you feel during these lessons?

PUPIL 3: Well, just hopeless. It was all too much, like a growing mountain on top of me. I never had a chance to get anything explained or to finish anything.

◊   ◊   ◊

PUPIL 4: That was in the first year. I remember it well.

INTERVIEWER: What happened then?

PUPIL 4: Well, the teacher was always picking on me.

INTERVIEWER: Picking on you?

PUPIL 4: Yes, and in one lesson she jumped on me. I wasn't doing anything, but she said, 'Come to the board and do this sum.' Fractions, it was. My mind went a blank. Couldn't do nothing; couldn't even begin.

INTERVIEWER: What did you feel then?

PUPIL 4: Awful; shown up. All my mates were laughing at me and calling out. I was stuck there. They thought it was great fun. I felt so stupid I wanted the floor to open up and swallow me. It was easy, you know. The teacher kept me there and kept on asking me questions in front of the rest. I just got worse. I can remember sweating all over.

In the last two stories, the pupils react to what was perceived as bad planning, excessive workload or public humiliation in the mathematics classroom with feelings of anxiety and stress. What is particularly thought-provoking is that such incidents seem adversely to affect pupils' confidence in their mathematical ability which could perhaps have more long-lasting consequences. There seem to be a wealth of similar insights that can be obtained by exploring how pupils are reacting to their everyday experiences in mathematics, if we can only find the time to hear about them. As one pupil said to me after an interview: 'I really enjoyed that, miss, you sitting there and listening to me. Makes a change somehow, doesn't it.'

Note

For more details of this work, please see the longer article by the author: 'The pupil's view of mathematics learning', *Educational Studies in Mathematics*, **13**(4), pp. 349–72.

Section II

School mathematics

Section introduction

With the advent of national curricula in the United Kingdom in the early 1990s, the mathematics to be taught in schools seemed to become well defined and its purposes made clear. There were dozens of statements of content which were devised by a particular group of people, who had their own understandings and predilections, not only for the topics they included, but also for the order in which these might be taught. What is remarkable is that the reasons for these choices – the aims of teaching them – are not included in the national curricula. Some aims are perhaps implicit in the listings, but they were possibly not even articulated by the working parties.

Teachers are thus compelled to teach certain subject matter, but the purposes for which it is intended children should learn these topics are unknown. Teachers have to supply their own aims and those they adopt will radically affect the emphases in their teaching. The chapters in this section each suggest that such aims are not obvious and interpreting statements in the national curricula has to been done with caution. All the authors, in their different ways, offer images of what school mathematics might be about, as well as providing *their* reasons for suggesting what they do.

In the first chapter, Angela Walsh looks at the impact of the calculator on the number curriculum for the early years and shows how this forces reconsideration of the aims of teaching number. Janet Ainley describes a typical primary school lesson on measurement and shows how the purposes of including the various strands of activity are being confused, so that little of *mathematical* value is being learned. In his consideration of geometry, John Mason looks beyond the naming aspects to the purpose of teaching geometrical facts. His conclusion is perhaps surprising and has considerable implications for the stressings that a teacher might give to work on shape and space. Martin Hoffman and Arthur Powell look at a device – number circles – quite often seen in mathematics courses. Frequently, however, the purpose of working with this is thought to be practice in computation. The writers show how it can instead be conceived as a tool for promoting algebraic thinking and symbolism. In the final piece, Alan Graham argues that the most crucial aspect of teaching statistics – the posing of questions that give a purpose to the rest of the work – has actually been left out of the national curricula.

6 The calculator as a tool for learning

Angela Walsh

I sat down beside seven-year-old Jane who was holding a calculator displaying 2000000. Seemingly unperturbed by my presence, Jane began to write the number down on her paper. My curiosity got the better of me, and I enquired about the number.

'It came from that', she said, pointing to a 'sum' on her sheet. 'The answer is two million – I did it on my calculator.'

'Where did the question come from?', I asked.

'I made it up', replied Jane. 'It's one hundred times two thousand', pointing to her paper showing 100×20000.

'Can you show me two thousand on the calculator?', I asked.

'Yes, look', she said, and displayed 2000. 'Oh! That sum can't be two thousand can it? ... But I don't know how to say that number' (pointing to the 20000).

Jane and her friends explained that they had been given the calculators by their teacher yesterday, and they were clearly enjoying using them. They had just spent the best part of an hour moving in and out of the operations of addition, subtraction and multiplication together with a range of single- to multi-digit numbers. They did not always get what might be termed 'right' answers, and it was not easy to discern what they did or did not know about the magnitude of the numbers with which they were dealing. Yet there appeared to be something about the action of pressing buttons which produced an immediate result that motivated and stimulated them to explore, experiment and conjecture.

A classroom situation such as this one, where young learners are offered the freedom to explore numerical ideas supported by the calculator as a tool, is not commonplace practice in schools. In discussion with many teacher groups, an account of just such a classroom episode evokes comments such as the following. Many are dismissive of the *task* as a worthwhile learning experience and as a trigger for appropriate activity for children of this age.

Seven years of age and using a calculator for number work?

Such large numbers – ridiculous!

Why confuse her by letting her introduce different operations simultaneously?

Clearly she doesn't or can't know what she is doing.

She's going to be helpless without a calculator.

She will never understand place-value learning in that way.

These teachers' comments reflect accepted beliefs held by many concerning the child's development of the concept of number. These beliefs are heavily influenced by at least eighty years of history and practice which has seen 'early years' mathematics as predominantly concerned with the need to develop successful users of standard paper-and-pencil arithmetic techniques. This emphasis on learning particular algorithms for the four operations ('the four rules') has, in its wake, determined the pedagogical approach and produced an orthodoxy for teaching about number. This orthodoxy has pervaded almost every textbook available for primary-aged children during the last fifty or so years. (For some examples of this, see Eddie Gray's chapter in this volume.)

A firm attachment to long-established teaching methods and approaches is understandable. Moving into a new area involving a perspective changed by technology, one where control of learning may need to be vested in both child and teacher and where development of the subject matter does not necessarily fit neatly into small sequential steps (as with Jane and her friends), is likely to be threatening. In addition, a belief in the adverse effects of the use of calculators by young learners is likely to be a genuine concern. Yet calculators are widely used in everyday life. Adults accept calculators in use at home, in shops, on television and in school; they are also accepted tools for use in the final years of compulsory schooling and even in many public examinations. It seems, apparently, that it is acceptable to forget about standard algorithms and to make use of a calculator, *provided* one has first learned the 'basics' – namely the standard methods for the so-called 'four rules of number' – so that one is a user who supposedly 'knows what they are doing'.

But evidence suggests that not only do the majority of primary-aged children see older people using calculators for number work, they also themselves profess either to owning a calculator or having ready access to one (see Shuard, 1986). Calculators are already a part of their world, at least outside school.

Calculators have the apparent advantages of speed, accuracy and ease of use. For example, it is far easier to remember how to multiply two numbers with a calculator than how to set down a complex algorithm incorporating paper-and-pencil methods including vertical columns of thousands, hundreds, ten and units. Calculators also free users from the need to remember how the method works, and allow them to concentrate upon the process of doing and making sense of the mathematics. What other advantages might calculators have to offer?

Given the advantages described above, and the evidence that calculators are generally available to and accepted by quite young children, it seems important to ascertain whether it is possible to harness the potential of the calculator to promote meaningful and successful mathematics learning for young children. In addition, it seems feasible to suggest that the potential outcomes of the use of a calculator might offer some insight into our understanding of children's learning with regard to number.

Evidence from a research and development project (The PrIME Project, 1991), which involved very large numbers of children aged 6–7 (including

Jane and her classmates) and which followed these children c
of several years, can provide at least some partial answers to thes
Throughout the three years of the project, the children had acces
to a wide range of practical apparatus and a calculator for use wh
at their mathematics. It was their choice when and whether to t
or none of these. No teaching of the standard approaches to the
of number was carried out.

The research findings suggest (as was the case with Jane and her classmates)
that many of the children encountered several mathematical ideas and
concepts which would not normally be met until much later. They appear
to be able to operate successfully with these more advanced ideas. They
seem to have developed intuitive approaches for dealing with processes
which often cause difficulty even for many older pupils and which have
generally been assumed to have to be learned in a strict order within a well-
defined structure. For example, they can operate with large and small
numbers; they know something of what a negative number is and can do
simple addition and subtraction with them; they have some appreciation of
both decimals and fractions; they show a well-developed understanding of
place value. The range of tasks that the children have worked with over the
last few years is enormous. A few examples are offered below, both to
provide evidence to support the statements above and to give a flavour of
the types of activity and the developments that took place.

Doing some 'sums'

Sophie (aged 6) decided to make up some sums. She used small numbers –
1, 3, 4, and the operations of addition and subtraction. She did lots of
calculation, but it didn't look like anyone else's recording. You might think
she was unhappy about larger numbers, but it transpired she had a special
reason for her choice.

Well done Sophie.

Developing understanding

Tony (aged 7) was working on different ways of 'making' the number he placed in the centre of the 'box', by placing numbers at each vertex. Tony chose the numbers.

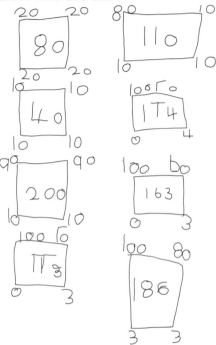

Maria (aged 9) when working on this activity decided to use a triangle and, after doing several of this type, wrote this one down with apparent ease.

After several trial-and-improvement attempts to reach a solution on the calculator, she recorded her findings.

33,333333

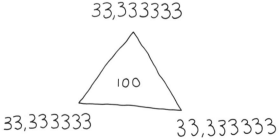

Her next attempt was as follows. She said it would produce a similar pattern, but she found the following solution.

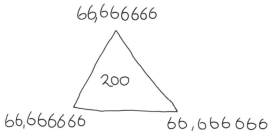

66,666666   66,666 666

After some minutes pondering, she set about finding a range of examples that gave either 0.333333 or 0.666666, etc. Not long after, she stated that they couldn't have any other answers except ones with these kinds of funny numbers or ones which didn't have any funny bits, like 9 or 42.

Jody (aged 8½ years) was looking at what happened to 1 and 4 using the four operations, to see if she could show the fraction ¼ on her calculator.

$$4 + 1 = 5 \quad 1 + 4 = 5 \quad 1 \times 4 = 4 \quad 4 \times 1 = 4$$
$$4 - 1 = 3 \quad 1 - 4 = -3 \quad 4 \div 1 = 4 \quad 1 \div 4 = 0.25$$

After further experimenting, Jody said, 'I think ¼ is the same as 0.25 ... because 0.25 + 0.25 + 0.25 + 0.25 = 1 ... 0.25 × 4 = 1.'

Andrew and Simon (aged almost 9 years) were trying to complete their cycle of operations. The aim was to get back to where they started.

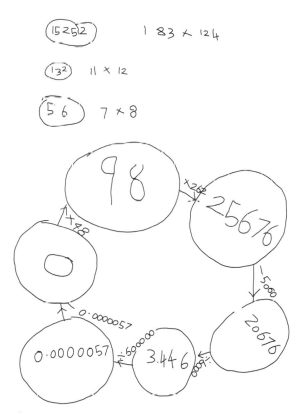

They became stuck when they reached 0.0000057. After a few minutes pondering, Andrew said, 'I know, you have to subtract that much', pointing to the display showing 0.0000057, 'and we get zero'. However, Simon added it, so producing a display showing 0.0000114. After a short while, Andrew said 'You have doubled it ... You must have pressed add ... Anyway, now subtract that 0.0000114 to get us to zero and then we can add 98 ...'

Problem solving

Sally, Julia and Katie (all aged 6½) decided they wanted to find out how many children were in their school. Their teacher was a little apprehensive, but decided to let them go ahead. After collecting their information, they recorded and totalled their numbers as follows, thus devising a working algorithm for themselves.

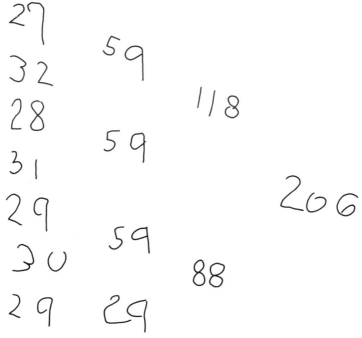

I posed the question: 'How much water do we drink at lunch time (either the whole class or the school)?' I chatted to each group, and asked them to explain how they had worked it out. One girl seemed to be in some difficulties. She had on her paper:

    10 glasses was 1200 millilitres

I asked how much 20 glasses would be. It was quite a time before she said 'Two of those', and wrote:

    20 glasses was 2400 ml

I asked how much 30 glasses would be. After what seemed like eternity, when she was working on another task, she wrote:

    30 was 3600 ml

She read out the number as 'Three hundred and sixty', but then immediately corrected herself and said, 'No it isn't, it's three thousand, six hundred'.

Talking about the number system with year 4 children (8–9 years)

TEACHER: What do you think is the biggest number in the world?

WENDY: A trillion.

TEACHER: Do you think you could tell me what that looks like? [Wendy fetches a pen.]

ANDREW: A million … it looks like a thousand with one more nought on the end. [Wendy writes 1.111121.]

GREGG: That's not big at all … it's just over one.

ANDREW: [Andrew writes 10000.] Or is it a trillion?

ANNA: A trillion … But I don't know what it looks like.

TEACHER: No idea?

ANNA: A one and lots of noughts.

TEACHER: Will it fit on your calculator?

ANNA: No, it's got too many noughts.

DAVID: Nine thousand million … It starts with a nine, but it won't fit on my calculator.

CLARE: There isn't a biggest number in the world, because it just goes on and on and on, because if it does, it just goes up to a certain number and then it goes on again like 1 2 3 4 5 6 7 8 9 and then back to 1 with two numbers.

TEACHER: Do you think you can get the biggest number on the calculator?

SAMANTHA: I do think it goes on and on, but the biggest number that I can find out is on the calculator.

HANNAH: A zillion and it's got twenty-six noughts as 'z' is the last letter.

LUCY: Three thousand and one million.

TEACHER: And you can't go any further?

SUZY: Three thousand and one million and one.

JOHN: As Clare said, there's only a number it can go up to … Well, it keeps going on, because it keeps going on into thousands and you end up in thousands … It keeps going higher into thousands and things like that and it isn't actually getting any bigger, because it's getting higher, but you think it's getting bigger – but it's not.

GREGG: The biggest number on the calculator is 99999999.

KEITH: Eight nines.

HANNAH: If there is a biggest number in the world, then the smallest number must be minus that.

ANNA: It stops at any number that you can stop at … It stops at any number you can't count to.

TEACHER: What do you mean?

ANNA: Like if you can only count to one hundred, it stops there for you.

These examples demonstrate that these young learners are making good use of the calculator – the technology of their era. They do it with apparent ease and, like Jane, seem to experience excitement in learning. They demonstrate confidence, the ability to make and monitor choices, to explore, to engage in challenge and, as the last example in particular shows, the ability to articulate their knowledge and ideas and the willingness to share those experiences with their friends. They are learning very much as one learns in life, constructing their knowledge in such a way as to allow for change and development.

Some questions for the future

Given the enhanced level of mathematical activity engaged in by many of these children, we need to ask where some of these children will be in their mathematical development by the end of their primary years, and also ponder the implications for later schooling.

How do these findings relate to a general perception of how children acquire number concepts and skills and to theories of cognitive development in mathematics? Both of these have contributed much to the view of progression and presentation of the content of mathematics for children in their primary years. This view sees mathematics being learned through the acquisition of skills and concepts within a hierarchical development, generally seen as linear or spiral and contributing to a well-defined, structured, sequential framework. Many of these pupils show abilities far beyond those one would assume possible for children of this age. Many are able to derive mathematical meanings for themselves from their experiences, and can make connections about mathematical ideas, thus appearing to 'know' things that they have not been taught.

I end with three questions.

- What roles could the calculator play in supporting such enhanced development of mathematical thinking?

- How may we best support teachers to respond to this challenge, namely to make effective use of the calculator as a teaching and learning tool for all children of *all* ages?

- How do we work towards a curriculum approach which addresses the question of the impact of technology on the teaching of mathematics in schools?

References

Hilary Shuard (1986) *Primary Mathematics Today and Tomorrow*, Longman.

The PrIME Project (1991) *Calculators, Children and Mathematics*, Simon and Schuster.

7 Is there any mathematics in measurement?

Janet Ainley

A class of eight-year-olds is in the middle of a mathematics lesson. The room is full of activity. Some children are sitting at tables, writing in their exercise books and discussing with their neighbours. Others are crouching on the floor in various parts of the room, moving paper cut-outs of feet and counting. Some are working in other parts of the room, measuring doors, window frames, tables, chairs or bookshelves with their cut-outs. The teacher is moving around, talking to individuals or pairs of children, reminding them how to use their foot measures correctly, placing a finger at the point the toe reaches before moving the shape forward and lining up the heel at the same point. Very occasionally, she has to comment on behaviour or intervene in territory disputes.

On the chalkboard is a table, and a reminder to record measurements in the correct units.

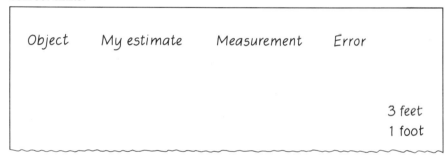

Children move purposefully around the room, from their places to objects they have chosen to measure, and back again to record results. Everyone is busy and engaged in the activity. There is a pleasing hum of conversation. The teacher and the children look confident and relaxed.

A glance at the exercise books which lie open shows similar tables drawn in previous lessons to record measurements of many of the same objects in different units: handspans, cubits, finger widths. These have been marked by the teacher, and in some cases the calculations of the 'Errors' have been corrected. Today, the children are filling in their tables confidently. A few children are clearly considering their estimates carefully and discussing their results.

A more careful look reveals a variety of approaches to the activity. In one group, several books have 'floor' in the 'Object' column, and all have '40 feet' given as the estimate. Their owners are busy measuring across the width of the room. Looking at the previous objects in the table, it is clear that the estimates given are the same in all these books, but they vary widely from the actual measurements recorded.

At another table, a book indicates that a child is measuring the notice-board. The 'Estimate' column is blank. The book's owner returns and writes '5 feet' in both the 'Estimate' and the 'Measurement' columns, and '0 feet' in the final column. Other books on this table indicate the same pattern of identical estimates and measures.

At the back of the room, two children are discussing their work:

> What did you just measure?

> The door.

> What did you get?

> Eight feet.

> I'll do that next then.

The second child carefully enters '8 feet' as an estimate for the door, and goes off to measure it.

At the end of the lesson, the teacher asks some children for particular results and questions the class about why these vary. The majority of hands go up, and the child chosen explains that some people have bigger feet than others. The teacher collects in the exercise books. In future lessons, there will probably be similar activities going on, using metre rulers, tape measures, trundle wheels.

What is this lesson about?

What does the teacher see? The children are learning to estimate and measure in non-standard units: they are also starting to see why these units have limited usefulness, and understand the need for standard units. Measurement is an important skill for everyday life, and it gives them a chance to use numbers in a practical activity. The children enjoy lessons like this one, where they have some practical work to do.

What do the children see? They enjoy the lesson. There is a clearly defined and not-too-difficult task. Not much writing is required. There is some calculation to do in working out the error, but, as we have seen, there are ways of avoiding this, or at least making it easier. It is a relaxed lesson: estimates are meant to be wrong, so no one is worried about failure.

As an observer, I see a lesson in which everyone is busy, but to no real purpose, with very little mathematical thinking going on at all. The whole idea of estimating first, and *then* measuring is a very odd one. Why would you want to do that? The only purpose of this sort of estimation is to see how good you are at it, and to get better at it, and that is not a purpose that means anything to the children. There is no pay-off for them in being good at estimation. Some children may, quite understandably, think that what is important is to get their estimate 'right', and so they tend to do the measuring first. It seems unlikely that anyone actually improves their skill at estimating lengths through this sort of activity.

Lessons like this go on in many, if not most, primary schools. It is the way we have come to teach measurement, not only of length, but also of weight and capacity. The teaching of measurement is traditionally part (and, in the case of primary schools, a sizeable part) of the mathematics curriculum. But where is the mathematics? I ask this question not just about the kind of lesson I have described, but about measurement as a topic. Is it appropriate to think of it as part of mathematics? By doing 'measuring activities' in mathematics lessons, are children actually learning either mathematics or a 'real-world' skill? Before answering these questions, I would like to look further both at what currently goes on in schools, and at what is really involved in learning about measurement.

It is possible to make a plausible a case for a progression in the learning of measurement which is generally followed by primary schools and commercial schemes. It could be summarized as:

- awareness of what is being measured – developing appropriate vocabulary (heavy, light, longer, narrower, etc.);
- comparing, sorting, ordering – by direct comparison or comparison with a chosen unit;
- measuring with a convenient, non-standard unit – foot-lengths, cupfuls, weight of marbles, etc.;
- using standard (metric) measures and understanding the system of units.

This progression is usually considered separately for length, weight and capacity, with slightly different programmes being followed for other measures, such as those of time, area or volume.

Looking at a progression like this suggests a coherent topic with a 'natural' line of development. It seems to me that this is far from being the case. There are at least four separate strands within the topic, none of which are often recognized or addressed. These are estimation, using measuring instruments, the structure of the system of units, and approximation and appropriate accuracy. I shall explore each of these separately to see what mathematics they contain.

Estimation

Having a sense of the size of common units of measurement is clearly an important aspect of measurement. If you have no idea of this, it is hard to know what degree of accuracy is appropriate. This is just one way in which estimation is useful. We also often estimate quantities without using any particular unit, using instead some form of comparison. As adults, we carry around reference points in our heads which we can use for the kind of estimates we actually need to make. For many people in Britain, this may involve rough conversions from imperial to metric units. You might like to make your personal list: some of my reference points are these.

- My handspan is about 8 inches (useful for checking the size of cake tins, or the length of knitting).

- I can visualize a pint bottle or carton of milk, and a litre carton of fruit juice.
- My own height is 5 feet 6 inches.
- A 50 g ball of wool is equivalent to a 2 ounce ball.
- A teaspoon is about 5 ml, which I know (but do not *believe*) is the same as 5 cm^3, or 5 centicubes.
- I can measure fabric in yards or metres between my nose and my fingertips.
- I know what a (1 kg) bag of sugar feels like.

These are all learned reference points for particular units. I also have some reference points which are intuitive, to do with 'having a sense of' the size of something.

- I can (usually) decide whether a parking space is big enough for my car.
- I know how long a piece of thread I need to sew on a button.
- I know what a pound of apples looks like.
- By feeling the weight of the kettle, I can tell if there is enough water in it for a cup of coffee.

My list has been accumulated over a long period, and reflects particular interests and experiences. As my personal concerns change, my range of reference points develops. Having a baby has meant that I have become familiar with a whole new range of measurements. I now know what eighteen pounds feels like!

All of these personal lists are built up through repeated experiences, or through needing to make reasonable estimates. It is interesting that in everyday life estimates are often in the form of 'Is it big enough?' rather than an absolute size, even in contexts where units might appear to be in use. If I buy fruit at the supermarket, I pick up a bag and put in it the amount I want. I rarely think about how much it weighs, even though the fruit is priced by weight, unless I want to follow a particular recipe or the fruit is very expensive. My decision about the quantity to buy is based on counting, or on assessing volume by sight. I am doing some estimating, but I am certainly not using any 'standard' units.

It would be unreasonable to expect children to have the same range or the same kind of reference points for standard units as adults have. They do not have the experience, or the need, to develop them. They might be encouraged to learn some, such as seeing how far up their own bodies a metre rule comes (though, of course, this will change with time!). Handling rulers and weights and pouring water into different containers may help them to get some local, immediate sense of the size of the units, but it seems unlikely that this will be long lasting or transferable.

However, this 'having a sense of' the units is only part of what is involved in making a good estimate. There is also a *process* of estimating, and this is what generally gets ignored. It is hard simply to look at a unit, and then estimate how many of them will fill a space, and it is even harder to do this with weight, which you cannot see but only feel. However, within a particular context, we can fairly quickly develop the ability to estimate. If I go into the greengrocers and ask for two pounds of apples, the shopkeeper gets a bag and puts some apples into it. Then she puts it on the scales to check, but on the whole the shopkeeper's estimate will be a very good one. She probably hardly needs to use the scales, though she needs to be seen to be using them. There is a real pay-off in terms of speed and efficiency in being able to estimate accurately, and she does it regularly within a limited range of weights. Apples do not vary too much in size, and so the process the shopkeeper uses is probably to count the apples, and to make some adjustment for large and small fruits as she goes along.

The key features here are a context in which the estimation takes place, a purpose for estimating, a limited range of outcomes, and immediate feedback on accuracy. Where these features are present, children too can become good at estimation in a short space of time. At the school sports day one year, I was judging the long-jump finals. A group of children was sitting by the sand-pit, helping to measure how far each jump was beyond the 3 metre mark, and then raking the sand smooth for the next jumper. All the distances we had to measure fell within a range of about 5 cm to 50 cm, and within a very short time the children were saying: 'That's a good one', 'That's better than so-and-so's', 'I think that's about 20', 'That must be more than 25'. They were spontaneously estimating, even though we were just about to measure accurately, because it mattered to them. They were interested in the result. Their estimates were soon very accurate, and I would suggest that this was because the situation contained the key features of context, purpose, limited range and rapid feedback.

The same happens when children are drawing pictures in Logo. They are constantly needing to estimate distances and angles. Within a short time, they became quite proficient, even though they have to work with relatively large numbers, because turtle steps and degrees are very small. Logo is a very nice context in which to develop the ability to estimate, because the computer gives instant feedback. If you have already drawn a line 100 steps long, or turned the turtle through an angle of 100 degrees, it is there on the screen as a reference point. It is possible to see children doing things to help their estimates, such as holding their fingers up to the screen to make comparisons. If your line is not long enough, or if it is too long, it is natural to adjust it by 'homing in'; moving smaller distances to fill in the gap. Children use the same process of 'homing in' for angles, turning the turtle to left and right until it is pointing in exactly the right direction.

In the typical measurement lesson, even though estimation is nominally part of the activity, most or all of the key features I have identified are missing. There will almost certainly be little discussion of the process of estimation: it is often described as making a sensible guess, suggesting that there is no technique which can be learned. The process of estimating may involve visualizing, counting, approximate calculations, sub-dividing the quantity to be measured: all these are important processes in mathematics.

Using measuring instruments

Obviously, there are particular techniques associated with the use of individual measuring instruments, and these need to be learned and practised separately. But essentially using any measuring instrument (except those which give a digital read-out of some sort) involves reading a number-line. Whether you are measuring length with a ruler or weight on a spring balance or telling the time or reading the electricity meter, it is all basically the same skill, though the scale on the line may vary. The ability to read the scale is largely independent of any understanding of the units in which you are measuring, or any sense of what the answer you get means.

In passing, it is worth noticing that once measuring instruments such as rulers and measuring jugs are introduced (or rather, introduced in the mathematics lesson – children see them regularly in everyday life), measurement is being done on a continuous scale, rather than by the use of discrete units. It seems to be part of the folklore of mathematics education that children must first measure in discrete, non-standard units before they can use standard units. I often wonder what sense children make of measuring things in foot-lengths when they have perfectly good rulers in their bags. In the 'real world', we rarely use discrete units for measuring things. There is some interesting research to be done here!

The importance of learning to use the measuring instrument is generally recognized in the context of time, where 'telling the time' or reading a clock is taught as a separate skill from understanding the units in which time is measured, or having a sense of what parts of the day the times shown on the clock relate to. Most classrooms are equipped with replicas of clock-faces on which children practise this skill in isolation. Would we consider doing the same for any other measuring instrument? Obviously, social pressures are at work here: clocks are by far the most commonly used measuring instruments in everyday life. However, a clock-face is also a particularly difficult instrument to read, since two different units must be read from separate pointers on the same dial.

With other measures, we do not generally give special attention to the skill of using the measuring instrument. It is seen as an incidental part of the overall learning about the particular measure. This stresses a tenuous connection (between the activity of using the instrument and understanding the measurement), while ignoring the similarities involved in reading the scales on different instruments, or indeed on the axes of graphs. There seem to be some mathematical ideas here which are being overlooked.

The structure of the system of units

This is another aspect of measurement which is largely independent of any understanding of the size of the units, or of the ability to use a measuring instrument. The metric system provides a common structure for the units used for measuring length, weight, capacity, area and volume, and indeed for relationships between these units. However, children usually meet the different units separately, and so may not see these connections. There are potential problems in the similarity of the names of units when the same prefixes are used (e.g. *kilo*gram and *kilo*metre), which might be eased by an understanding of the whole system.

I do not wish to engage in discussions about whether imperial measures should still be taught in schools. They do not form an integrated system, since they arose originally from the formalization of relationships between many idiosyncratic units which were convenient for different purposes. Hence the sizes of individual units are sensible, but the relationships between them are chaotic, in direct contrast to the metric system. However, both systems share the same overall structure of different sizes of units with a fixed exchange rate between them (something which is entirely absent, incidentally, from all that measuring with discrete, informal units which we spend so much time on).

Money is sometimes included under the heading of 'measures'. It is not easy to see what money is a measure of, but again there is a structural similarity which could be brought out. The whole notion of a system of related units is an important one which involves a lot of mathematics.

Approximation and appropriate accuracy

Making any measurement involves some degree of approximation. However small a unit or part of a unit you choose to use, the result will still be 'rounded off'. If you use a measuring instrument which involves you in reading a scale, you have to make a decision about where to stop, that is, what degree of accuracy is appropriate for that particular context. In many 'real-life' situations, fairly coarse units are appropriate. If you are deciding how much of something to buy, it is generally better to have too much than too little, and so the sensible strategy is to round up to the nearest whole unit in which the thing is priced. In situations where greater accuracy is needed, such as ordering glass to fit a window frame, you need to consider not only the acceptable margin of error, but also the accuracy of the particular ruler you are using.

Approximation when reading a scale is to some extent a visual skill. You can round off by sight to the nearest part of a unit that you want to consider, without necessarily looking at the most accurate reading you could make. You can choose how much information you want. Measuring instruments which give a digital read-out pose different problems. With these, you have no control over the degree of accuracy you get, but this may mean that you actually get too much information. Digital clocks and watches provide a clear example. When I glance at my watch, I often do not want to know exactly what the time is. More often, I want to know something like, 'Have I got time for a cup of coffee before my eleven o'clock lecture?' I can see this from the spatial arrangement of the hands on my analogue watch, but if I look at a digital clock which says 10:43, I have to interpret whether this means before or after a quarter to eleven.

In some cases, a good strategy for approximating a digital read-out would be to ignore the last digit. As I am writing this chapter, I occasionally get the word processor to do a word count to see how close I am to my allocation. I am not interested in knowing exactly how many words I have written, but ignoring the last two figures gives me a close enough measure. In deciding whether to put the kettle on, however, reading the time as 'ten forty-something' is too inaccurate.

I cannot tell whether I have this problem with digital clocks only because I use them less often than analogue ones. With increased experience, I may become able to make an approximation of the time from a digital display more easily. In using a less-familiar measuring instrument than a clock, I probably would find a digital display less awkward. However, there do seem to be situations in which the accuracy of a digital display gives too much information, so that it actually gets in the way of understanding. The stop-watch facility on most digital watches allows children to time events to hundredths of a second: provided, of course, that they can stop and start the watch accurately enough, and that they can interpret the results when they get them!

Deciding how much information you need, choosing an appropriate unit or part of a unit, and making a sensible approximation all involve mathematical thinking, as well as developing a reasonable feel for the relative sizes of numbers.

Where is the mathematics?

When I began this article by examining a typical measurement lesson, my impression was that there is very little mathematics in measurement. I was prepared to suggest that measurement should be taken out of the mathematics curriculum at primary level. After all, measurement is not included as a mathematical topic at secondary level. Some measurement of area or volume may be needed in geometry, but this is generally found by calculation. Any teaching of measuring skills takes place within science or technology lessons, in contexts where these skills are needed. There seemed to me to be plenty of worthwhile mathematics that we could be doing in the time that is currently taken up with filling yogurt pots and pushing trundle wheels.

However, the more deeply I have looked into what is actually involved in measurement, as opposed to what we currently do in primary schools, the more I have been surprised by how much mathematics there is. The activities which provide purposeful contexts for learning about and using measurement may well be ones which are not overtly mathematical, but I now realize that this is not because there is no mathematics involved. There is mathematics in measurement; but it does not happen to be in the bits which currently get given priority in mathematics lessons.

8 Questions about geometry

John Mason

In this chapter, I want to approach these four questions about geometry.

- What is geometry?
- Where is geometry?
- Why do we learn geometry?
- How can we teach geometry?

I am conscious that what I offer can only be *an approach*, and that any initial conjectures will need to be modified and refined. Before I begin real work, let me tell you where I am headed. I want to test out with you the following conjectures about geometry in schools.

What is geometry?

It is the dynamics of the mind; what is 'seen'; incidence properties invariant under isometries and similarities.

Where is geometry?

Apparently in the physical world, but actually in the mind, or in the world of mathematics accessed through the mind.

Why do we learn geometry?

To strengthen and help organize a sense of space; to educate awareness that there are certain geometrical facts; to gain direct contact with the world of mathematics accessed through the mind.

How can we teach geometry?

By encouraging and supporting pupils in *working on* rather than *working through* mathematical tasks; by bringing attention to the power of mental imagery, and extensions of the mental screen on paper and electronically.

I shall approach these conjectures through a series of tasks, which I hope you will carry out. My intention is that they will highlight particular aspects of geometry for you, focusing your attention, and perhaps sharpening what you notice as you work. I also offer comments and reflections on how I see the tasks relating to my questions.

Hands-on geometry

There has been much talk about the role and need for practical equipment in mathematics classrooms ever since the first published educational reports. Of course, there is more to the use of practical apparatus than the apparatus itself, as the first task may demonstrate:

Take a folded piece of card (or thick paper) and make two cuts as indicated in the first diagram.

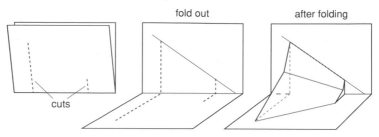

Now open up the card and focus attention on one half. Draw a straight line from the top of the long slit down to some point on the crease of the fold, as shown in the second diagram. Push the part of the card between the two slits from behind so as to make a fold *along only that part of the line which is between the two slits*. Make a firm crease.

Now re-fold the card along its first fold, preserving the new fold. You will force a third fold at the other end of the two slits, and a fourth fold somewhere near the part of the original crease. Make these creases firm.

Now open up the construction, draw a line which follows the third crease (the one which matches the one you made) and extend it to meet the original crease. Now observe what happens to the creases as you open and close the construction.[1]

So far, all you have done is cut and fold some card. From a mathematical point of view, the important question is whether what you have just done is mathematics, or, if not, where mathematics might come in. Is this just another task that a teacher might set at Christmas time, or does it contribute to some aspects of the national curriculum?

The invitation to *observe* suggests that I have something in mind which I am stressing, and that you will notice it too, if only you look. Unfortunately, this is not always a successful strategy, and can induce people to try to guess what is in my mind rather than to observe. What is intended is that you see what I see, stress what I stress and ignore what I ignore. To help with this, attend closely to what is happening to the three creases you have made as you open and close the construction.

If you are reminded in one way or another that there was one crease to begin with, that you made one crease yourself, at random (more or less), but that now there are three creases; if your attention is drawn to the fact that the three creases (if extended) appear to intersect – and always at the same point as the construction is opened and closed; if someone asks whether *any* three creases will create the same effect; then you may become aware that there are some geometrical facts present.

After trying the construction in different ways, you might become convinced that there must be a geometrical fact which makes the construction work, and you might even formulate some sort of explanation of why this fact will always hold. In which case, you will have experienced a particular case of those quintessentially mathematical processes of generalization and of convincing yourself and others (which used at one time to be called *proof*). You may have made contact with the geometrical aspect of *seeing* that things must always be so, without necessarily proceeding to the algebraic aspects of using words and symbols *to argue* that these things must be so.

You might like to contemplate for a moment different classroom contexts in which pupils might make use of this construction (for example, by using the mechanism to make different things pop up, or to explore just how complex a pop-up you can make by making pop-ups within the pop-up, ...). I suggest that this task has a lot in common with much work on tessellations, and with practical tasks more generally. It seems mathematical, but often pupils are left simply having cut out some shapes or having drawn some pictures. Their attention needs to be drawn to the mathematical features of the task.

The whole exploration could make use of the distinction between *giving an account of* some observation (what seems to happen when you open and close the construction), and *accounting for* it, by seeking some explanation based on simpler terms. Some pupils may be totally convinced by their seeing, while some other pupils will become aware that although they seem to see, others may not be so easily convinced, and so some justification might be needed.[2] Such a framework or structure could infuse all mathematical activity in the classroom, so providing a basis for exploring without the guidance of the teacher.

What sort of behaviour might be expected from pupils in order to suggest that they have developed their geometric awareness as a result of this or associated tasks? One could test their ability to make some particular thing pop up, but that would be testing engineering. It would be testing their knowledge of particular facts and whether they can make the pop-up happen in practice. You could ask them to describe how to go about making something pop up, but almost certainly they would attend to the details of a particular example – unless they had been trained in thinking beyond the particular, to the particular as illustrating the general. What is wanted is access to their sense of there being geometrical facts, and to their awareness and acceptance of the many adjustments to and modifications of conjectures as they developed confidence with pop-ups. One of the roles of a teacher is to draw attention to global themes which pupils are likely to miss in their attention to detail, and so to provide an extension of their consciousness.[3]

There are numerous other sources for such 'hands-on' geometry. There are the many aspects of paper folding (fold several times then make some cuts, then predict the effect on opening out[4]), geoboards, tiles for tessellating the plane, regular and semi-regular polyhedra (especially using ATM mats), and so on. All of these can provide engaging tasks, and all provide access to mathematical experience. In particular, they focus attention on *the fact that there are geometrical facts*. Some things have to happen, and will always happen, while other things are coincidences, requiring special conditions in order to happen, and some things can never happen.

There are other sources for practical geometrical thinking. Think back to the last time you went through a swing door that would open in either direction. How does the hinge work? Can you make a cardboard hinge which illustrates how such a hinge works? You might have to inspect a hinge – even so, the challenge to make a cardboard version is likely to expose aspects of mathematical thinking, and convert your awareness of the fact of double swing hinges into an awareness of the geometry on which they are based.

The examples so far use physical objects, and the geometry lies within or comes from the object. A different access to physical geometry can be effected through taking part in the geometry yourself.

> Form a group of six or eight people, join hands to form a circle, and then practise turning as a circle around the centre, then around some other point (it helps if a person takes up that position) or along a wall, or round another circle (of people). Direct experience is obtained of what it is like to be point on a wheel rolling along.

This task has some value in terms of general awareness of motion, but it also indicates the value of directly entering the experience of some part of a geometrical situation in order to work out what is going on. Here are two more examples.

> Contemplate the following diagram, not as an entity, but as something to be re-drawn. But you are a turtle. You crawl around, following Logo instructions of Forward so much, Left or Right so much, and so on. Try to find at least two different ways of instructing a turtle to re-draw it.

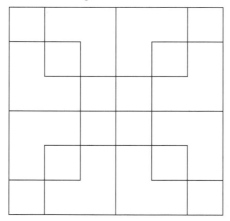

'Playing turtle' is an important aspect of gaining mastery of the Logo turtle commands, of giving access to a sense of relative geometry – the geometry of participant rather than the geometry of an external, 'elevated' observer. As such, it can contribute to pupils' sense of mastery (and hence self-confidence), to their creativity and sense of control (making it do what *I* want), as well as access to important mathematical processes such as conjecturing and modifying conjectures (debugging), breaking a problem into manageable and checkable bits, and so on.

> Two people take up positions a few feet apart. Others then take up positions twice as far from one of them (specified) as from the other.

There are many variations of this sort of task, both dynamic and static,[5] but the task is just a task, and it can be carried out in just as an unthinking, unreflective manner as can any other. Tasks are relatively easy to come across or construct. What makes a task mathematically useful in the classroom is the potential that it creates for:

- evoking surprise or other forms of involvement;
- exercising mathematical thinking processes;
- automating useful behavioural skills, such as ways of speaking (and hence thinking);
- bringing people up against important ideas, especially those in which the focus or nature of attention needs to shift or alter in some way.

The main point of this section was to note not only that geometry can be detected in the functioning of the physical world, but that geometry actually lies in the seeing, rather than in the seen.

Eyes on geometry

> Here is a drawing to contemplate.

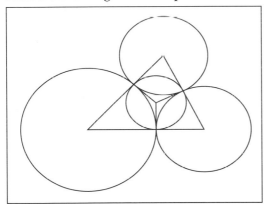

> I could ask you to do some mathematical work on it, but I want to use it simply to remind you of what geometrical diagrams used to be like – static and un-informative. Now consider this sequence of drawings.

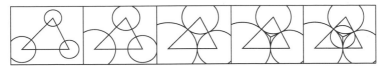

> The fact that I show you a sequence already suggests that there must be some story which links them together, in order to account for what you see.

> Say what you see to a colleague (failing any companion, say it to yourself). Concentrate on giving an account *of* what you see, rather than trying to account *for* it for the moment.

There is a lot more to *saying what you see* than there appears to be at first. You soon discover that other people are seeing something different from you, and that you do not always manage to say precisely what you are seeing. Everyone, no matter what their mathematical experience, benefits from attending to what they are seeing, and from trying to give a brief but vivid description of it to others.

> With your colleague, try to account for what you see, by constructing a story which links the diagrams together.

Even if I could show you a film which connects the diagram sequence continuously, there still remains the same work to be done: to give an account *of* what is observed, and then to try to account *for* it.

One result of work on a sequence of diagrams (thought of as selected frames from a film), or on a film itself, is that you become aware that there is some inevitability about the sequence, some generality being illustrated. In that generality, some features can change (does the shape of the triangle matter?) while others remain the same (the fourth circle always seems to fit perfectly into the triangle). Again, we have an example of a geometrical fact. It is not crucial that every member of the population knows and remembers this fact, but it *is* important that pupils become aware that there are geometrical facts which constrain what is possible. Certain things *must* happen, and certain things *cannot* happen. Being alert to the fact that there are such facts is what is important, among other things, in order to appreciate the technological society in which we live.

There is a lot to be said for the dynamic images obtained through film or animation, but these do not function entirely on their own. Most pupils these days are familiar with very sophisticated animation, and without some sort of accompanying work, phenomena such as animations are likely to remain just phenomena. They need some intentional 'making-sense-of' in order to produce their full impact. Where pupils' experience of school is of *working through* mathematical and other exercises, they develop a sense of mathematics as getting answers to questions, of getting the work finished, and so on. Where they are helped to develop and refine techniques for *working on* stimuli, such as film, drawings, posters, physical objects and situations, they are exposed to an enquiring attitude, to the disciplined enquiry which we call mathematics, and to habits which will serve them in good stead independently of any current or future contents of national curriculum attainment targets.

In the absence of film and of building on the images which it offers, we can now contact the main vehicle for geometrizing. Instead of a film on an outside screen, we construct one on an inner screen.

Imagine a triangle. Imagine a circle tucked in one corner, touching the two sides. It grows in size, always touching the two sides of the triangle, getting bigger and bigger, until it touches the third side as well. Let it grow even bigger, until it is entirely outside the triangle, but touches all three sides (two will need to be extended). Then let it shrink back down until it is tucked back in the same (starting) corner.

Now let it grow again, but this time let its centre leave a trace or track. Let the circle grow until it touches the third side of the triangle as well. Since it touches all three sides, we can allow it to 'let go' of a different side, and then shrink until it is tucked in a different corner. Experiment with that for a while.

Allow it to grow until it is outside the triangle but touching all three sides, then 'let go' of a different side and shrink. Where can its centre get to in all this movement?

Any statement of what you are seeing is a geometrical theorem. The significance of your theorem will depend on whether others can recognize what you are seeing, and agree to its generality, to its applying to any triangle. Discussing with a colleague can be very helpful, as can drawing a diagram. But observe that the diagram is a summary of what you have already seen, extending your inner screen and helping you to stabilize details. It signals a theorem, but to detect that theorem you have to know what to stress and what to ignore so as to be able to 'read' it.

There are many things which can emerge from such a task, depending on the experience of the participants. The same device of *say what you see* can be used, with no one allowed to use their hands, much less to draw a picture – so that people will contact that deep desire to illustrate, to extend their mental screen, to use a diagram. Someone else's diagram has to be worked on and made sense of, but your own diagram is a tool for your thinking.

Individual tasks can have enormous potential for seeing, for being geometrical and mathematical, but still more is required. Mathematics is not a smorgasbord of random tasks. There is sense, order and structure to be discerned. To see what I mean, consider the next task.

The diagram with the circles centred at the vertices and the diagram arising from the previous task both concern circles connected by a triangle. Try to construct a story which links the two together. Then try to find common elements other than mathematical facts which they both share.

The purpose of the task is to indicate that it is possible to link the two previous tasks together, both at the mathematical level, and at a meta-level. Mathematically, they are both about bisectors of angles, but it is not terribly important that you were able to say this yourself. More important is that there are geometrical facts which connect certain circles formed within triangles. It is the fact that there are facts, and that facts can be related or connected which seems to me the most important awareness to come from the task. Attributes of pleasure, engagement, or mathematical thinking are significant, but not primary.

Films and drawings are simply devices: they are not mathematics, not geometry. But they are aids to sharpening that amazing faculty which we all share, the ability to form and manipulate mental images. There is not space to undertake a full discussion of mental imagery here, but I do want to stress that film and diagrams can be thought of as a means first and foremost for awakening mental imagery and the awareness of it as a power which all pupils possess. Secondly, films and drawings are ways of augmenting, extending and strengthening mental imagery and hence mathematical thinking.[6] If I have felt strongly the need to draw a diagram to help my thinking, I am more likely to use diagrams to help myself in the future, whereas if I am constantly being told to 'draw a diagram', not knowing what to draw or why, I am unlikely to benefit greatly from such instruction.

I find it useful to think of mathematics as a world which one enters – not a world in which something is either true or false, but a world in which one experiences contexts in which there is truth, falsehood and unknowability. Geometrical activity is one excellent way of gaining access to that world, through the power to form mental images, through seeing *through* diagrams to the world of generality which can be read into them. It is one way to encounter the discipline of mathematics, where convincing people *why* something must be a fact is as important as finding out what the fact is.

What and why (or that and must)

Imagine a computer screen showing the following diagram.

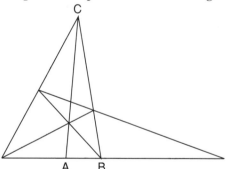

You move the mouse, and as the cursor approaches one of the vertices, an icon showing thumb and forefinger appears, inviting you to grab and move the point. You press the mouse button and drag. The point comes with you (though it may be confined to a line or a circle), and so do the lines through it, together with some of the other lines. As you move the mouse you have a sense of some things changing, and of others staying fixed in the diagram.[7]

One of the features of the dynamic aspect of geometry, as manifested in film and in certain computer programs such as Cabri-geometry, is the direct contact which can be made with *some things changing and some things staying the same*. It was the German mathematician Felix Klein who formalized the idea of geometry as the study of properties of objects which do not change under isometries (similarities are sometimes allowed), or more generally, under different groups of transformations. Before computer graphics, it was necessary to appreciate this idea totally through mental imagery. Attention had to be drawn away from the particularity of individual diagrams or drawings to the general case.[8] The general case could not be displayed, only spoken of. Now we have access to what I call *mouse mathematics*. Through the movement of the arm (guiding a mouse), you can get direct contact with the scope of generality, with what is permitted to change and yet observe relationships which remain fixed throughout the movement. You can *see* much more 'graphically' what seems to be true. Thus, with the two constructions of the previous section, a Cabri version enables you to drag the vertices of the triangle around, and to see all the circles following, and that no matter which triangle you start with, the construction seems to work.

For many people, this level of convincing will be adequate. But it is more important that people have a well-developed sense of the fact of geometrical facts (together with an underlying scepticism of anything machine-generated), than that they are pushed through tedious and for them meaningless computations and reasonings that purport to provide a proof, but which remain mysterious incantations. It is possible to raise the question of proof, of trying to convince yourself that certain facts must hold, and even to be intrigued by the plethora of interconnections between different facts, but this need not be demanded of everyone.

As Freudenthal observes, geometry for younger pupils is about seeing, seeing *that* something is the case. For example, the following diagram is suggestive.

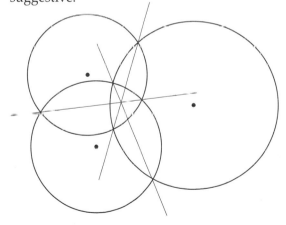

but suggestive of what? Many pupils may not be aware at all that there is at least one generality implied by, or better, readable into, the diagram. The expression *seeing the general in* or *through the particular* applies here. It pervades mathematics, and often lies at the heart of misunderstandings between teachers and pupils, for the teacher sees the general in or through the particular, but the pupils see only the particular.

You may have been reminded that it is sometimes quite hard to see what it is that someone else has in mind, to be able to stress and ignore in the same way that they are doing, without further cues. Much more effective is to show you a sequence of diagrams, so that you can look for what is the same and what different about several examples.

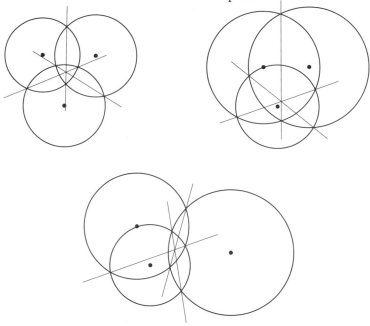

Better still, by using a program such as Cabri-geometry, you can experience for yourself the scope of generality available. It is hard not to be convinced that those lines will always intersect at a single point. We can then see *that* something is 'always' true, but we have nothing to say yet about why it *must* be true. We have not reached a point of proof, of convincing others, apart from 'go through the same experience as me and adjust the circles in any way you choose'.

This sense of *mustness* which arises from an argument using previously accepted facts, showing that something must indeed happen is quite sophisticated. I am certain that it is not so sophisticated that we are justified in excluding it from the syllabus, but I acknowledge that young pupils do not see a need to offer justification, apart from 'I see that it is so'.

One reason for pupil reluctance is that they do not see a problem. Indeed, they may be concentrating fully on the particular diagram, and not even be aware of the implied generality that the teacher is seeing.[9] By finding ways to show a myriad of cases so as to be aware of the vast variety of possible but untested cases, and by sowing seeds of a background doubt (perhaps it is an artifact of the computer's calculation/program), the important aspect of proof, which is essential to mathematics as a disciplined enquiry, can be brought to the attention of pupils. I believe this can be done at quite a young age. George Polya suggested[10] that there is a big difference between a conjecture which has a lot of support, and something that we know for certain. This mathematical awareness can certainly be appreciated by young people. Pupils spend so much of their time accepting what people say to them as fact (or at least appearing to do so), that it can be quite refreshing for them to encounter an honest and open mathematician who reminds them of what they really know and what they only surmise.

But our notion of proof in mathematics may be changing. I predict that one of the long-term effects of computers will be to establish a mode of certainty which lies between the too-easy acceptance of a generalization from one or two cases and the rigour of mathematical proof. Programs like Cabri-geometry enable the user to experience a huge range of particular cases, and by appeal to continuity, an infinite number of cases. This plethora of confirming instances will be highly convincing for many, if not most, people. I find this entirely reasonable. Any 'fact' that holds under such a wide range of conditions as can be quickly explored using Cabri, must be due to some underlying theorem (or bug in the program!). I conjecture that this same phenomenon will pervade a whole range of mathematical (and perhaps other) disciplines in the near future. Truth will be ascribed to observations made in a huge range of cases explored rapidly on a computer. Mathematicians will begin to formulate theorems of the form: 'If something holds in such a range of cases, it holds in general' – where 'such a range' is made precise.

Some reflective remarks

What is the same about the various tasks proposed above? I have tried to draw attention to a more precise interpretation of the words *sense of space* which appear so frequently in unelaborated form in, for instance, the England and Wales national curriculum documents of 1989. There is more to it than time spent tessellating the plane! There is, for example, contact with the mathematical world of brief-but-vivid descriptions of what is seen, and the process of trying to refine that description so that it convinces others that they too see the same. There is experience of the generality lying behind so many apparently innocuous statements about triangles and circles, hinges and structures. There is awareness of the dynamic that lies behind the static drawings encountered in texts, seeing a diagram as a single frame from a film. There is experience of that eternally difficult task of *saying what you see*, in terms which others can relate to.

I have attempted to help you harness your emotional energy so as to concentrate, at least for a while, on mathematical thinking. I have tried to draw upon your awareness of the world of mathematics, and to draw your attention to mathematical processes through direct participation, and to suggest that they are of some significance. I have tried to indicate some mathematical behaviour which is worth gaining facility in, such as *saying what you are seeing*. I put before you my two main conjectures:

- that what is important about geometry is being aware of the fact that there are facts, rather than mastery of some particular few facts;

- that geometry takes place in a world of forms and images, entry to which is gained through the power of mental imagery, augmented and extended by dynamic images, drawings on paper, and discussion with colleagues.

This was my main aim. In the context of implementing a national curriculum by manifesting programmes of study, I find it useful to bear in mind three interlinked aspects of human experience:

- harnessing pupils' emotional energy (motivation) to concentrate on, attend to, and engage in mathematical thinking;

- educating pupils' awareness through the evocation of their faculty of mental imagery and their powers for making sense;

- training pupils' behaviour in the exercise of skills in language use, and in physical and symbol manipulation.

How then can pupils be invited to demonstrate through their behaviour that they have developed and refined a geometrical awareness, a sense of space, as required by particular national curricula?

It is all too easy to fall into assessing knowledge of particular geometrical facts (Pythagoras, one or two facts about circles, and trigonometric ratios). I am not suggesting that every pupil should *know* the pop-up theorem, or the theorem about the angle bisectors of a triangle meeting in a point. Such results are of limited value in themselves, except in rare instances, when they can be looked up in a book. What is important is to become aware that *there are geometrical facts,* and that they can be worked with, exploited and applied, and looked up or sought out when needed. In order to become aware of the existence of constraints and 'musts', what I have been calling geometrical facts, it is necessary to explore several domains in some detail, but without being seduced into treating the facts as the goal. In exploring a domain (such as three-dimensional solids, Pythagoras, triangles and circles, tessellations, or rotational and reflective symmetry) thoroughly, it may be necessary to automate certain language patterns (associated with more elementary facts) and some motor skills (in using compasses or a computer program like Logo or Cabri). These are needed in order to explore the fact that there are connections between geometrical facts (so that given some facts you can deduce others); but again, the automating (gaining mastery over) of some facts is merely a means to an end and not the end itself.

In terms of teaching geometry, what probably matters most is the 'mathematicalness', the mathematical being of the teacher. Decisions made by teachers in the moment depend on their noticing an opportunity, and are informed by their mathematical knowledge and their awarenesses of different aspects of mathematical thinking.

Rather than having *a way I always do things* (for example a way I always introduce Pythagoras), it is probably more sensible to use static and dynamic sources, extended screens and directly evoked mental imagery at different times and in different ways. If teachers can re-enter or re-awaken surprise in themselves, the wonder at the fact of geometrical facts, they are likely to inspire at least some of their pupils to wonder as well. I am not advocating the *wow!* school of thought which simply says 'Wow!' at each encounter with a geometrical fact, but rather, to move from a sense of wonder to a specific 'I wonder if it is always true' and to an exploration of the meaning of both *always* and *true* in the particular context, and thereby to achieve access to that mathematical process of convincing others.

The enthusiasm and interest of the teacher play an important role in any teaching. When you become unimpressed with certain geometrical facts, when they become stale and obvious, it seems to me sensible to look elsewhere for a time. There is so much that is amazing and striking about the (co-?)incidences of points and lines in the plane, that it seems a shame to have thrown it all out just because it was hard to teach as a deductive science. Unfortunately, what has happened in the past is that experts have become bored and developed enthusiasms for totally new approaches. By reminding their colleagues of their dissatisfaction with pupils' responses to current content, they managed to get support for sweeping changes. We have seen geometry according to Euclid give way to coordinate geometry, which in turn gave way to transformations (with and without matrices), and then the demise of matrices. Such big swings are not needed in order to remain fresh and intrigued in the classroom. Pupils' responses to and discovery of geometrical facts, and their gradual appreciation of the fact that there are facts is surely intriguing enough for any teacher.

As Nitsa Movshovits-Hadar reminds us,[11] it takes only a little effort to re-enter the astonishment that certain incidences *must* occur, no matter what triangle you start with. For me, the real importance of geometry is as a domain in which the fact that there are necessary and inescapable facts can be experienced, developed, manipulated to produce new facts, and for those who wish, organized into a deductive scheme.

Some pupils will be activated by challenges to explain how physical things work, and may be led to a discovery of the mathematical world which, as it were, lies behind the facts of the material world. Others may be inspired by the sheer complexity or beauty of geometrical relationships, and still others by the neatness of attempts to organize the plethora of geometrical facts into some sort of overall structure. Surely almost everyone could be drawn into geometry in some form, since it lies at the heart of their experience, both of the physical world, and of the world they inhabit through their minds.

Notes

1   I am indebted to Malcolm Swan, Shell Centre for Mathematical Education, Nottingham University for acquainting me with this theorem. The classroom materials 'Be a paper engineer' are published by the Shell Centre.

2   In his book *Weeding and Sowing* (Reidel, 1978, pp. 275–9), Hans Freudenthal uses the expression 'I see it so' as the response of pupils to the question 'Why?'. He suggests that such an answer is entirely reasonable. He observes that around the age of eleven or twelve such responses disappear, but whether because pupils no longer see, or are aware of its inadequacy, or have been blocked from seeing by formal instruction, is unclear even to him. Freudenthal is by no means the first to dwell on seeing, for Plato distinguishes between *theoria* (literally 'vision') and referring to ideal forms, and practice, embodying *theoria* in physical forms. Freudenthal uses the term *condensation kernels* and mentions 'Say what you see and draw a picture' or 'Make a model of what you see' as two examples (p. 280).

3   In *Actual Minds, Possible Worlds* (Harvard University Press, 1986, pp. 73–6), Jerome Bruner refers to Vygotsky's notion of the *zone of proximal development* (what pupils are capable of with the help of someone more experienced which they could not do unaided), and the role of the teacher as being a vicarious consciousness, able to hold onto global aims and themes when pupils' attention is diverted to detail.

4   A favourite one of mine, suggested by Peter Gates, is to fold a square along its diagonal, then fold the result along its line of symmetry, and repeat this a few times. Finally, cut along the line of symmetry of the current shape, and predict the number and shape of the pieces when unfolded.

5   See, for example, the excellent book *Curves*, published by The Leapfrog Group and available from Tarquin Publications, Diss, Norfolk.

6   In *Interaction of Media, Cognition and Learning* (Jossey-Bass, 1979), Gabriel Saloman uses the term *supplanted images* to refer to the strength and robustness of dynamic images encountered in films, and signalled by the remark 'I don't want to see the film, because I so enjoyed the book'.

7   The program being described is just part of *Cabri-geometry*, available for the Apple Macintosh from CEDIC-VIFI, CNRS, University of Grenoble, France. The word *Cabri* is an acronym of 'Cahier brouillon informatique' (French for a 'computer roughwork notebook'), which provides an image for how the designers envisaged users of the software might work with it.

8   In the diagrams drawn earlier, the same triangle was used throughout, yet somehow you were expected to appreciate that the particular triangle was unimportant, noticing only that it was a triangle!

9   Hence the value of practising *saying what you see*, so that others will feel able to say 'I see what you are saying'.

10 George Polya proposes this in the film *Let Us Teach Guessing* (1963), published by the Mathematical Association of America and available from distributors in the UK.

11 See N. Movshovits-Hadar (1988) 'School mathematics theorems – an endless source of surprise', *For the Learning of Mathematics*, 8(3), pp. 34–40.

9 Circle expressions and equations: multivalent pedagogical tools

Martin Hoffman and Arthur Powell

For some years, we have taught remedial and developmental mathematics and, for these and other contexts, have developed a number of multivalent pedagogical tools. By the phrase 'multivalent pedagogical tool', we mean a technique and variations of it, which can be used as a vehicle for teaching and learning a number of interconnected topics.

In this short chapter, we describe how teachers and pupils can use certain pedagogical tools for examining algebraic structures and conventions while providing opportunities for improving computational ability in the four basic operations using integers, fractions, decimals, percentages and exponents. In addition, these tools, which we call circle expressions and circle equations, can provide pupils with insight and facility in solving a category of equations. We developed these tools in the context of our work with older pupils, who, after repeated failed attempts to master these topics, approach them with anxiety, and often hold the view that 'mathematics is something you do, not something you understand'.

When working with teachers, we frequently observed an indifference to the pedagogical and mathematical challenges inherent in teaching these topics. Many, given time constraints, find it difficult both to cover the content and to provide pupils with opportunities to attain understanding of the involved conventions and mathematical structures. By using circle expressions and equations, we have been able to balance the imperative of time with the need to enable pupils to acquire mathematical insights.

In this chapter, we discuss specific uses and variations of circle expressions and circle equations related to the school mathematics curriculum. The first of these tools, circle expressions, is particularly useful not only for revealing mathematical structures underlying arithmetic computation but also for providing interesting and varied computational practice. The open-ended nature of many circle-expression activities provides teachers with a powerful instrument for evaluating pupils' understanding of computational techniques and certain mathematical structures.

We start with the following simulated dialogue which will illustrate how one might introduce circle expressions. The teacher places a circle on the chalkboard with, say, the numeral 5 inside it.

⑤

TEACHER: Do something to 5.

PUPIL: [Possibly after some hesitation.] Add 3.

TEACHER: What's the result?

PUPIL: 8.

⑤ —+3→ ⑧

TEACHER: Do something to 8.

PUPIL: Multiply by 4. The result is 32.

⑤ —+3→ ⑧ —×4→ ㉜

[At this point, pupils are likely to be aware of the task's basic conventions and to respond without verbal prompting.]

PUPIL: Subtract 7; the result is 25.

TEACHER: Starting at 5, can you find other ways to arrive at 25?

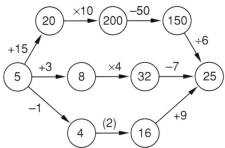

The two additional circle expressions shown here represent other possibilities generated by pupils at different levels. (In the bottom circle expression, the notation (2) is used to indicate 'squaring – second power'.) At this juncture, a teacher could direct this task along one of several routes. For instance, you may wish to focus your pupils' attention and practise on particular types of numbers or operations or both. This can be accomplished by imposing restrictions on the task, where pupils are asked to create circle expressions satisfying constraints or conditions such as the ones in the table opposite. Also, either individually or in small groups, pupils could construct such a table and exchange their challenges among themselves.

Problem	Start	End	Constraints
1	49	3	three steps; different operations
2	19	0	use +, ×, – at least once
3	5	–9	four steps; pass through 10
4	1	56	use a factorial
5	7	11	$7 \xrightarrow{+} \bigcirc \xrightarrow{\times} \bigcirc \xrightarrow{-} 11$
6	3	219	use two different exponents
7	$1^3{}_4$	$7^1{}_4$	three steps; no repeated operation
8	46.3	21.3	three steps
9	3	219	use at least one fraction

The types of 'start' and 'end' numbers and 'constraints' in the problems only begin to illustrate the range of possibilities at this stage. Each problem in the table contains one or more points of explicit focus. In problem 3, for instance, one focus is on the arithmetic of signed numbers. A teacher or pupil could design a sequence of problems to focus on almost any aspect of the school arithmetic curriculum.

At one level, a purpose of this type of exercise is to provide pupils with varied, interesting, and challenging practice in the basic operations in a format which can be used throughout the school curriculum. At another level, the open-ended nature of the problems allows pupils an opportunity to explore their own thinking and knowledge of mathematics. Moreover, the problems that pupils solve and create provide a teacher with feedback on the mathematical functioning of pupils that is qualitatively different from that normally associated with textbook exercises which require pupils to find a single correct answer.

By re-examining, for example, the middle circle expression in the previous diagram, one can become aware of another facet of the multivalent character of circle expressions. When pupils attempt to translate this or other circle expressions into standard notation, they are naturally led to a discussion of the conventions governing the order of operations.

$$5 \xrightarrow{+3} 8 \xrightarrow{\times 4} 32 \xrightarrow{-7} 25$$

When translating the circle expression given above, pupils must decide *whether* and, if so, *where* grouping symbols are needed so that the expression $5 + 3 \times 4 - 7$ will equal 25. In this example, unlike the textbook problem of evaluating an expression such as $(5 + 3) \times 4 - 7$, they are involved in using grouping symbols and applying the order-of-operations convention in a cognitively richer and more active way. To develop further proficiency in applying the order-of-operations convention, it is instructive for pupils to translate expressions written in standard notation into circle expressions and to discuss each other's attempts. Furthermore, if the top circle expression in the diagram is considered (see below), and the fraction bar is understood to be a grouping symbol, then several expressions in standard notation are possible.

$$\left(10\,(5 + 15) - 50\right) \div 6 = 25$$

$$\frac{10(5 + 15) - 50}{6} = 25$$

$$25 = \frac{-50 + 10(5 + 15)}{6}$$

With a slight modification, yet another facet of the multivalent character of circle expressions is revealed, namely when they are used to represent what are known as 'What's my number?' or 'Think of a number' problems. A classroom presentation of a 'What's my number?' problem might proceed as follows.

TEACHER: I'm thinking of a number. I divide it by 4 and then subtract 5. The result is 7. What's my number?

PUPIL A: It's 48.

TEACHER: How did you arrive at that?

PUPIL A: I first tried 40, but when I divided by 4 and subtracted 5, I didn't get 7. Then I tried 48 and it worked.

PUPIL B: I worked backwards from 7. I know that 12 minus 5 is 7 and that 48 divided by 4 is 12. So the answer is 48.

PUPIL C: I also worked backwards. I added 5 to 7, got 12 and then multiplied by 4 to get 48.

In the above simulated interaction, pupil A used a trial-and-improvement approach which has obvious limitations if the stated problem contained more operations, involving difficult computations. Pupil B introduced the idea of working in the reverse of the order that the operations were stated by the teacher, but did not explicitly suggest the use of inverse operations. Pupil C, however, did explicitly describe the ideas of reversing the order of the operations and using inverse operations.

We use 'What's my number?' problems to force awareness of the two mathematical structures that pupil C described. Any 'What's my number?' problem can be translated into a circle expression. This is particularly convenient to do when a stated problem involves more than two operations. 'I'm thinking of a number. I subtract 1 from it, raise it to the second power, and add 9. The result is 25. What's my number?' The diagram below contains a translation of this problem into a circle expression.

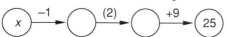

The first circle contains a variable to represent the unknown number. In this form, we refer to such expressions as *circle equations*, and like circle expressions, they can be translated into standard notation. A translation of the above circle equation is $(x - 1)^2 + 9 = 25$.

At this stage, pupils have three alternative representations of an equation: the *verbal* 'What's my number?' statement of the problem, the *graphical* circle equation, and the *symbolic* standard notation. These representations provide pupils with bases for forming both verbal and visual images of equations. On paper or in the mind, pupils can translate one representation into another. Consequently, these three equivalent representations of equations provide pupils with a richer set of connections and platforms from which to construct meanings than conventional introductions to solving equations.

The investigation in which pupils engage to answer that 'What's my number?' problem, represented by the above circle equation, forces awareness of the inverses of operations and their role in solving equations. It is likely that some pupils are already aware of the inverses of the four basic operations; however, some discussion is probably needed for them to know how to write the inverse of the whole-number powers as unitary fractional powers. As a natural notational extension, opposite-facing arrows are drawn to accompany their corresponding operational inverses.

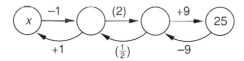

The solution to the circle equation is found by performing the inverse operations, while reversing the original order in which the operations were performed. (At this stage, pupils rarely find both solutions of this equation; however, the method of circle equations can be extended to handle both.)

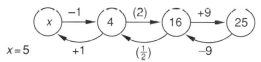

If pupils can translate complex-looking circle expressions into standard notation and vice versa, they can also translate such circle equations into the standard notation for equations. Naturally, any equation for which the unknown appears only once can be translated into circle equations. This provides a basis for solving a large category of equations. For example, the equation $6[(y + 3)^3 - 4]^{1/2} + 5 = 71$ can be translated into the circle equation given below.

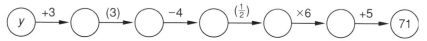

It can be solved by performing the appropriate inverse operations in their appropriate order. With practice, pupils can imagine that a given equation is expressed as a circle equation and solve the equation, as it were, by sight.

Extensions and refinements of the technique can be developed to handle a wider range of equations, including the ones below, taken from a recent examination.

$$3(x - 5) = 21 \qquad\qquad 4x^2 - 39 = -3$$

$$\frac{(2.5t + 2)^{12}}{2} = 1 \qquad\qquad [4(100y^{-2} + 4)^{13} + 1]^{12} - 9 = -6$$

$$(\sqrt{(x! + 1 - 3)})^5 - 1 = 31 \qquad [5(x^{23} + 5)^{12} + 1]^{14} + 1 = 3$$

There are many equations encountered in algebra which cannot be translated into circle notation (only equations in which the unknown appears once can be directly translated into circle notation). However, the pedagogical importance of working on circle equations lies elsewhere. First, working with circle equations provides pupils with a number of important insights into the nature of certain equations and their solutions. Second, in the context of creating and solving equations, pupils gain varied practice in computation. Third, at an affective level, pupils can gain confidence in their ability to do mathematics at a level beyond traditional expectations.

Furthermore, the positive affective impact and pedagogical value that pupils derive from working with circle equations and expressions is evidenced in the important mathematical features they reveal. For many, it is an arcane notion that, in a given mathematical expression or equation, there exists an explicit and codified order in which operations are performed or undone. Indeed, the convention codifying the order of operations is not manifest in the standard notation of expressions and equations. When doing mathematics, pupils (as well as mathematicians) often find it useful to have a mental scheme for depicting, in this case, algebraic information and processes.

Circle expressions and equations provide pupils with a linear representation, visual images, of the order of operations of expressions and equations written in standard notation and the process of evaluating or solving them. In addition, this multivalent tool enables pupils to become aware of the fundamental difference when the order-of-operation convention is applied to evaluate expressions and to solve equations. For these reasons, we have found that circle expressions and equations are effective pedagogical tools to enable pupils of varying mathematical backgrounds to acquire powerful insights into certain mathematical structures, *while* they are gaining computational facility.

References and further reading

Caleb Gattegno (1988) *The Science of Education, part 2B: The Awareness of Mathematization*, Educational Solutions Inc.

Guy Gattegno and Martin Hoffman (1976) *Handbook of Activities for the Teaching of Mathematics at the Elementary School*, Human Education Inc. (Section II.A.5).

Martin Hoffman and Arthur Powell (1988) 'A multivalent tool for computation', *Mathematics in College*, Fall/Winter, pp. 43–51.

David Wheeler *et al.* (1967) *Notes on Mathematics in Primary Schools*, Cambridge University Press, pp. 329–31.

James Wirth (1975) 'The Christmas-present principle', *Mathematics Teacher*, **68**(9), pp. 636–9.

10 Where is the 'P' in statistics?

Alan Graham

Although the main focus of this chapter is on the handling of data which arises as a natural part of any investigation, it is clear that the term 'data handling' can be viewed as something much wider than this. In a sense, data handling could be thought of as being the sort of information processing which we are performing every waking minute of our lives. This could include checking that it is safe to cross the road before setting off, judging the qualities of a piece of music, or deciding how you should vote at a general election. However, when people talk about data, they are normally referring to a collection of numerical information about something, and it is in this more restricted sense that I explore ideas of data handling here.

Handling data is the theme of AT 5 in the current mathematics national curriculum in England and Wales (1991), and there are similar sections in the equivalent requirements in Scotland and Northern Ireland. The programmes of study state: 'Pupils should collect, process and interpret data and should understand and find probabilities'. AT 5 also makes mention of recording and representing data, making a total of five aspects in all.

In order to emphasize that these five aspects of data handling are often sequential, I have set them out in a flow chart. Taken together, they might seem to comprise a fairly comprehensive list. However, there is a crucial absent element here, without which it is hard to carry out any of the other stages sensibly. The missing stage comes at the very beginning.

It is actually very hard to handle data *to a purpose* unless you know why they were collected in the first place. There must have been an initial question which provided the impetus to collect the data. I would like to propose that it is this initial question which provides the main criterion for making decisions and choices about all the other stages in the data-handling process. In tackling the initial question, there are decisions to make about which data to collect and record. Trying to answer the initial question will be what determines how the data are to be processed and represented. And, finally, the interpretation of the results needs to be seen in terms of how well your analysis has helped you to answer the question that you started with.

There seem to be four clearly identifiable stages here.

Stage 1 P – Pose the question.

Stage 2 C – Collect the data (collecting and recording).

Stage 3 A – Analyse the data (processing and representing).

Stage 4 I – Interpret the results (interpreting).

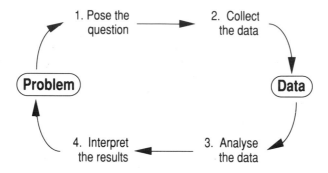

These stages describe the main features of what might be called a 'statistical investigation', and will be referred to here as the *PCAI* cycle. It has been my central hope in promoting this view of statistics that pupils might come to see data-handling techniques (drawing graphs, calculating averages, and so on) as genuinely useful skills which can help them to answer questions which they might pose for themselves. As a result, they may become active statistical investigators rather than merely passive handlers of data.

Posing questions

This section looks at the crucial element in any data-handling task which gives it purpose and direction – posing an initial question. Here are some examples of questions which might form the basis of investigations and give pupils the opportunity of handling data purposefully.

- How much shelf space is needed for the lunch boxes or wellies?
- How quickly can we get everyone out if there were a fire?
- Is a particular book sexist or racist?
- How good are we at estimating length/weight/temperature/...?
- Do estimation skills improve with practice?
- Are we taller or shorter than the children in class X?
- Do children watch more TV than adults?
- Can taller people run faster?
- What sort of balls are bounciest?

It would be difficult to answer any of these questions without collecting data of some sort. Of course, we all already have quite a lot of information stored in our memories on the basis of a wide variety of previous experiences. As adults, we may 'know' that a tennis ball will bounce higher than a squash ball. Children, particularly young children, have neither access to such a variety of previous experience, nor may they have had much practice at posing similar questions for themselves.

But where are the various questions which are to form the basis of classroom investigations to come from? There are many possible sources. I will look briefly at just three here. The first might be to start with questions already being posed in other areas of the curriculum, particularly science and CDT.

Science

A quick glance at the *Science in the National Curriculum* document (1990), and its associated *Non-Statutory Guidance* notes, reveals a large number of interesting investigations. Here are some questions which should ensure that children engage in purposeful data handling.

- Do light objects float? (AT 1 level 2)
- Which balls bounce highest? (AT 1 level 3)
- How does a plant grow over time? (AT 1 level 3)
- How do objects change when they decay? (AT 2 level 4)
- How could you insulate your house efficiently? (AT 1 level 6)
- What factors affect the growth of cress? (AT 1 level 7)

There is nothing very radical in exploring science concepts in this investigative way. On the contrary, the *Non-Statutory Guidance* notes say this about the learning of science.

> Skills of investigation do not develop in isolation from the subject matter or ideas being used. In making observations, hypothesising or planning an investigation, there is always a specific problem.
>
> *(Section 6.2)*

In the 'Interpreting the results' section, a number of starting-points for investigations are offered, which may take the form of observations, hypotheses or problems. These may be posed by either the teacher or the pupils and may lead on to a number of subsidiary investigations.

Maths schemes

Maths textbooks or work schemes can provide alternative starting-points for data-handling tasks. However, the initial problem setting may need some adjustment. This may require little more than rephrasing a rather closed task into the form of a more open question, and this change should be sufficient to ensure that the pupils get the chance to go through the *full* data handling cycle. For example, you might have a go at rephrasing the following rather closed activities given as examples in the mathematics national curriculum document for England and Wales (AT 5 level 4).

- Find and record the number of pupils born in each month of the year; produce a chart for display.
- Calculate the mean and range to compare the scoring records of two hockey teams which have played different numbers of games.

As you can see from the wording of these examples, the focus is very much on the 'C' and 'A' stages of the PCAI cycle. Here is one possible way of rephrasing them to open up the pupils' thinking about *why* data are collected and how they could be interpreted *to a purpose*.

- Do you think that more babies are born in the autumn than during other seasons? How could you check? Why might this be?

- Do you think the school team was more successful this year than last year? Why? How could you compare the two?

With these (or similar questions) as their starting-points, pupils should have some basis on which to decide what to do at each subsequent stage of their investigation.

One problem with the approach suggested by these rephrased questions is that they have been posed entirely by the teacher. From the children's point of view, the 'P' stage has been done for them. Perhaps this is an inevitable difficulty of using printed resource materials as the starting-point for activity which could otherwise be fairly open ended. An alternative is to look at a more likely context for children to pose their own questions – theme work.

Theme work

Usually, topics or themes tend to break down into a number of smaller related investigations, questions or areas of interest. The experience of many teachers in this area suggests that the *need* for mathematical thinking in theme work only really comes to light when the children are seeking answers to questions. To take the example of 'birds' flight', children might be curious about how a bird can fly and what size of wings *we* might require to be able to fly. Here is a question which invites purposeful data handling – there is then a desire or *need* to measure the wing length, find the bird's weight, and so on.

Sometimes, the questions being investigated can be too relevant, to the point of intruding on individuals or groups of children in the class and causing embarrassment. Clearly, therefore, sensitivity is needed when choosing, or supporting pupils in choosing an area for investigation. Where a possible area of embarrassment can be foreseen, the teacher is better prepared to know how to deal with it. The table below illustrates one teacher's preparation in this area when considering possible themes.

Theme	Possible area of embarrassment
Body proportions	Some children are very sensitive about their size, weight, etc.
My family	Some children will not want attention drawn to their family composition.
Christmas presents	Ditto above. Also, not every child may celebrate this Christian festival.
Holidays	Many families will not be able to afford one.

There is great scope within theme work for purposeful data handling to occur. Children's natural curiosity and their capacity to pose questions just need to be given a little encouragement for quantitative approaches to follow quite naturally. Even beyond the confines of theme work, everyday events in school and at home occur which give rise to the wish or need for children to handle data in order to answer some question or solve a problem. For example, a new pupil may have just joined the class from Somalia. What a lot of questions the children will want to ask her! Or perhaps someone will have heard on Blue Peter about how quickly the Amazon rain forest is shrinking. How quickly? At this rate, how long will it last? (See the book by Hugh Burkhardt (1982), listed at the end, for a useful discussion on how to elicit children's own questions.)

Collecting data

Basically, there are two ways of collecting data – either getting them yourself directly, or from someone or somewhere else. *Primary* data you collect yourself (perhaps from an experiment or a questionnaire), while *secondary* data are collected from elsewhere (from the library, newspapers, etc.).

Surveys and questionnaires

Before pupils collect and record data, some organization and planning are needed. Administering a badly designed questionnaire can sometimes be a valuable learning experience. More often, however, it is frustrating for all concerned and can cause disruption around the school. In fairness to teaching colleagues and pupils in the school (and, indeed, the general public), pupils conducting a survey should be expected to give considerable thought to the purpose and organization of any questionnaire they prepare. They can be invited to think in advance about what use they will make of the information. Use of a pilot survey can enable pupils to correct many of the more obvious problems in their questionnaire in advance and to anticipate what may be involved in processing their results. Another idea is to give pupils a poorly worded and badly structured questionnaire and ask them to improve it. An example is shown below, one where the purpose of the survey has not been clearly thought out.

Questionnaire on health

1 How healthy are you?

2 Do you think you are fit?

3 How old are you?

4 What sort of things do you eat?

5 What is your name?

6 Do you take exercise?

7 Are you overweight?

8 Will you agree to take part in this survey?

Choosing a sample

Before grappling with the details of *how* to select a sample, it is worth pausing to consider *why*. Collecting data from a large population is usually too costly or time consuming to contemplate. Choosing a *representative* sample of the population allows us to investigate the characteristics of the whole population by looking at only a selection of its members.

Two eleven-year-olds, Sean and Mario, conducted a class survey in order to find which were people's favourite sports. Their results showed a remarkable preference for soccer and, in particular, support for Everton. Further questioning revealed that their sample consisted of eleven boys, all from their class! Their results may have revealed something about eleven boys in their class, but not necessarily a lot about people's preferences in general. As a means of finding out about options and preferences of a wider population, surveys must choose samples which *represent* that population. Thus, the sample should be selected to try to ensure representativeness. This is often achieved by (a) random selection, and (b) the sample being reasonably large.

The task of selecting fairly and deciding on a suitable sample size is not easy, but one useful check is to test for replicability. In other words, if another sample is chosen and the survey is carried out again in the same way, given that there will be some degree of variation, do the same general patterns emerge? If the answer is 'yes', then there is some evidence that a generalization about the wider population can be made from the results. Of course, if Sean and Mario had chosen another five boys from their class as their second sample, it is quite likely that the same result would have occurred, simply because they would have replicated the same sampling bias!

Recording and storing data

Recording data can be rather like the children's game of 'Chinese whispers'. The more often data are transferred from one piece of paper to another, the greater the chance of them being corrupted or mislaid. There are also occasions when data present themselves too quickly to be recorded (when conducting a traffic survey, for example), and it is difficult to find a way of recording them accurately. These are two reasons why it is useful to have given some thought to how the data should be recorded *before* collecting them.

One solution is to have a blank chart prepared in advance and to record the data directly onto it. This will require having some idea of the expected categories, the range of likely values or range of intervals, and a quick pilot survey or simulation can be of great help here. Thought also needs to be given to the degree of accuracy to which the data should be recorded. This will depend on how accurate you need to be, but also on how accurate you are *able* to be.

It is important for children to come to realize that some things are very difficult to measure with any great accuracy. A useful classroom task here might be to choose an individual in the class and ask five pupils to measure that person's head size, leg length and handspan (keeping their measurements secret until everyone has completed their measurements). They should discover that there is a surprisingly wide variation in results. Indeed, even if one of the five measurers repeated the experiment, it is likely that some of the results would show a variation from the previous values.

These questions of variation, accuracy and ambiguity in what is actually being measured are non-trivial and they are well worth introducing, even to very young children. Here are some possible ideas.

- Bring in a paint chart and explore what we mean by the terms 'green' or 'yellow'. At what point does green start to look like blue?
- Estimate the number of shoelace holes in class by counting the numbers of holes in one shoe. Then check how good the estimate was. Discuss why it wasn't 'correct'.
- Estimate the passage of one minute. Do you improve with practice?
- How good is your memory? Do you improve with practice?

The national curriculum (for England and Wales) design guidelines for key stage 1 specify that pupils should be taught 'how to store, select and analyse information using software, for example, using a database'. It is also a key stage 2 requirement in mathematics. For example, AT 5 level 4 requires pupils to be able to interrogate data in a database.

What this means is that every teacher will be expected to incorporate the use of the computer appropriately into their teaching right from key stage 1. So information technology (IT) will be a significant and increasingly important element in teaching. Data handling is an obvious area in which IT, in the form of computers and calculators, has much to offer. For example, at the 'C' stage of the PCAI cycle, the data can be recorded directly into a database or spreadsheet. Additionally, a graphics program will help at the 'A' stage to present the data in different formats. Also useful at this stage is the calculator – particularly for calculating totals, averages, costings, converting measurements, and so on. Finally, the 'I' stage may involve a project write-up, and there is an obvious application for the word processor here.

Analysing data

One way of analysing data is to do a calculation, such as finding an average. But perhaps the most useful technique for analysing data is the drawing of graphs – block graphs, pie charts, scatter graphs, and so on – and indeed, these are central themes of AT 5 Handling data.

Graphs are powerful ways of analysing and interpreting data and should be seen by pupils primarily as useful, rather than decorative! By the time they reach the final stages of primary school, most children are already familiar with seeing numerical information represented in tables, block graphs (both bar charts and histograms) and pie charts. Some may even have used scatter graphs. But what about infant pupils? Can they have direct access to graphical representations and, if so, what is the best way to introduce them? Concrete (physical) embodiments are usually good starting points for young children, and graphs are no exception. For example, here is an account of how a class of five-year-olds used Multilink cubes to draw a three-dimensional block graph.

> I asked the children (5–6 years old) what different ways they could think of to travel around. They came up with quite a long list of things like bus, train, helicopter, walking, and so on. Each child then drew onto a card one of the ways of travelling and we stuck the cards onto the side of my desk. I then gave everyone a Multilink cube and they came up, in turn, to place their cube

beside the card that showed how they came to school. (Not surprisingly, the helicopter and space rocket categories remained unfilled!) Each pile of cubes was then made into a tower and by now our three-dimensional bar chart was complete. We spent some time talking about the most popular and the least popular ways of coming to school. I also asked them questions like how many cubes they thought there were altogether.

Voting is a classroom activity which offers the double virtue of encouraging fair collective decision making and also providing interesting data-handling opportunities. Here is a suggestion from one infant teacher.

> I find it useful to have, as a class resource, a set of cards with each child's name written on one of them. Then whenever there is to be any voting or choosing to be done, each child takes their own card and places it against the picture of their chosen option.

Most people tend to skip over tables of figures when reading an article in a book or magazine. One explanation may be that, on their own, a set of figures may not reveal any great insights. However, when they have been plotted onto a graph, it is surprising how often clear trends and patterns can become apparent that were just not evident from the raw data. Of the graphs which genuinely help pupils to form sensible conclusions from their data, the most useful are the histogram, stemplot and scatter graph.

A histogram allows pupils to see where a typical value in their sample is likely to lie and, at a glance, they can get a feeling for the extent of the variation. If two samples are being compared, two histograms overlaid on acetate can help give an impression of the similarities and differences between the two data sets. (For example, this approach might be used to compare class estimates of an unknown length in metric units with their estimates in imperial units.)

A stemplot is a less common form of representation in schools, but it is a simple and powerful alternative to the histogram. Instead of each value in the data set being represented by a 'block', the space is filled by a digit corresponding to the value of that data item. Taking the example above, where the class may wish to compare their estimates based on using metric and imperial units, the two sets of data could be set out side by side using a back-to-back stemplot. (See Graham, 1987 and 1990, for further details of stemplots.)

A scatter graph gives a useful picture of the nature of the relationship between two different things (the relationship might be that as one thing increases, the other decreases). For example, children may wish to carry out an experiment to investigate the connection between the amount of water given to different plants each day and their rate of growth. Plotting the results on a scatter graph will help them to see a picture of the nature of the relationship (in general, the more water, the more growth – but not beyond a certain point). The scatter graph also allows some insight into the strength of the relationship, based on the degree of scatter of the points.

There is no doubt that computer graphics programs can take the hard work out of drawing graphs. However, they may increase the likelihood of children producing a variety of inappropriate ones. For example, it may be perfectly *possible* to produce a pie chart depicting the prices of four different magazines – but does it mean anything? To take a positive view of this, 'silly' graphs drawn on the computer at least provide the teacher with opportunities for making interesting teaching points!

Finally, it is worth stressing again the central theme of this chapter which is that all these types of graphs can be *useful* in helping children to answer questions about their data which they might not be able to answer without them.

Interpreting the results

One of the difficulties with project work in mathematics is that it does not always provide a clear end-point for the children where they can perform or present to others what they have done. This contrasts sharply with certain other areas of the curriculum, where the pay-off to the pupil is more tangible. For example, the rewards for practising a piece of music or drama may be to be able to perform it for others. The reward for pursuing craft/design tasks is, to a large extent, the pleasure of holding in your hand something that you have made yourself.

A partial solution to this problem of a lack of 'product' in maths is to encourage the children to do work which can be displayed on the walls of the classroom or corridors. This may have the benefit of helping to motivate the children to achieve a high standard of presentation, so that their efforts will be seen and approved of by other pupils, teachers and parents who see it. However, this is only a partial solution, because what is being judged is sometimes the form rather than the content of their work. In other words, the block graph on the classroom wall will tend to impress if it is neatly drawn, rather than if its use were appropriate.

The next account raises the question of how children view some of these questions concerning the form and content of their work.

> My class of third-year juniors had been working on their 'news-paper' theme and had collected data about the various papers and magazines which were read at the homes of members of the class. Bar charts of their data were duly drawn, shaded and coloured. I wanted them to think about what they had drawn, so

asked them to spend about five minutes, working in pairs, noting down what sort of things they could tell from their bar chart. Fay and Melody produced the following.

> information about how many people get the magazines and paper. How many different paper + magazine there are.

Liam and Amit came up with a rather different list.

> Colours   Paterns
> Numbers   Titles
> Names   Shapes
> Squares   Width
> lines   Length

Clearly Fay and Melody were attending to the meaning and interpretation of their bar chart and seemed to recognize that its primary function was to *provide information* about their survey. Liam and Amit, on the other hand, focused on the *form* of their drawing and, in particular, on the component parts that went into drawing it. Within their own terms of reference, both sets of answers were excellent, but it is likely that Liam and Amit would be less willing and able to use graphs confidently as a *tool* for handling their data than Fay and Melody.

As the following account suggests, when it comes to presenting information appropriately, children are not always sure what is being judged.

> Our school lost property box had become full to overflowing, and Bal and Marti (year 6) kindly volunteered to check the boxes each day and keep a record of all the items they found there. By Friday, the job was finished, and Marti carefully wrote out her findings to stick on the notice board. A sample of what she wrote is shown below.

> The number of socks on...
> > Monday 5.
> > Tuesday 5.
> > Wednesday 8.
> > Thursday 8.
> > Friday 15.
> The number of combs on...
> > Monday 0.
> > Tuesday 0.
> > Wednesday 3.

Chatting to Marti later, I thought I would gently reveal to her the delights of laying information out in a table. Then I noticed something on her desk, which looked like this.

	Mon.	Tue.	Wed.	Thur.	Fri.
Pens	1	0	1	1	0
Combs	0	0	3	3	3
Socks	5	5	8	8	15
Rings	0	0	0	0	0

She explained that she had used the table as an easy way of collecting the information day by day.

'Didn't you think the table would have been a good way of presenting the information to the class?' I asked.

'Oh, no!' she replied. 'The table just has numbers in it. It wants to be written up properly with words.'

The difficulties pupils have in handling and presenting data appropriately tend to be less in evidence if the investigation has been driven by a clear, purposeful question right from the beginning. In the adult world, the end-point of posing a question is, in general, finding a sensible and satisfactory answer. Thus, merely displaying pie charts on the walls is rarely a suitable end to the sort of statistical investigations described here. Drawing graphs enables children to gain a better understanding of the data which they have collected, and so come to a reasoned conclusion about the central question of their investigation. This may take the form of a recommendation to the headteacher (e.g. to agree on a re-organization of storage of equipment), or perhaps provide supporting evidence for a letter to the local paper (one school conducted an energetic campaign to prevent Ernie, the lollipop man, from losing his job), or provide them with the means to help answer a curious question for its own sake (e.g. can people with long legs run faster?).

Developing a healthy scepticism is, perhaps, one of the most useful qualities that we can encourage in pupils. 'Things are rarely what they seem' is an apt aphorism in the area of data handling – children need to learn that for every plausible interpretation of the results of handling data, there may be several other equally plausible explanations. In particular, good detection skills are often rewarded when graphs and tables of data are read critically.

Notes

A fuller version of the ideas in this chapter is contained in *Handling Data*, one of the five Open University books which together comprise *Supporting Primary Mathematics* (PM649).

The Open University pack *Statistical Investigations in the Secondary School* (PM646) covers similar issues, but with a particular focus on the eleven- to sixteen-year-old age range.

The Open University data-handling software pack *Statistical Investigations in the Secondary School* (PM646SFT) provides the facility of drawing and printing data represented in a pie chart, bar chart, stemplot, histogram or scatter graph. However, the quality of such software improves all the time and free advice on the best offerings currently available is provided by NCET.

Further information on the above can be obtained from the Centre for Mathematics Education, The Open University, Walton Hall, Milton Keynes, MK7 6AA. All are available from the Learning Materials Sales Office, The Open University, PO Box 188, Milton Keynes, MK7 6DH.

The National Council for Educational Technology (NCET) specializes in the application of IT to educational needs. As well as producing their own materials, they offer advice and training in this area. For a free resources catalogue, contact: NCET, Sir William Lyons Road, Science Park, Coventry, Warwickshire, CV4 7EZ.

References and further reading

Hugh Burkhardt (1982) *Mathematics and the Real World*, Blackie.

Alan Graham (1987) *Statistical Investigations in the Secondary School*, Cambridge University Press.

Alan Graham (1990) *Investigating Statistics – a Beginner's Guide*, Hodder and Stoughton.

PME233 Mathematics Across the Curriculum (1980) The Open University. (Further details available from the Centre for Mathematics Education at The Open University.)

Edward R. Tufte (1983) *The Visual Display of Quantitative Information*, Graphics Press.

Edward R. Tufte (1990) *Envisioning Information*, Graphics Press.

The Castle of Knowledge.

The Sphere of Destinye.

The wheele of Fortune.

Sphæra Fati

Sphæra Fortunæ

QVOMODO SCANDIT. COR RVETSTATIM.

whose governour is Knowledge.

whose ruler is Ignoraunce.

TO KNOWLEDG is this Trophy set,
All learninges friendes will it support.
So shall their name great honour get,
And gaine great fame with good report

Though spitefull Fortune turned her wheele
To staye the Sphere of Vranye,
Yet dooth this Sphere resist that wheele,
And fleeyth all fortunes villanye.
Though earthe do honour Fortunes balle,
And bytells blynde hyr wheele aduaunce,
The heauens to fortune are not thralle,
These Spheres surmount al fortunes chance.

~ 1556 ~

Section introduction

In the United Kingdom, the introduction of the various national curricula has exerted a powerful influence over the thinking of all concerned with the teaching of mathematics. Within the education system, both teachers and advisers have had to rethink their practices; meanwhile, the authors of textbooks and schemes have been busily producing new books or adapting current ones to their perceptions of the relevant national curriculum.

Although teachers pick and choose among schemes, and in recent years they have been offered lists of criteria for making such choices, they are not usually invited to look behind the different presentations of subject matter to the underlying ideological and pedagogical assumptions. The mathematician René Thom writes: 'As soon as one uses a textbook, one establishes a didacticism, an academicism, even if the book be so written to promote individual research'. Three of the pieces in this section attempt to reveal some of the normally taken-for-granted aspects of written materials.

Through several examples from the past, John Fauvel examines one aspect of texts – the tone and manner in which the writer of a textbook or scheme addresses the pupil. In a situation where schemes in which pupils do a large part of their work unaided are very widely used in both primary and secondary schools through the United Kingdom, this is a concern with everyday implications. It also reflects George Santayana's remark: 'those who do not learn from the past will be condemned to repeat it'. Eddie Gray examines the changing styles of primary texts over the last hundred years and shows both changes and unexpected continuities in their assumptions. He also indicates that the tension between addressing the textbook to the teacher or directly to the pupil is still a live issue. Paul Dowling looks closely at a very widely used secondary mathematics scheme – the texts for the last three years of the SMP 11–16 course – and draws conclusions concerning the implicit collusion between mathematical ability and social class.

The last two chapters, by Jill Adler, and Zelda Isaacson and Jane Coombe respectively, focus on comparisons between the proposed national curriculum under discussion in South Africa and those in the United Kingdom. In the former case, the premises on which such a mathematics national curriculum will be based are the subject of much debate. These linked pieces inform each other about the range and plausibility of some of the justifications offered in favour of national curricula, as well as highlighting some inherent problems of their implementation.

11 Tone and the teacher: instruction and complicity in mathematics textbooks

John Fauvel

The use of books in the classroom is a complicated matter. Whatever the overall structure of use – whether all pupils have copies of a book or only the teacher does, whether pupils use the book in class or only during homework, and so on – they provide a fresh set of challenges, with both benefits and problems. A feature of mathematics texts which is useful to think about is the relationship between the author and the reader which is built into the book: how has the author set up the pedagogic interaction between text and pupil? What conception of the pupil is implied? What function is the teaching seen as serving? The way the text is written, and its pedagogical presuppositions, obviously constrain what the teacher, as one corner of a book/pupil/teacher triangle, can or should do in relation to the book's use in the classroom.

The purpose of this chapter is to open out some aspects of the *tone* of mathematics texts; that is, how the author has worked to influence the way that readers must respond to the book to benefit in the way intended. I will do this by exploring three arithmetic books written over a wide period: Robert Record's *The Ground of Arts* (1543), Thomas Dilworth's *The School-master's Assistant* (1743), and David Eugene Smith's *Number Stories of Long Ago* (1910). My reason for choosing books from the past is that we can see certain features of them more clearly than in contemporary texts, precisely because of our distance from them. This is not a historical survey, however – the fact that our three books were written so far apart is interesting, but is not really the point. It just so happens that these books provide good clear material for comparison, to bring out some of the different ways in which authors can structure and use texts for teaching and learning purposes. You should find that some of the features found in the old texts speak of decisions which textbook writers today must also face.

The first book we look at was the most popular mathematics textbook written in English during the first couple of centuries after the invention of printing, and thus significantly contributed to the flowering of British mathematical practice in the century leading up to the work of Isaac Newton.

Robert Record's *The Ground of Arts* (1543)

Record was a Welshman, born in Tenby about 1510; he graduated from the University of Oxford in 1531, and became a Fellow of All Souls. Like others of the period, he combined mathematics and medicine, taking a Cambridge MD degree in 1545; but his later public career was as a civil servant, controller of the Bristol mint in 1549 and from 1551 to 1553 surveyor of mines and monies in Ireland. But he did not manage to plot his way skilfully enough through those politically dangerous times, and a longstanding quarrel with the powerful Earl of Pembroke landed him in jail, in the King's Bench prison in Southwark, which is probably where he died in 1558, when only in his late forties.

So Record was a child of the generation of English humanists, brought up in the new spirit towards learning inculcated by such as Erasmus and Sir Thomas More. Secular education had become enormously important, and Record was really the first person to think through what mathematics should be taught, and also how to teach it, in the circumstances of increasing literacy, growing trade and prosperity, and new technological capabilities for peace or war. His strategy was an ordered series of textbooks, the first of which, *The Ground of Arts*, set out to instruct its readers in the basics of elementary arithmetic: numeration, addition, subtraction, multiplication, and division. The Hindu–Arabic numerals, and the decimal place-value system which they use, were fairly novel to most people, and earlier editions of the book explain how to do these operations both in the new numerals and on the counting-board, which up until then was the standard way of doing numerical computations.

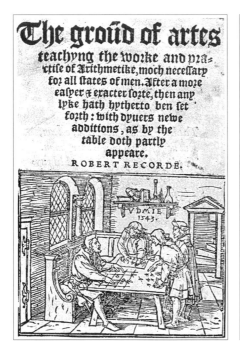

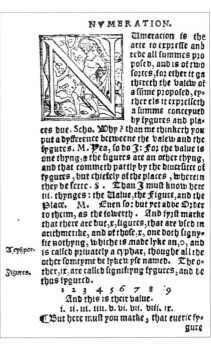

The Ground of Arts, first issued in about 1543, was extremely popular. Four or five editions came out during Record's lifetime, and it was regularly re-issued thereafter, passing through the hands of several editors, for a century and a half – the last of the fifty or so editions came out in 1699. Record has a rather characteristic style, which was fully formed from the start: the *Ground* begins with a 'declaration of the profit of arithmetic' which introduces Record's dialogue form, his humanist pedagogical policy, and not least his propensity to versify at the slightest opportunity. Here the two characters who converse through most of his textbooks, Master and Scholar, make their appearance, discussing why numbering is a good thing. The scholar says he wants to learn, to which the master responds:

> **Master**: I am very glad of your request, and will do it speedily, since that to learn it you be so ready.
>
> **Scholar**: And I to your authority my wit do subdue; whatsoever you say, I take it for true.
>
> **Master**: That is too much; and meet for no man to be believed in all things, without showing of reason. Though I might of my Scholar some credence require, yet except I show reason, I do not it desire.

We immediately notice Record's care to set out the aim of leading the scholar to think for himself. A theme running through all the books is the balance between authority and reason as the proper grounding for knowledge. Record gives the most forthright formulation of his views in a later work, his astronomical text *The Castle of Knowledge* (1556), when in discussing the work of Ptolemy, the master remarks to the scholar:

> yet must you and all men take heed, that both in [Ptolemy's] and in all men's works, you be not abused by their authority, but evermore attend to their reasons, and examine them well, ever regarding more what is said, and how it is proved, than who saith it: for authority often times deceiveth many men.

Throughout the texts, remarks to this effect are dropped about balancing the sources of knowledge: reason and authority, reason and custom, reason and learning by rote, reason and observation. In this way, Record gradually imparts a world-view in which thinking for oneself, using one's reason aright, is a prime duty. The messages that come over to the reader are far more than the narrowly mathematical. This is true, in fact, of all textbooks – what messages in this respect come from the texts which you use?

Mathematics, too, is something established on a basis of reason, rather than, say, an empirical craft. But the emphasis on reason is not a call for providing immediately a full panoply of mathematical justification. Indeed, Record's geometry text *The Pathway to Knowledge* (1551) explains the constructions and theorems of the first four books of Euclid's *Elements* without giving a single proof. This was part of a careful strategic judgement that the beginners he was writing for had to understand what the results were about, in the first place, and only later see their demonstrations. In short, we see in numerous aspects a most carefully considered pedagogy informing Record's texts.

Dialogue form

Crucial in Record's pedagogy was his choice of a dialogue form. He explains this in the preface to *The Ground of Arts* in a simple and straightforward way.

> I have written in the form of a dialogue, because I judge that to
> be the easiest way of instruction, when the scholar may ask
> every doubt orderly, and the master may answer to his
> question plainly.

This statement rather underplays the enormous versatility the form takes
on in Record's hands. It enables him to engage with subtle teaching points
and convey the learner through difficulties which might be hard to handle
in any other way. It has two global advantages as well: it forces the author
to be constantly putting himself in the place of the reader, to raise and
respond to any difficulties that the learner might have, so there is greater
and more persistent reader-friendliness than in most texts of a more one-
sidedly didactic form. Secondly, from the reader's perspective, the dialogue
form gives a dramatic momentum to the text which encourages the reader
to persevere through any hard passages, and generally makes the task of
learning more productive as well as more agreeable. It does, though, require
the reader to read in a fairly connected, persevering way – a reader with too
short an attention span will not benefit very much!

Teaching in written dialogue form is somewhat rare nowadays. The roots
of Record's choice of form are fairly clear: as a well-educated Oxford
graduate, he was quite familiar with the works of Plato, then as now the
paradigm for philosophical dialogue. Several features of Record's dialogues show a familiarity with Plato's style, most notably his dialectical use
of error to move towards truth. The point is not just a dialogue *form*, of which
there are other precursors of a more or less tedious nature (as we will see in
the next example!), but the handling of that form to lead the reader towards
greater skill and enlightenment.

A sign of Record's genius in handling the form is the character of the scholar.
Far from the placid inquirer of the conventional catechism, the scholar is
lively, ready to speak his mind, slightly over-self-confident, but emphati-
cally committed to learning, quite bright, and unafraid of making mistakes
– but making enough mistakes for all readers to be able to empathize.
Indeed, the scholar's errors are a critical part of the teaching process,
enabling ambiguities to be cleared up and common mistakes and miscon-
ceptions to be guarded against. What he does wrong is as instructive as what
he does right. And that he can go wrong at all, and be led back onto the right
path in a gentle, friendly, supportive way, carries a crucially important
pedagogic message.

A simple example of learning through error is found early on in *The Ground
of Arts*, where the scholar is getting to grips with addition. After the master
explains what to do, through an example, the scholar is confident of being
able to do likewise, and indeed of being able to devise his own example. But
he stumbles on both counts, and has to be rescued by the master.

> **Master**: … So that now you see, that 160 and 136 do make in all
> 296.
>
> **Scholar**: What? This is very easy to do, me thinketh I can do it
> even such. There came through Cheapside two droves of cattle;

in the first was 848 sheep, and in the second was 186 other beasts.
Those two sums I must write as you taught me, thus,

848
186

Then if I put the two first figures together, saying: 6 and 8, they
make 14, that must I write under 6 and 8 thus,

848
<u>186</u>
14

Master: Not so, and here are you twice deceived. First, in going
about to add together two sums of sundry things, which you
ought not to do, except you seek only the number of them & care
not for the things … [and secondly] in writing 14, which came of
6 and 8, under 6 and 8, which is impossible: for how came two
figures of two places be written under one figure and one place?

The warnings that Record is trying to impart at this stage are on two levels:
one a technical detail about carrying digits when the sum goes over 9, and
the other the principle of not mixing numbers which refer to different things
(though this seems an unfortunate instance of 'do as I say, not as I do', since
the master's own example was a sum of Latin books and Greek books). As
the sum progresses, there are other very plausible difficulties which the
scholar discusses with the master, and from which we can see how experienced a teacher Record was.

Thus, Record conveyed his learners (provided only they could read) from
innumeracy to quite a sophisticated handling of a range of mathematical
practices. In fact, we may judge from the numbers of editions that not many
readers ventured onto the higher ground in the textbooks he wrote after *The
Ground of Arts*: but it was the lower level that needed consolidation in Tudor
England, anyway. The very real grounding that Record supplied made
possible the development of mathematical arts and sciences in Elizabeth's
reign in such fields as navigation, and other activities of mathematical
practitioners, and in constructing an appropriate mental attitude towards
mathematics and its value for society.

How, then, do Record's texts work as teaching documents? Throughout, we
get the impression of an author who carries in the forefront of his mind what
the person studying the text is supposed to do with it, which can broadly be
characterized as getting inside, empathizing with, the learning situation
represented on paper. The author is very present in the texts, and the reader
too inhabits the mind of the scholar, so as to learn along with him. The book's
success as a teaching text therefore depends on how well the author has
anticipated the degree to which the mind of the reader and the scholar work
similarly. Obviously, not every misunderstanding of every reader can be
foreseen, but Record makes a more creditable effort in this respect than most
later textbook writers. Working in dialogue form helps the author here; it is
harder to skim over, or indeed not notice, difficulties when in constructing
the text there is an empty space on paper, as it were, needing to be filled by
the scholar/learner's response to the immediately previous material.

On another level, a further way in which the texts work is that some characteristics of the scholar's moral personality may by example transfer to the reader, who absorbs an understanding of what it is to be an inquiring mathematician, as well as the details of mathematical skills and techniques. This level of moral understanding gleaned from books is particularly important for distance learners, who may need guidance and reassurance in the very business of being a student, of inquiring into knowledge.

Of course, there are problems in learning from Record's texts also: the pacing of the text cannot be quite right for every reader, one's attention span needs to be longer than a minute or two, the crowded black Gothic type of early editions is rather hard to skip back or forwards through, and one may not realize just how complicated a 'simple' arithmetical technique is until the master describes it in words!

Textbook writers and distance teachers today may gain inspiration and food for reflection from re-examining the pedagogic techniques employed in Robert Record's teaching texts. Of course, every textbook writer is a teacher at a distance, and has to make the choice of how far to appear in the text. And perhaps classroom teachers can benefit from Record also. It might be that his dramatic scenes could be transmuted into modern classroom activities; could children be encouraged to explore their growing understanding by constructing dramas around mathematical ideas, techniques and errors? What about having them write teaching dialogues for pupils lower down the school?

The next example is of another highly popular school textbook, first published just two hundred years after Record's.

Thomas Dilworth's
The Schoolmaster's Assistant (1743)

Thomas Dilworth, who died in 1780, was one of the most successful textbook writers of the eighteenth century. He was a teacher in London, at Stratford-le-Bow Free School around 1730, and later (*c*.1740–1770) at the Academy at Wapping New Stairs. His arithmetic text *The Schoolmaster's Assistant* first appeared in 1743, and there were some 45 editions in Britain, the last in 1816, while nearly 70 editions appeared in the United States, between 1773 and 1832. So this is a book which found favour with a very large number of teachers on two continents for nearly a century.

The tone of Dilworth's book is markedly different from Record's. There is still a large question-and-answer component, but the relation between reader and writer is no longer conversational. It is, rather, in the form of a didactic catechism, much as in religious instruction – a style which predates Record, and comes down from medieval church practice. There is little possibility of the reader empathizing with the answerer – it seems fairly clear that it is the answers which are to be learned rather than the reasoning underlying them. By comparison with Record's texts, the balance between reason and authority has swung far in the latter direction. Dilworth had indeed made a conscious decision to adopt this pedagogic style, as he explained in the preface.

I have thrown the Subject of the following Pages into a Catechetical Form, that they may be the more instructive; for Children can better judge of the Force of an Answer, than follow Reason through a Chain of Consequences. Hence also it proves a very good examining Book; for at any Time, in what Place soever the Scholar appears to be defective, he can immediately be put back to that Place again, without the formal Way of beginning every thing anew.

This passage throws light on Dilworth's aims, and perhaps helps to explain the success of his book in the circumstances of the late eighteenth century. To use a book for *examining* children, in Dilworth's sense, would never have crossed Record's mind! But Dilworth, two centuries later, shrewdly read the new social needs which society had of the educational system, and helped prepare the climate of opinion which led to the fully fledged examination culture of the following century. This culture (also discussed in Eddie Gray's chapter in this volume) had further, more sophisticated, elements, such as attaching numerical gradings to examination results. There is also a clear conception, embodied in the style of Dilworth's book, of mathematics as a body of content rather close to religious doctrinal truths. It is worth assessing any textbooks you use in these respects: what is its conception of mathematics? Does it explain its pedagogy, and what is it?

What purpose for teaching is implicit in the tone of the book – to entertain pupils? To help them to pass examinations? To lead to growth in their understanding? Or something else?

Further, Dilworth has made a more cynical – or more realistic? – assessment of the attention span of pupils. A child unable to persevere with Record's humanistic prose should still be able to learn short, catechetical questions and answers and, as Dilworth points out, it is easier to pin down just what answer has been memorized incorrectly and refer the pupil back to relearn it. Dilworth does not, perhaps wisely, dwell overlong on the subject of the level of pupils' understanding which is reached through this procedure. It is still valuable to ask of texts today which are constructed in a climate of assessment: what balance is achieved between helping pupils to learn and understand, and preparing them for assessment?

Dilworth wrote in a period when 'the child' was just coming to be invented as a special socio-educational category (this claim is to over-simplify a rather complex and contentious historical debate, but it is helpful as a first approximation). In Record's book, the scholar was of indeterminate age, and may indeed have been a learner of any age. By the time of our final example, in the early twentieth century, it is clear that a whole psychology of the child has been developed as a framework of assumptions within which to write a school-book.

D. E. Smith's *Number Stories of Long Ago* (1910)

David Eugene Smith lived from 1860 to 1944, and was professor of mathematics at Teachers College, Columbia University, from 1901 to 1926. Many of his works are still in print, notably his two-volume *History of Mathematics* (1923) and his *Source Book in Mathematics* (1929). He was one of the most distinguished mathematical historians and mathematics educators of the century, a towering figure in a wide range of fields and activities. Although remembered now as a historian, Smith was in the first instance a teacher of mathematics, with the profound belief that in order to develop a good pedagogy for the subject one must know and understand its history.

Number Stories of Long Ago is a very carefully crafted book aimed at children of primary school age, and we can learn quite a lot from it about Smith's pedagogical conceptions, about the conceptualization of childhood implicit in the text, about the role he sees for history at this level, and about the use of the book as an object. The pedagogical approach is remarkably clear: it is one of empathy and identification – indeed, complicity. There are two prefaces, and the contrast between them sets the tone for the book.

Preface number one: just between us, and worth reading

Preface number two: for the grown-ups, and not worth reading

The contrast of prefaces is notable. They are written in quite different linguistic styles. The first preface is in the clear, simple, rather beautiful language in which the book as a whole is written.

> You who read these stories should imagine yourselves sitting by the great log fire and listening to the Story-Teller. You should seem to see in the flames and the shadows the moving pictures of those who played their parts in Number Land when the world was learning as you do.

The second preface is written in Smith's usual adult style, far less clear and flowing, explaining that the book is 'intended for supplementary reading in the elementary school'. 'Reading' is meant literally, as the first preface indicates – Smith intended that the child would not be read to but would read the book for himself or herself, and use it to enter into a new imaginative world.

NUMBER STORIES OF LONG AGO

ADDITION.
Master.

The easiest way in this arte, is to adde but two summes at ones togyther: how be it, you maye adde more, as I wil tel you anone. therefore whenne you wylle adde two summes, you shall fyrste set downe one of them, it forceth not whiche, and then bp it draw a lyne crosse the other lynes. And afterwarde sette downe the other summe, so that that lyne maye be betwene them: as if you woulde adde 1659 to 8341, you must set your summes as you see here.

And then if you lyst, you maye adde the one to the other in the same place, or els you may adde thm bothe tohither, in a new place : whiche way, because it is most plynest

PAGE FROM ROBERT RECORD'S BOOK

This page from Robert Record's "Ground of Artes" was printed nearly four hundred years ago

caster," meaning a man who could calculate only with counters and not with pencil and paper as we do. We sometimes use counters to-day in keeping the score in games.

58

Robert added numbers much as Caius did, placing the counters on the lines and in the spaces. When he had five counters on a line or in a space he took them up and carried one counter to the next place. You now see how we came to say "carry one" when we add, a counter being actually carried to the next place in the days of Robert Record.

When Robert became a man he wrote several books and used his influence to have the English people give up the Roman numerals.

We are apt to smile at Robert's use of counters and to think that we are much wiser than he because we use pencil and paper. But it is well to know that most of the world to-day finds it better not to use pencil and paper for computing. The Russians very generally use an abacus, many Persians use one, the Chinese

A MODERN ADDING MACHINE

This kind of machine is used in banks and in many large establishments

59

To add to its attractions to a child, the book is beautifully illustrated. There are eight coloured plates, including Ahmes and the Priest at the Temple gate, Ahmes studying fractions, Hippias on the Acropolis of Athens, Robert Record learning the use of counters, and Michael Stifel and his teacher. The picture titles give a clue to the book's strategy: Smith takes authors of past arithmetic texts, where possible, and talks about their work through imagining the author as a child, how they would learn to calculate and so on, and describes the improvements made in their own books when they grew up. So several messages permeate the text: empathy with past mathematical writers as children, perhaps the message that the reader when grown up may also create fresh work, and certainly a message of tolerance and relativism.

'Did they really count like this?' asked the Tease.

'Really,' replied he of the curious book.

'I think it is funny,' said the Tease.

'No funnier than your way would seem to Ching,' said the Story-Teller.

The text is not simply a succession of straightforward stories. A complicated effect of further complicity is created by the interaction between narrator, who is called *The Story-Teller*, and the children, called *The Crowd*, consisting of one main female child called *The Tease*, as well as Charles, Dorothy, Edward, Fanny, George, Gertrude, Maude, and Will. This interaction can have a slightly arch quality, but may also contain instructional humour – perhaps deriving a little from Lewis Carroll – which has quite a ring of realism.

'Now we are getting near the end of our number stories,' said the Story-Teller as the Crowd rushed into the room.

'Which end?' asked the Tease. 'A line has two ends.'

'Never mind which is the end of a line. One thing is sure, that I am near the end of my stories.'

'Yes, but *which* end of the stories?' persisted the Tease.

'The end that we are near,' said the Story-Teller.

A further pedagogic feature built into the text is 'the Question Box', which is an elaborate way of incorporating end-of-chapter questions both into the text and into the use of the text by schoolchildren. Smith says in the adult preface that the Question Box is a supply of questions that can be used either for conversation or for written work. They are questions like: 'What need have we for counting that Ching did not have?', 'Which numerals seem to you the easiest, those of Chang, those of Lugal, or those of Ahmes?', 'Can you arrange a magic square of nine figures in a different way from the one shown by Ching and Gupta?', or 'Count the number of figures used by Adriaen and Michael in the galley method of dividing 1728 by 12, and then count the number used by us in our method. Then compare the space required in the two cases. Can you see why the world refused so long to use our method?'. Within the story-line of the book, the Question Box supplies questions that the children must tackle before they are told the next story. They are part of the fun and play activities that the children enjoy, and which indeed move into number puzzles and conundrums towards the end. So the genuine read-and-enjoy quality of the book is enhanced or overlaid, depending on your perspective, by the presence of questions at the end of chapters, a reminder that a teacher is supposed to watch over the whole process and keep a check on how the child is developing knowledge and understanding.

Smith saw mathematical education not as an end in itself, but as part of a much broader inculcation into culture and understanding. This is seen here in his remark at the close of his adult preface that he hopes the book 'will create a new interest not merely in the study of arithmetic but in the story

NUMBER STORIES OF LONG AGO

decimal fractions about as we do to-day. We have not yet agreed upon the decimal point, however, for children who go to school in England write decimal fractions with the point halfway up (3·14), and in the rest of Europe they use a comma for a decimal point (3,14).

Explicatiō du donné. Il y a trois ordres de nombres de Difme, defquels le premier 27 ⊙8①4②7③,le deux-iefme 37 ⊙8①7②5③,le troifiefme 875 ⊙7①8②1③.

Explication du requis. Il nous faut trouver leur fomme. Conftruction. On mettra les nombres donnez en ordre comme ci joignant, les aiouftant felon la vulgaire maniere d'aioufter nombres entiers;en cefte forte:

⊙①②③
27 8 4 7
37 6 7 5
875 7 8 2
941 3 0 4

HOW SIMON STEVIN WROTE DECIMALS

This is the first book ever published on decimal fractions. The first number is 27.847

So the world's ideas grow just as yours grow, and fashions change as the years go on. For this reason the fashion of decimal points varies from time to time and from country to country very much like the fashions of men's collars, of women's hats, of cutting boys' hair, and the ways of wearing belts on a girl's dress.

"Do you mean that we have fashions in arithmetic just as we have fashions in clothes?" asked Emily.

"Certainly; why not? We have been seeing fashions in reading and writing numbers, in adding, subtracting, multiplying, and dividing. Why do you call the answer in multiplication a product and not a sum? Nothing but fashion! It was once the fashion to use the word 'product' for the answer in addition, and the word 'sum' for the answer in subtraction. It is the fashion in school to speak of a dividend as a number to be divided, but it is not the fashion with business men to use it in this way. It is the fashion for you all to go to bed at this time, and —"

"But you say that fashions change," said the Tease.

"This fashion does n't change at all," replied the Story-Teller.

"And the fashion of telling us number stories at night does n't change, either," said the Tease.

"Neither does the fashion of the Question Box," laughed the Story-Teller as the Crowd started for bed.

of the development of our civilization'. One quotation at the head of the text is rather striking; it appears to prefigure Foucault – 'There is no knowledge that is not power' – but this is in fact a quotation from the nineteenth-century American essayist Ralph Waldo Emerson.

Tone and the teacher

In each of these books, the writer has chosen a different way of relating to the reader, and what the reader is supposed to *do* with the text varies. Some of these differences may arise from the authors having different kinds of pupil in mind, of different ages or with different expectations. But there are also clear differences in pedagogy, which are independent of these features and worth thinking about.

Of course, these three examples do not exhaust the ways in which writers determine the tone of their books. The tone of the most popular textbook ever written, for example, Euclid's *Elements* (*c*. 300 BC), is notable for the reader making no appearance in the work at all! Euclid's succession of definitions, axioms, theorems and proofs follow one another without any explicit or even implicit awareness of there being a reader of these inexorable truths, let alone anyone trying to learn from the book. It is clear that so lofty and detached a style is not incompatible with great popularity (among teachers, if not pupils) – apart from the Bible, Euclid's *Elements,* over the centuries, has passed through more editions than any other work.

12 The primary mathematics textbook: intermediary in the cycle of change

Eddie Gray

A recurring feature of the primary mathematics curriculum since the inception of compulsory state education in 1870 has been debate. Hardly a decade has passed without concern being expressed over the level of children's attainment, the nature of the mathematics curriculum or the quality of children's learning. In response, politicians, parents, mathematicians and mathematics educators have each presented various philosophies for the mathematics taught within the schools. But as each has had the opportunity to play the dominant role, so too has each initiative been subject to the accusation that it has failed children and/or society. Unfortunately, there has been discord, even contradiction, between each group's perception of the curriculum and its purpose.

Classroom teachers do not usually take part in the broader philosophical or socio-economic arguments. Despite observing from the sidelines, they are highly conscious of the debate. Most accept that if innovation dominates, they may need to encompass a change in direction; although predominantly passive in creation, they are active in implementation. However, the eloquence of a reformer's rhetoric does not provide most teachers with the means to accomplish this. Widespread implementation of mathematical innovation proceeds when the change in emphasis is tangible, usually with the publication of a textbook: an intermediary in the cycle of change.

The primary mathematics textbook is a resource that is taken for granted within most modern primary classrooms. It is hard to imagine what we would do if we did not have one available. We expect so much from it; a maths curriculum, child appeal, the ability to cope with the individual, administrative flexibility and even the encouragement of different teaching styles. Traditionally, they were no more than a permanent collection of suitable problems to support teaching. In their modern role, the function of primary mathematics textbooks has expanded to include attempts to:

- help teachers respond to the mathematical requirements of society;
- remedy and prevent weaknesses in children's levels of mathematical attainment;
- provide a structured and sequential development of mathematics;
- develop motivation through presentation and learning through understanding.

However, perhaps because of their wider function, textbooks do not always satisfactorily provide a coherent approach to the various elements of a broader mathematics curriculum. If a mathematical strand – for example, arithmetic – has a clearly defined hierarchy, textbooks can provide sound support. Curriculum elements without an agreed hierarchy – for example, shape – usually receive fragmentary treatment and teachers need to look for supplementary material. Sometimes, it appears that mathematical structure and continuity loses out to other features, particularly the textbook's attempts to motivate children's learning.

In initial teacher training, many students, invited to consider an appropriate textbook to support their teaching, focus on visual appeal. Criteria such as the need to be 'visually attractive', to have a 'child-centred approach' and to be 'accessible to children' seem to precede mathematical considerations. Words such as 'attractive', 'lively' and 'fun' permeate students' evaluations of textbooks, but they are also words that flow easily from the pens of those who attempt to describe the qualities of the texts they promote. Over the past few years, the pre-publication material for new textbooks has claimed that a particular series was 'setting new standards of child appeal', was 'highly motivating' and 'purposefully illustrated in full colour with lively and varied drawings and photographs'. It appears that if a modern textbook can inspire motivation, interest and enthusiasm and 'cater for the individual', then it has overcome an important hurdle in the selection stakes.

Advances in print technology and the extensive use of peripheral writing combine to strengthen the view that the modern primary mathematics textbook is addressed directly to pupils. Innovation in printing and reproductive techniques has enabled publishers to make extensive use of colour at relatively little cost to ensure that textbooks have 'child appeal'; within some texts, the use of actual pictures has replaced schematic representation. Introductory remarks such as 'Do you remember when …' or 'Let us investigate …' are now coupled with attempts to jolly readers along through cartoons, suggestions, statements and comments. These writing styles complement more usual instructions to the child to do something and supplement the extent to which teaching components are contained within textbooks. Textbook writers now communicate a view of the mathematics curriculum within books that are becoming increasingly more personalized for the children who use them.

Publication of the national curriculum requirements in mathematics (1989) leaves us in no doubt as to the mathematical content identified for primary schools and the place of this content in terms of continuity and progression throughout the child's schooling. The translation of these explicit requirements into action within the classroom may increasingly make teachers continue to turn to textbooks for topic definition, stage-by-stage mathematical progression, and mathematical activities for children. If history is anything to go by, writers and publishers will respond to the need.

That politicians should now be making statements about content and attainment in primary school through a national curriculum in mathematics is not new. They did so in the first decade of state education in Britain and set the ground rules for the dominance of arithmetic in the primary school curriculum: 'The demand of parents for thoroughly good arithmetic appears to us to be one which must be satisfied, whatever else has to give way to it. Both for its utility and for its educational power, nothing else can stand in its way (Taunton Commission Report, 1868).

Arithmetic became a compulsory part of the curriculum for the child of the 1870s and its place was further ensured by the 1876 Education Act which introduced what has become known as 'payment by results'. As a result of this act, 50 per cent of the children above seven years of age were assessed in arithmetic, reading and writing. If over one half of the children tested failed in one subject or more, the school faced the prospect of no longer being certified as efficient.

Of course, at that time, the textbook was not the partner in the attainment of the appropriate level of achievement that it was to become in the future. Costs for schools were prohibitive and few, if any, texts on the market were suitable for the public elementary schools. The blackboard was the medium through which most problems were set. Children carried out their calculations with slate and chalk. However, primary textbooks did attempt to help the teachers in their task: 'To ensure the *Excellent* Merit Grant teachers should adopt these little books, which afford ample practice in every variety of problem set by the Department' (Capel, 1887, introduction).

The Department of Education requirement that the children of Standard 2 (eight- to ten-year-olds) should deal with numeration to 100 000 and the four simple rules to short division gave the text plenty of scope to provide examples for practice.

> A gardener gathered 7008 apples from twelve trees and each tree produced the same number. How many from each tree?
>
> What number is multiplied by eleven to give the answer 10,208?
>
> Divide the product of 19 and 20 by half the sum of 19 + 1.
>
> *(Capel, 1887, p. 12)*

Such was the pace of this little book that children of Standard 7 were faced with this lovely example.

> A owned $\frac{4}{17}$ of a vessel and sold $\frac{3}{11}$ of $\frac{2}{9}$ his share for £ $\frac{33}{400}$
>
> What was the value of $\dfrac{1\frac{2}{8}}{4\frac{1}{4}}$ of $\frac{2}{5}$ of the vessel?
>
> *(Capel, 1887, p. 82)*

A standardized curriculum for arithmetic in the latter part of the nineteenth century did not lead to attempts to standardize the texts that schools used. Neither did a prescribed curriculum, outlined within *Codes of Regulations*, which was 'designed in the first instance to serve the necessary purpose of setting forth the conditions which an elementary school must satisfy to obtain the parliamentary grants available for public elementary schools' (Board of Education, 1901), and accompanying assessment lead to success. These, together with conscientious but uninspired teaching, conspired to reduce arithmetic teaching to a soulless routine of the same kind of sum day in and day out, week in and week out, until mechanical accuracy became a habit and the required percentage of passes in the annual examinations could be guaranteed.

The centralization which dominated the curriculum of the elementary schools gradually receded so that, by the 1920s, the initiative within the classroom gradually moved from the teacher as teacher to the child as learner. The cycle was beginning to move. Success had not been achieved through centralization and a process-driven curriculum which had taken very little account of the appropriateness of the content.

The reorganization of elementary schools into junior and infant schools gave an impetus to the publication of textbooks to 'meet the needs of the new type of school organization' (Ballard, 1926). The infant sector was largely omitted from these attempts to provide the mathematics curriculum through the medium of the textbook; there were considered to be too many practical problems, not least being one of reading level.

Authors of the new school texts, many of whom were drawn from the inspectorate within local authorities or from the ranks of tutors within teacher-training establishments, made assumptions about the level of attainment in arithmetic that children would have by the time they entered the junior school and responded to general concerns about standards. 'Our scholars are, in fact, weak in the fundamentals, and it is this weakness that these little books are specially designed to remedy' (Ballard, 1926, 1, p. 17).

Fundamental Arithmetic (Ballard, 1926) not only included a permanent set of problems, but attempted to remedy weakness by providing a systematic training in the fundamental processes of arithmetic, while also giving direct attention to speed as well as accuracy. The author, within the answer book that also contained some comments on the philosophy of the series, suggested that the texts were suitable for individual work and could take most of the labour of marking from the teacher's shoulders; children could mark their own exercises using the answer books provided with the texts.

Within the schools, the series, for all its claims, proved to be 'rather difficult for children of average mental calibre' and the outcome was the publication of *The London Arithmetic* (Ballard, 1934), which was a series of less difficult books intended for less mathematically-minded children.

Meanwhile, the second Haddow report (1931) had given the term 'mathematics' respectability. Although some textbooks were: 'compiled to meet the requirements of Junior Pupils as indicated in the Recent Report of the Consultative Committee of the Board of Education on the Primary Schools' (Potter, 1933, p. 3), arithmetic remained the dominant feature.

> From 1,000,000 take the product of 567×678.
>
> From 102,010 take 98,765.
>
> $865,943 + 345$.
>
> *(Potter, 1933, Book IV)*

Disclaimers were to become regular features of textbook commentaries, and no doubt, those to be published in the near future will contain such a disclaimer referenced to the national curriculum.

The advent of more opportunities for children to go forward into secondary school led to enhanced concern that there should be continuity between the primary and secondary sectors. The Board of Education (1935) claimed that: 'the result of the teaching of arithmetic in schools should be to secure that a certain body of knowledge is thoroughly and permanently known' and that 'primary school children should be introduced to certain processes and notions which would be further developed in the secondary school'.

The influence of a more liberal approach, together with the outcomes of research into the development of computational skills, combined to bring about a radical change in the content, style and presentation of textbooks. Even though *Right from the Start Arithmetic* (Schonell and Cracknell, 1937) took note of contemporary trends, it focused on a recurring issue: 'to prevent the development of those weaknesses which careful study of post-primary pupils has disclosed' (Book 1, p. 3). The series used a contents list to indicate how the 'carefully graded material based on a careful consideration of available research into arithmetical processes' was presented throughout the texts.

The use of a textbook enabled the teacher to make the work for the children a little more personal; they could direct children to work individually. But not until the 1930s was the child directly addressed by the text:

> You already know the multiplication table up to 6 times 12.
>
> You can therefore multiply by 2, 3, 4, 5, or 6.
>
> Now you must learn to multiply by 7, 8, 9, 10, 11 and 12.
>
> *(Ballard, 1934, Book 2, p. 9)*

and examples of procedure added.

EXERCISE 28.—EASY DIVISION OF MONEY

Examples:

(a)
$$3)\overline{19\ \ 16} \\ 6\ \ 12$$

£19 ÷ 3 = £6 + £1 over.

20s. + 16s. = 36s.

36s. ÷ 3 = 12s.

Check:

£6 12s. × 3 = £19 16s.

(b)
$$8)\overline{27\ \ 5\ \ 4} \\ 3\ \ 8\ \ 2$$

£27 ÷ 8 = £3 + £3 over.

60s. + 5s. = 65s.

65s. ÷ 8 = 8s. + 1s. over.

12d. + 4d. = 16d.

16d. ÷ 8 = 2d.

Check:

£3 8 2 × 8 = £27 5 4.

(Ballard, 1934, Book 2, p. 34)

This was the start of a trend that we are now so familiar with; textbooks that set out to teach directly to the children.

Acknowledging that the child was the person reading the book and, in addition, making use of the book as a teaching medium were features that Schonell and Cracknell took a considerable stage further. In Book 2, for example, two pages devoted to writing numerical values for numbers up to 10 000 written in words are immediately preceded by three pages of exposition. These pages, which are intended to be directly led by the teacher, use diagrams and explanations linked to appropriate vocabulary and notation in an attempt to foster the child's understanding of place value. Also, the series also introduced new ideas without reference to the teacher.

Despite the move being gradually towards the textbook as a direct teaching medium, Fleming, in the teacher's book published with *Beacon Arithmetic*, cautioned as follows.

> No series of books intended for pupils' use can take the place of the teacher whose mind is alert to the needs of every pupil. No series of books can crowd between its covers those wider experiences which should be drawn from the pupils' everyday surroundings to bring added interest and meaning to the arithmetic work.

(Fleming, 1939c)

Beacon Arithmetic made considerable use of relevant research to categorize the development of numerical skill, and presented a mathematics curriculum which included spatial work and an introduction to graphs. Language development was also a feature of the texts; a 'number reader' was included with the series, and so too were books for infants – *The Beacon Number Books*.

LONG DIVISION (*continued*)

Book	Part	Chapter	Type of example	
Three	Two	II	$72 \overline{)\ 496}$	The first figure of the divisor is the trial divisor, but the trial quotient is one larger than the true quotient. Some remainders. One or two figures in quotient
			$28 \overline{)\ 212}$	The trial divisor is to be thought of as one larger than the first figure of the divisor. The trial quotient is the true quotient. One figure in quotient
			$39 \overline{)\ 2526}$	As above. Two figures in quotient
			$26 \overline{)\ 184}$	The apparent trial quotient is one less than the true quotient
			$13 \overline{)\ 103}$	More than one trial is necessary
			$61 \overline{)\ 26292}$	Three figures in quotient
			$51 \overline{)\ 11232}$	Zero or zeros at the end of

(Fleming, 1939c, p. 215)

To achieve its aim of helping the teacher to 'lay a firm foundation for the mastery of the basic combinations of addition, subtraction, multiplication and division' (Fleming, 1939c), the series made use of research to introduce 390 basic number combinations in each of the two parts of Book 1 and the first part of Book 2. These included addition and subtraction facts to 20 and the multiplication and division facts up to 9×9.

The teacher's books, now becoming much more than simple answer books, provided an appendix which indicated the order of presentation of types in each process. The 17 stages for addition of up to three four-digit numbers pales into insignificance when considered alongside the 49 stages for division. Graphical work was introduced in a very abstract form in Book 3.

Beacon Arithmetic offers the first real example of the use of a comprehensive teacher's book which contains reinforcement material for teachers. It provides an indication that such a resource could be used for introducing teachers to material they are unfamiliar with.

Both *Beacon Arithmetic* and *Right from the Start Arithmetic* were, for me, influential textbooks. The former I used as a child in school. Considering it again for this chapter brought back memories of a class of fifty children seated in paired iron-frame desks working from the pages of sums. The teacher seemed so far away as she sat at her pedestal desk. We worked in silence, but periodically were called to present our exercise books for marking. I loved ticks by my sums. If there were crosses, corrections had to be done in the afternoon when other children played with Plasticine.

The latter I used as a student undergoing initial training. Indeed, *Right from the Start Arithmetic* underwent fifteen impressions between 1937 and 1955, and both of these editions gave the following problem:

BILLS

SET ONE

		s.	d.
A. $\frac{1}{2}$ lb. bacon (back) at 1s. 4d. per lb.	. . =		
$\frac{1}{4}$ lb. lard at 6d. per lb.	. . . =		
1 lb. salt butter at 1s. 1d. per lb.	. . =		
$\frac{1}{2}$ lb. margarine at 8d. per lb.	. . . =		

(Schonell, 1937, 2, p. 60)

By the late 1950s, inflation was beginning to play havoc with other publications. *Alpha Junior Arithmetic* (Goddard and Grattidge, 1957) indicated that prices for the similar items had increased at least two-fold. In 1985, *Nuffield Mathematics* was suggesting that children obtained the cost of such items from home. No doubt expediency was one of the factors behind this suggestion; it indicates that there is a perceived need for 'reality' to prevail in the presentation of problems.

Attempts to provide suitable problems to illustrate the application of the arithmetical skills that children have learned can tax the imagination of textbook writers. Resolution of the difficulty up to the end of the 1930s centred upon what children were expected to do with the arithmetical

SHOPPING.—4

(Bullard, 1934, 2, p. 56)

skills they had acquired. The guiding principle was not the reality of the child as child, but the reality of the child as future adult; boys were expected to enter employment in the industrial or building industries, while girls entered the service industries or required a course in 'household arithmetic'. Both required the 'arithmetic of citizenship'. The production of pictures in textbooks provided an additional complication. Whose reality would be displayed – the child's or the textbook writer's? It was the comfortable middle-class world of the latter that dominated. Although the focus of learning was moving towards the child, the focus of 'reality' remained in the adult world.

There is a girl at the cash desk in this tea shop. If, when you grow up, you want a job like her's you must be able to do money problems quickly without mistakes.

(Fleming, 1939a, 3, p. 62)

Both in the gradual expansion of the mathematics curriculum, with its move towards the child as the focus, and in the development of the textbook, the 1930s had seen considerable development. There may have been further gradual progression over the next two decades had not the constraints of war time and post-war years led to a period of developmental stagnation.

Expansion, when it did come, gained momentum slowly in the 1950s and in the 1960s drastically changed our view of primary mathematics. It underwent rationalization in the 1970s, was questioned in the 1980s and leaves us in a sense of deep foreboding that in the 1990s we may be turning back to prescribed content and its allied problems, not least of which is the possibility that it will become *the* primary mathematics curriculum.

The 1955 Mathematical Association report provoked unprecedented interest in the teaching of mathematics of all types and urged the teaching of *mathematics* in the primary school as opposed to simply arithmetic.

> At first sight the word mathematics may seem pretentious when used in the Primary School. The words number and arithmetic … are equally so, and they have the disadvantage of suggesting limitations in aspect rather than elementary treatment.
>
> *(MA, 1955, p. vii)*

The report's compilers believed that the main aim of primary mathematics teaching was to lay the foundation of the child's mathematical thinking and it recommended that the syllabus should be extended to include more spatial work, not the formal geometry of Haddow, but spatial relationships such as symmetry and tessellations, angle relationships, nets of common solids and natural curves.

A very popular series of the period was *Alpha Junior Arithmetic* (Goddard and Grattidge, 1957), which carried forward the tradition of the texts of the late 1930s. As its title was meant to convey, within the teacher's handbook, the authors indicated that the series was intended 'for children of good average or above average ability' (p. 5). The concern of Goddard and Grattidge was that most books on arithmetic, although comprehensive in their aim of supplying a variety of examples on each topic, tended to devote much of the content to the 'special needs of the backward and the retarded' (p. 5), with the consequence that the syllabus tended to be limited. The authors recognized, even in 1957, the extraordinary progress that was being made by our overseas business competitors and that the nation was becoming more and more dependent on scientists and skilled technicians: 'the arithmetic that is taught has an eye on the future and has a broad enough base on which further building is possible' (p. 7). The texts, again responding to widespread dissatisfaction with the then-current position regarding the teaching of mathematics, claimed to interweave the old and the new and their motto was summarized as 'REVISION, REVISION, REVISION' (p. 13).

Later, the authors produced the *Beta Junior Arithmetic* which, following the pattern of *The London Arithmetic*, was intended for the average and below average children. Beta contained the same material presented at a slower pace taking five books instead of the Alpha's four; however, there was very little content differentiation between the two series. It was not unusual to see whole schools adopting either the Alpha series or the Beta series without really considering who the texts were designed for. In one never-to-be-forgotten experience, I once visited a school where all of the children worked first through Beta Book 1, then Alpha Book 1, then Beta Book 2, and so on. It had not been noticed that Alpha 1 and Beta 2 were almost the same books.

By the start of the 1960s, the primary school curriculum in arithmetic had been honed to the point where there was a general agreement about its structure. Its modification, during the 1970s, with the move towards decimalization of currency and measures, involved greater emphasis on understanding the base-ten numeration system, but it was believed that up to a year could be saved on 'delivery'. Consequently, many schools had the time to focus on a broader mathematics curriculum which had been consolidated within two publications: *Mathematics in the Primary School* (1965) and the *Nuffield Mathematics Project* (1967, etc.).

Mathematics in the Primary School recommended that children's understanding of mathematics should be broadened so that it became embedded in the relationships underpinning the processes that children use. To this end, it was suggested that bases other than ten be considered and the vocabulary of 'sets' be introduced. The latter was presented for teacher discussion, and it was indicated that introduction of such vocabulary depended on the interest, the enthusiasm and the willingness of the teacher. Rejecting earlier caution from the Mathematical Association about graphical work, the book gave a sound outline of the work that may be covered in the primary school and which, in fact, children had taken to with ease. The movement to focus on the child's mathematical thinking had the effect that considerable change became apparent within the curriculum and mathematics now became referred to as 'modern mathematics'.

Initially, textbook writers responded to the new trends in such a way that the new material was simply tacked onto existing work. Certainly this was the case with the Alpha and Beta series. In a new edition, published in 1969, separate chapters on 'Sets' and 'Venn diagrams' were added. However, they could hardly be identified as a unifying factor for mathematics. Many other new texts presented 'base work' without any effort to extract any generalizations.

Of course, there was another cost in expanding the mathematical content in a text; add something in and we must take something out. There was a noticeable decline in numerical examples that may be used for practice and consolidation of skills. It is also obvious that many of the textbooks published immediately after the legitimization of the new content were produced before the implications of the suggestions had had time to be considered. Although colourful and attempting to have child appeal, many lacked what may be called a sense of urgency.

The watershed created by *Mathematics in the Primary School* and the *Nuffield Mathematics Project* was not fully realized within the classroom until a text which attempted to embrace their philosophy and wider content was developed. This vacuum was filled by *Mathematics for Schools* (Fletcher, 1972), which is a fine example of how the role of the textbook was again being modified. Textbooks were now taking on some of the responsibility for teaching new ideas that teachers were not familiar with.

The series was designed to provide a structured and sequential development of mathematics for children aged from five to thirteen, with a philosophy based upon a recognition that mathematics is a universal language of communication. Six strands of mathematics were integrated into an ongoing structured course: numeration, pattern, algebraic relations, pictorial representation and statistics, measurement and, lastly, shape. Five of these strands are now easily recognizable as major components within the current national curricula for mathematics.

Perhaps because of its enhanced style, teachers began to use the series for 'individualized learning' but, of course, it was not designed for this: no textbook is. This use, together with the extensive inclusion of new mathematical language, invoked heavy criticism which Ruth Walker, a co-editor, responded against in 1977. '*Mathematics for Schools* does not, and cannot, relieve the teacher from teaching, and in the case of the non-mathematicians, from learning. Nor does it remove the children from memorizing number bonds and tables at the appropriate stage'(Walker, 1977).

The HMI publication *Mathematics 5–11* (1979) gave respectability to, and provided a structure for, most of the topics now advocated for the primary school, while *Mathematics Counts* (DES, 1982) pulled together the philosophy for mathematics teaching within primary schools.

Many textbook publishers immediately after this period were quick to identify their publications with *Mathematics Counts* in particular.

> The Cockcroft Report states, 'Practical Work is essential throughout the Primary Years ...', and emphasizes that practical work can only be truly effective and worthwhile if it is 'properly structured with a wide variety of experience and clear stages of progression, and is followed up by the teacher by means of questions and discussion'.
>
> Ginn Mathematics gives the same emphasis to practical work.
>
> *(Publisher's presentation, Ginn Mathematics, c. 1983)*
>
> The Cockcroft Report supports fully the philosophy on which Nuffield Maths was based.
>
> *(Publisher's presentation, Nuffield Mathematics, c. 1983)*

The strength of *Mathematics Counts* was not that it produced much that was new, but rather it pulled together contemporary thinking based upon the best of earlier recommendations. Problem solving and investigations were areas of primary mathematics which have received considerable attention since. The former had received recognition in 1930s textbooks and we find that a recently published text inherited a similar treatment.

Beacon Arithmetic, 1939 (p. 21)	Ginn Mathematics, 1983 (5, p. 30)
An adult approach to problems is by general analysis of the following type:	Remember:
1 What does the question mean?	A Read the problem and find the question.
2 What are we told?	B What are the facts?
3 What are we asked to find out?	C Decide what to do.
4 How can we find the answer?	D Answer the question.
5 What is the answer likely to be?	E Does the answer seem right?

The impetus for publication of primary mathematics texts has now largely moved from the mathematician or the mathematics educator like Ballard and Fleming, into the hands of private foundations such as Nuffield and SMP, or publishers like Ginn and Macmillan. However, a commercially produced mathematics scheme is no longer simply a mathematics text containing problems. Teachers books, enrichment cards, investigations, assessment packages, mathematics profiles, and computer tapes or discs may now all be part of the general package. Commercial workcards and workbooks make up the complete scene available to teachers. The quality of pictures, graphs and drawings, a vast improvement on that of previous decades, has also greatly improved in the last decade. Not for the first time has the printing industry effected an influence on mathematics. This, of course, will be beneficial in developing one aspect of the curriculum – the more we see graphs and pictures, the more we will think in terms of graphs and pictures.

In the field of primary mathematics textbooks, the 1980s saw schools spoiled for choice, but perhaps it was the availability of choice which created the potential for divergence in the primary mathematics curriculum. While some texts remained closely allied to more traditional aspects of primary mathematics, others were innovatory. I believe that *Mathematics for Schools* was one of the latter. Adopting such a series required a change in many teachers' thinking about mathematics. The school's freedom to choose its mathematics texts could result in two different mathematical experiences for children; a longitudinal development which followed the arithmetical philosophy of practice, speed and accuracy with numbers, or the lateral development which involved the best of what *Mathematics in School* was attempting to do. Of course, there were many shades of development in between, but the extremes of curriculum led to an artificial dichotomy which meant that, in the long term, something like a national curriculum for mathematics was inevitable.

Future textbook writers now have a prescribed curriculum to guide their deliberations. Given the structure and development of the levels within the mathematics attainment targets, I suspect that the numerical and graphical elements of the new books will receive rigorous treatment, while that given to shape and space will continue to be fragmentary. In the first instance, the algebraic components may well receive treatment similar to that given to sets and base work in the late 1960s. It will all depend upon interpretation, because there are aspects of the mathematics national curriculum attainment targets which structurally are unsound, indicate piecemeal compilation and, no doubt, will be subject to revision sooner rather than later.

In the future, I doubt whether there will be a move towards a textbook overtly being identified as the National Primary Mathematics Textbook. This does not mean to say that, almost by default, a textbook will not take on this role. The impetus for the publication of new primary mathematics textbooks now largely comes from publishers. Content reliability is obtained by appointing chief editors and advisory editors drawn from among mathematics educators and local authority advisers. Validity for the development of the text and the examples used is often achieved through involving teachers in the writing and piloting versions of the textbook series in schools prior to final publication. There is a possible scenario where a mathematics education establishment or some national foundation will place appropriate bids and receive funding from publishers to produce a 'definitive' national curriculum textbook. Should any designers of the mathematics national curricula in the United Kingdom or the people experienced in the design of mathematics assessment packages be available for the roles of chief editor or advisory editors, such a series will claim a credibility that is going to be hard for teachers to ignore. Truly, such a textbook may well believe its own claim that it will 'take forward more quickly and more comprehensively the achievement of high standards and be an effective way of ensuring that good curriculum practice is more widely used' (NCC, 1988, p. 3).

However, the final transmission of the perceived view of the subject matter that is important is the responsibility of the teacher. In that sense, very little has changed. The content of the primary mathematics curriculum has been influenced by concern with standards, a need for expansion, and a wider understanding of the ways in which children learn mathematics. The use of a textbook can secure, through reflection on priorities and the needs of the child, the professional integrity of the teacher. On the other hand, the textbook can be used as a prop for the teacher's lack of knowledge. Almost by default, textbooks have taken on their role as intermediary – currently neither local authorities nor schools have had sufficient resources to provide either extensive, longer-term, in-service training for all teachers or the time for teachers to reflect upon measured responses to the new initiatives. Within today's climate, given all of the tasks that the busy teacher has to accomplish, it is an answer to the question 'What do I do in maths this afternoon?' which is paramount. The primary mathematics textbook is available to provide an answer. The danger signals inherent in both question and answer should be obvious. Only when teachers are confident with the material they have to teach, and have a deeper awareness of how children learn, will they look beyond the gloss within textbooks and consider the mathematics and the ways they may interact with textbooks.

Textbooks are not individualized learning programmes and neither do they attempt to provide material for what may be described as distance learning techniques. Fleming's reminder about the teacher's position within the classroom is as relevant now as it was fifty years ago. So too are Ruth Walker's comments. We may allow the textbook to take on some of the responsibility for disseminating a perceived view of the primary mathematics curriculum to the teacher, but it is overstating its value for us to believe that it can take on the responsibility for teaching. I have yet to meet a child who, left to work individually, takes any note of the teaching points within a textbook. Not only are most superfluous, but they cannot possibly go much beyond a schematic development of process. Within the confines of books intended for children, writers cannot be expected to cater for all of the eventualities within the classroom. Textbooks may provide a structure and a collection of suitable tasks, but their ability to make more than passing comment to the qualitatively different ways in which children do mathematics is beyond them: only the teacher can respond to this issue. Unless this is faced, there is no doubt that in five to ten years' time, children's weakness in aspects of mathematics will become a subject of controversy again.

References

Albany, E. A. (general editor) (1985) *Nuffield Mathematics* (second edition), Longmans.

Ballard, P. B. (1926) *Fundamental Arithmetic*, University of London Press.

Ballard, P. B. (1934) *The London Arithmetic*, University of London Press.

Board of Education (1901) *Code of Regulations for Day Schools*, HMSO.

Board of Education (1905) *Suggestions for the Consideration of Teachers*, HMSO.

Board of Education (1931) *Report of the Consultative Committee on the Primary School*, HMSO.

Board of Education (1935) *Senior School Mathematics*, Educational Pamphlet 101, HMSO.

Board of Education (1937) *Suggestions for the Consideration of Teachers*, HMSO.

Capel, A. D. (1887) *The Problematic Arithmetic for the Seven Standards*, Joseph Hughes.

DES (1979) *Mathematics 5–11: Handbook of Suggestions for Teachers*, HMSO.

DES (1982) *Mathematics Counts: Report of the Committee of Inquiry into the Teaching of Mathematics in Schools*, HMSO.

DES (1989) *Mathematics in the National Curriculum*, HMSO.

DES (1989) *The National Curriculum – From Policy to Practice*, HMSO.

Fleming, C. M. (1939a) *Beacon Arithmetic Series*, Ginn.

Fleming, C. M. (1939b) *Beacon Number Books*, Ginn.

Fleming, C. M. (1939c) *Beacon Arithmetic Teacher's Manual*, Ginn.

Fleming, C. M. (1939d) *Beacon Number Reader*, Ginn.

Fletcher, H. (1972) *Mathematics for Schools – an Integrated Series* (first edition), Addison-Wesley.

Goddard, T. R. and Grattidge, A. W. (1969) *Beta Junior Mathematics* (second edition), Schofield and Sims.

Goddard, T. R. and Grattidge, A. W. (1957) *Alpha Junior Arithmetic, Handbook for Teachers*, Schofield and Sims.

Hollands, R. (chief editor) (1983) *Ginn Mathematics* (first edition), Ginn.

Mathematical Association (1905) *The Teaching of Elementary Mathematics*, G. Bell.

Mathematical Association (1955) *The Teaching of Mathematics in the Primary School*, G. Bel.

Ministry of Education (1868) *Schools Inquiry Commission*, vols I and II. HMSO.

Nuffield Mathematics Project (1967) *Teachers' Handbooks*, John Murray.

Potter, F. (1933) *Common Sense Arithmetic for Juniors*: Books 1–4, Isaac Pitman and Sons.

Schonell, F. J. and Cracknell, S. H. (1937) *Right from the Start Arithmetic*, Books 1–5, Oliver and Boyd.

Schools Council (1965) *Curriculum Bulletin 1: Mathematics in Primary Schools*, HMSO.

Walker, R. (1977) 'Mathematics for Schools, six years later', *Mathematics in School*, **6**(3), p. 266.

13 A touch of class: ability, social class and intertext in SMP 11–16

Paul Dowling

The sub-title of Paul Willis' seminal book (1977) is 'how working class kids get working class jobs'. At a time when unemployment is increasing (again), this might almost be read as the title of an optimistic handbook! But Willis' interest is in the tendency for people from working-class origins to end up in working-class, rather than middle-class, destinations.[1] In the decade of Willis' book, there was considerable interest in the relationship between schooling and social class – books by Bourdieu and Passeron (1977), Bowles and Gintis (1976) and Bernstein (1977) are among those which made the greatest impact – but perhaps academic times have changed since then, and the 1980s saw even the radical, Marxist ideas of Bowles and Gintis commuted to liberalism (Bowles and Gintis, 1986). Furthermore, mathematics, as a school subject, has rarely been seriously interrogated with regard to its relationship with social class.[2]

Nevertheless, it remains the case that the social nature of one's origins is an effective indicator of one's educational and economic destinations. In this chapter, I am taking it as axiomatic that there exists a significant correlation between educational performances and social class,[3] and that we can discount biologistic explanations for this such as propounded by the eugenicists of the nineteenth century (see, for example, MacKenzie, 1981). My interest is in the role of schooling in *producing* this correlation, but this is a focus which does not exclude the possibility of others. I do not intend to place the whole burden of responsibility for all the ills of society on teachers, who necessarily work within a social environment which is already structured by inequality; teachers do, however, play a part in the reproduction of social class, and this involvement should be placed under scrutiny.

Two examples will serve to illustrate my point. Firstly, some time before Willis' book was published, Ray Rist (1970) studied a group of children in a black 'ghetto' school in the United States as they moved from their entrance to the kindergarten class to the second grade. Before meeting the children, the kindergarten teacher (who was also black) had some details of their home backgrounds – including whether the parents were on welfare support, etc. The teacher's first action upon meeting her class was to divide it into three groups, sitting at separate tables and interpreted by the teacher as 'fast', 'medium' and 'slow' learners respectively. While this division could not have been made on the basis of any knowledge of 'academic' performance, Rist found that the 'slow learners' overwhelmingly tended to come from the poorer homes. Furthermore, over the three-year period of the observation, there was virtually no mobility between the groups named, by the second grade, 'Tigers', 'Cardinals' and 'Clowns'. Rist argued that the teacher's original assessments were made on the basis of knowledge of objective factors – whether the family was on welfare support, etc. – and on physical appearance and linguistic and other immediately apparent forms of behaviour; differential treatment subsequently ensured a differentiation of academic performance which progressively widened.

Rather more recently, Shirley Heath (1986) has reported the results of a study which compared the distinct forms of language used in a black, working-class community, in a school serving that community, and in the homes of the teachers working in the school. The differences in the use of questioning between the working-class families, on the one hand, and the teachers – whether at home or at school – on the other, were striking. Again, evidence of a middle-class cultural origin appeared to be a prerequisite for success at school.

School mathematics and ability

School mathematics certainly differentiates between school students through, for example, the use of differentiated curricula.[4] The *SMP 11–16* scheme (Cambridge University Press) divides pupils in the third year of secondary schooling into four groups, one of which ('those with special learning difficulties') it does not recognize as falling within its catchment area. However, this partition is not made on the basis of social class – at least not explicitly – it is made in terms of 'ability', as this extract from the *Teachers' Guide* to Book G1 explains.

> The Y series is for the most able group of pupils (roughly speaking, the top 20–25 per cent or so, although the proportion is likely to vary from school to school). The B and R series are for the 'middle' group (the next 35–40 per cent or so) and the G series is for lower ability pupils (apart from those with special learning difficulties).
>
> *(p. 4)*

The question to be addressed in this chapter is: 'What does this "ability" hierarchy mean?' I shall begin by examining the nature of the differentiation between the Y series of books (for those with the 'most ability') and the G series (for those with the 'least ability' – apart from 'those with special learning difficulties'). I intend to show that the polarizations that appear within this division connote another division within contemporary culture, one which is closely associated with social class. The connotation of – or indirect (and often unintended) reference to – meanings within one text or cultural practice by another text is what I mean by *intertextuality*:[5] my argument is that in reading the Y–G opposition within the *SMP 11–16* text,[6] *intertextual connotations* which are encoded within our culture, and which I will outline below, enable the reading of an equivalence between 'ability' and social class. In this respect, the *SMP 11–16* scheme might be said to exhibit a differentiation which is very similar to that produced by Ray Rist's kindergarten teacher.

Firstly, in terms of physical detail, the main textbooks of the G series (books G1 to G8) not only contain fewer pages overall than those of the Y series (books Y1 to Y5) – 512 pages as opposed to 832 – but there are also more G 'books' (eight compared with five Y books). This means that each G 'book' has very many fewer pages than the Y books (G1 has 60 pages, Y1 has 156), and they are stapled as booklets whereas the Y books are bound as books.[7] Considered as a whole, the G series comprises eight books of 60 pages each together with 'G booklets', three 'G resource packs', 'G supplementary booklets' and 'topic booklets' (shared with the B series). This gives a total of 31 G items (apart from 'teachers' guides') listed in the price list, as compared with seven Y items (the five main books and two 'extension' books). The diversity of the G series is referred to in the G1 *Teachers' Guide*.

> We have taken the view that lower ability pupils need a wide variety in their mathematics – variety of presentation, content, method of working and so on. The G materials reflect this view.
>
> *(p. 7)*

The result is that the Y materials – taken individually – are far more physically weighty than individual G materials, and this is enhanced by the difference in binding. The content format is similarly dichotomized in the two series of books, the Y series being more verbose and the G series more highly illustrated.

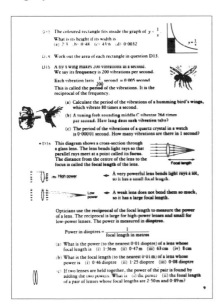

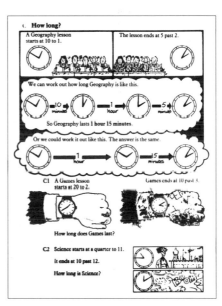

(Y1, p. 9)   *(G1, p. 37)*

The ratio of words per page in chapter 1 of Y1 to words per page in chapter 1 of G1 is approximately 2:1, whereas the corresponding ratio for pictures per page is approximately 1:2.[8] Furthermore, in the chapters concerned, approximately 68 per cent of the illustrations in Y1 are diagrammatic and 32 per cent pictorial, whereas in G1 the approximate figures are 18 per cent and 82 per cent respectively.

The front cover of Y1 (above, left) offers one of the few jokes in the book. It is a contour map (signifying section E of chapter 11), but it is a contour map of a face. This is no belly-laugh joke, it is intellectual, even enigmatic: is it a mathematizing of humanity or a humanizing of mathematics? The other Y covers are similarly – though, perhaps, not so strikingly – enigmatic: an M. C. Escher drawing for Y2; an attractive, white girl, casually dressed and posing between two mirrors facing each other for Y3; the parabolic shadow cast by a lampshade for Y4; an icosahedral 'globe' showing Africa and Europe for Y5. These cover illustrations signify enigmas that are to be resolved within the text: the Y1 and Y5 covers are strange mathematizings which are to become less strange; the Escher drawing looks wrong, but why, and how is the effect achieved? – all will be revealed; how and why are the girl's reflections produced, what is the nature of this curve? – see within for details. The designs are inviting those seeking knowledge and enlightenment.

The covers of the G books are different. G1 has drawings of a digital watch, an analogue watch and a carriage clock: there is a chapter on 'time'. G2 has a man in a white coat weighing a mouse in a beaker on a digital set of scales: there is a chapter on 'scales'. G3 (above, right) shows two surveyors (a man and a woman) using a tape measure on a building site: there is a chapter, much of which concerns reading from drawings of 'a surveyor's tape measure'. In the first case, the cover shows measuring instruments the use of which is assumed by the tasks in chapter 4; G2 and G3 show measuring instruments being used and so directly signify the tasks in the corresponding chapters. In all three cases, the connotation is a mundane, manual skill: telling the time, weighing, using a tape measure.

G4, G5 and G6 show diagrams of various types. G4 shows a windmill drawn from different viewpoints and with lines added to illustrate the relationship between plan and elevation. This is not quite an engineering drawing because the pictures are shaded to look solid and grass bents are drawn in. There is a promise of something technical, however, a promise which is broken by the use – in the relevant chapter – of 'spotty paper' and a worksheet on which the 'front view' of a shed has already been started. The G5 cover signifies two chapters at once by superimposing on a street plan a plan view – that is, a drawing from above (which includes a man and a woman), not an engineering drawing – of the ground floor of a house. The corresponding chapters involve using street plans and making, reading and drawing plans; any hint of the 'technical' is again expelled by the ubiquitous 'spotty paper' and the need for scissors and glue. G5 has an exploded diagram of a single-roomed, thatched cottage: the corresponding tasks in the book[9] involve answering questions about exploded diagrams of an audio-cassette and a model car. G7 shows a photograph of a cheetah which might relate to the chapter on 'speed'. There is nothing about cheetahs in the chapter, but you might refer to G1 if you want to know how fast a cheetah goes – 116 km/h, apparently. G8 – a mildly exotic cover – shows the stellated polyhedral construction in Disneyland which is referred to in the book as approximating to a sphere.

Whereas the Y covers are enigmatic and promise intellectual exploration and enlightenment, the G covers are far more explicit, connoting the mundane – banal manual skills and technical practices – or providing simple illustrations: the cheetah has 'speed', this building is (nearly) spherical. The G covers also connote outside of the classroom in a way that the Y covers do not: clocks, street plans and exploded diagrams connote the everyday; the technician weighing – a 'scientist' wouldn't be doing this – and the surveyors measuring connote the 'world of work'; the cheetah and Disneyland connote the mildly exotic. Perhaps only the windmill stands out: drawing a windmill from above seems an unlikely thing to do.

The Y covers are all distanced from the mundane, either through unusual juxtapositions (a table lamp projecting a curve onto graph paper; a map of the world printed on an icosahedron; a contour map revealing a face; the girl between *two* mirrors) or, in the case of the Escher drawing, through the representation of the impossible. The G covers represent the world as already comprehended: there is nothing more to understand, merely skills to be developed and practised; a vocabulary, perhaps, to be enlarged. The Y covers celebrate the spirit of academic enquiry: the world is fascinating and unknown, but can be approached through the erudite study of mathematics. Not that the contents of the Y series are entirely distanced from the mundane. However, whereas the Y contents frequently escape from the everyday into the purely mathematical, the G contents rarely do.[10]

The illustrations inside G1 and Y1[11] are of a number of different forms. Both books contain diagrams which are referred to or which are used in the various tasks; both books contain straightforward illustrations – a question about a horse's consumption of hay is accompanied by a drawing of a horse with a nosebag (Y1, p. 34); both books contain strip-cartoons which provide instructions or algorithms. However, G1 also contains strip cartoons which substitute for a prose narrative or which provide a mathematically irrelevant but jokey commentary on it. Some of the straightforward illustrations in both G1 and Y1 are also jokes, but whereas the Y1 jokes directly connote the mathematical content of the associated tasks, the G1 jokes connote the non-mathematical in much the same way as the jokey commentaries in the strip cartoons.

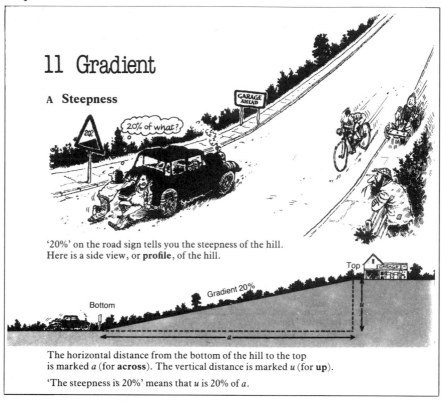

11 Gradient

A Steepness

'20%' on the road sign tells you the steepness of the hill.
Here is a side view, or **profile**, of the hill.

The horizontal distance from the bottom of the hill to the top
is marked a (for **across**). The vertical distance is marked u (for **up**).

'The steepness is 20%' means that u is 20% of a.

(Y1, p. 122)

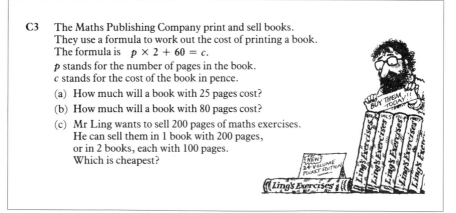

C3 The Maths Publishing Company print and sell books.
They use a formula to work out the cost of printing a book.
The formula is $p \times 2 + 60 = c$.

p stands for the number of pages in the book.
c stands for the cost of the book in pence.

(a) How much will a book with 25 pages cost?

(b) How much will a book with 80 pages cost?

(c) Mr Ling wants to sell 200 pages of maths exercises.
He can sell them in 1 book with 200 pages,
or in 2 books, each with 100 pages.
Which is cheapest?

(G1, p. 29)

Thus, the joke concerns the dissonance in the labelling of a twenty-four volume set of books as a 'pocket edition' and, perhaps, a reference to the absurdity of anyone ('less able') wanting to buy twenty-four volumes of maths exercises; there is also a 'private joke' in the reference to John Ling, the SMP 11–16 team leader. The anti-academic connotations are echoed throughout G1. Thus, later in G1 (see p. 139), geography is represented as boring in contrast to popular magazines;[12] games is represented as a brawl for which it is not even necessary to change out of everyday clothes; science is about making explosions.

Manual work forms an important part of many of the tasks in the G series. The *Teachers' Guide* to G1 asserts the importance of manual work – labelled as 'practical experience', with all of the quasi-Piagetian connotations of this expression (see the analysis by Corran and Walkerdine, 1981).

> We hope that it will be possible to give pupils as wide a range of practical experience as possible. Some (like weighing) we have included in the work. In other places it is very desirable to have practical work alongside, or in place of, the written work. So, for example, alongside book G1 we would hope that watches and clocks could be used in chapter 4, 'Time', and that dials, meters and scales of various types can be brought into the classroom for use in chapter 1, 'Estimating and scales'.
>
> *(p. 9)*

Manual tasks in the Y series are not referred to explicitly as 'practical' work and are generally intellectualized. The two 'probability' tasks shown below illustrate this manual–intellectual division.

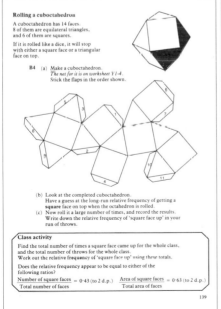

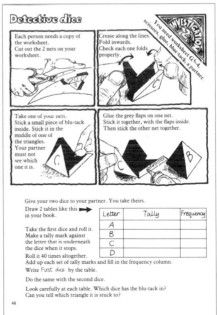

(Y1, p. 139)   *(G1, p. 48)*

Both tasks concern the transformation of a polyhedron into a biased dice for the purposes of an exercise in probability, but there are clearly a number of differences between the tasks. 'Detective dice' is a game, this is connoted by the title – it is a detective game – and by the hint of competition between partners – 'Your partner must not see which one it is'. But this is a manual game: the manual acts of cutting out the net, folding it, putting in a piece of blu-tack (surreptitiously) and gluing the dice together are illustrated with hands or fingers clearly visible – hands, fingers and pencils in the acts of manipulating, measuring, writing are frequent illustrations in G1. The pictures and the verbal instructions are very explicit: 'You need worksheet G1-4, scissors, glue, blue-tack,[13] a partner'; 'Take the first dice and roll it. Make a tally mark against the letter that is underneath the dice when it stops'; 'First dice' and the labelling of the table are rendered in 'handwriting', so there will be no mistake as to who is to write them. 'Rolling a cuboctahedron', on the other hand, suppresses the manual activity which is inevitably involved in the task. The term 'cuboctahedron' is introduced and defined ('tetrahedron' is not mentioned in 'Detective dice'). Furthermore, cuboctahedra are *not* dice (and their faces are not even labelled), but they may be rolled *like* dice: the transition from metaphor to simile in moving between the two tasks creates a distance in the Y task between mathematics and games. The net in Y1 is presented, as it is on both worksheets, as a net; no fingers or hands or glue are visible; no blu-tack is needed because the polyhedron chosen is not regular. The instructions in Y1 are distanced from the manual mechanics of the task: 'Make a cuboctahedron. *The net for it is on worksheet Y1-4.* Stick the flaps in the order shown.' There are no 'handwritten' tables or arrows to show which illustration the text refers to. The final badge of mathematics is awarded in the language of the final lines of the 'class activity'.

> Does the relative frequency appear to be equal to either of the following ratios?
>
> $$\frac{\text{Number of square faces}}{\text{Total number of faces}} = 0.43 \text{ (to 2 d.p.)}$$
>
> $$\frac{\text{Area of square faces}}{\text{Total area of faces}} = 0.63 \text{ (to 2 d.p.)}$$

That the Y books are concerned with serious, intellectual activity is announced by their 'contents' pages. The chapter titles are plainly descriptive, making use of mathematical terms which would be rarely used – or used very differently – outside of mathematical discourse: some examples are given below:

> algebra, algebraic expressions, cosine, direct proportionality, exponential, functions, inequalities, inverse proportionality linear equations, linear relationships, loci, mappings, periodic graphs, quadratic, sequences, sine, trigonometry, vectors.

The chapter titles in the G books, on the other hand, include very few mathematical terms and most of those used are also found in non-mathematical discourse. The list below includes *all* of the mathematical terms in the contents pages of books G1 to G8:[14]

%, angle, area, averages, calculate, calculating, calculator, capacity, circles, co-ordinates, cylinders, decimals, diagrams, enlargement, estimating, evens, formulas, fractions, graphs, lines, multiplication, negative numbers, numbers, odds, percentages, perimeters, plans, point, polygon, probability, rates, ratios, rectangles, reflection, sixteenths, spheres, squares, tables, thousandths, three, units, volumes.

Again, the banality of the G series contrasts with the erudition of Y.[15] A few of the G titles move beyond the straightforwardly descriptive to the mildly sensational: 'Escape!', 'Cheapo rulers', 'Detective dice', 'Say it with numbers', 'Bullet holes', 'See-through dominoes'. This slight tendency to sensationalism is also occasionally present in the contents as illustrated below.[16] The connotations always lead away from the mathematical to the everyday or to the sensational; the connotations in the Y texts are more often introspective in relation to the mathematical domain.

(a) **The dwarf in this picture is about 100 cm tall. Estimate the height of the giant.**

(b) **The giant in this picture is about 220 cm tall. Estimate the height of the man on the right.**

(G1, p. 3)

In summary, the division between the 'less able' and the 'more able' in the G and Y series of SMP 11–16 is made in terms of opposite orientations to the intellectual or academic. The textual strategies of the G materials move one away from the academic towards the mundane. This is achieved, for example, through the lightweight 'booklet' binding of the main series; it is achieved through the use of transparent and explicit language which connotes everyday discourse, occasionally even the mildly sensational; and it is achieved through the movement from prose to pictures. This *centrifugal* force of the G books is apparent in the frequency with which jokes appear, jokes which connote the non-mathematical, jokes which are even anti-academic. Finally, the G series celebrates the manual over the intellectual in its emphasis on the quasi-Piagetian notion of 'practical experience' and the orientation towards the practical activities of measurement and drawing in many of the cover illustrations.

The direction of textual forces in the Y series is *centripetal*, the orientation being towards the academic through the preference for prose over pictures and the use of esoteric mathematical language. Jokes in the Y books are cerebral and linked to the mathematical content, and the cover illustrations celebrate the enigmatic and the erudite. It is inadequate to define 'manual' in terms of 'using the hands' and 'intellectual' as 'using the brain': writing demands both, as does fixing a car engine. The two are to be understood in a more dialectical manner.[17] Thus, the Y series *intellectualizes* the manual through the use of highly technical language and trivializes necessary manual activity by providing the briefest of instructions. The mundane inevitably enters the domains of both series, but whereas, in the Y books, the everyday world is sacrificed on the altar of mathematics, in the G series, the everyday appears as an effusive apology for the tentative intrusion of the academic.

Ability and social class

Having described the 'more able'/'less able' division in terms of the oppositions academic/mundane and intellectual/manual, it is necessary to give some attention to the recognition of the rules by which 'less able' and 'more able' students may be identified in order that they may be assigned to the appropriate curricula. What intertextual connotations give meaning to academic/mundane and intellectual/manual? I want to assert that this differentiation closely mirrors the division between the 'serious' and the 'popular' press – between the 'heavyweight' and 'lightweight' newspapers.

> The 1947–49 Royal Commission referred to 'quality' and 'popu-lar' national newspapers. Other nations have had similar dis-tinctions – in France the *Grand* and *Petit* press – but in Britain this tradition is particularly long; it dates back to *The Times* and its radical rivals of the 1830s. To some extent the distinction be-tween the large size prestige papers of the 1980s and the popular tabloids reflects real differences in education, reader interest and income. These real differences have become exaggerated be-cause the two types of paper have not only, since the 1970s, acquired different physical sizes, but they rely on different prime sources of revenue. The 'prestige' papers operate pri-marily from an *advertising* revenue base; this forces them 'up market' more than a sales revenue base would require – because advertisers are willing to pay several times as much to reach readers who are several times as wealthy.
>
> (*Tunstall, 1983, p. 77*)

As with the *SMP 11–16* texts, 'heavyweight' and 'lightweight' are not simply metaphors relating to the style of prose and content – although this is true as well – but they signify real differences in the physical weight of the papers. On 21 March 1990,[18] the *Daily Telegraph* contained 48 broadsheet pages and *The Times* 56 (in two sections): the *Sun* and the *Daily Star*, on the other hand, contained only 32 and 36 pages respectively. Since the tabloid format is only half the size of the broadsheets, the 'quality' papers cover approximately four times the page area of the 'populars'. As with the SMP materials, there is also a difference in the quantitative relationship between prose and pictures. As Jeremy Tunstall notes: 'typically about 60% of a tabloid's contents is in fact 'looked at' material – pictures, headlines, cartoons and display advertising ... '(p. 134).

The use of prose is similarly differentiated, as is illustrated by two lead story headlines. 'Major tries to draw sting from poll tax and boost savings: extra on drink, smoking, petrol and company cars', from the *Daily Telegraph*, is not devoid of imagery, but is primarily descriptive and stands in contrast to the *Daily Star*'s 'Save of the Century: chancellor's banking on your cash', which, despite its brevity, is pleonastic. In terms of the budget, the *Star* headline twice denotes an initiative on savings, but this allows the inclusion of two jokes: the allusion to the popular TV show 'Sale of the Century', and the duality of the literal and metaphorical meanings of 'banking'. Both papers are explicitly sympathetic to the government. The *Telegraph* constructs the budget as an intellectual exercise in economic management:

> MR MAJOR, the Chancellor, lifted the gloom among Tory MPs yesterday with a skillfully-packaged Budget which coupled the first overall increase in taxation since 1981 with radical measures to encourage saving and take the sting out of the introduction of the poll tax next month.

However, the *Star* presents the Chancellor as the warrior, St George, as well as a bookkeeper, and includes another joke on the ambiguity of his name:[19]

> *The ice-cool Chancellor scored a Major triumph as he balanced the nation's books yesterday.*

> He wielded the economic sword to slay the dragon of inflation in a bold and imaginative Budget designed to encourage people to *SAVE, SAVE, SAVE.*

The class dichotomy between the two papers is apparent in their respective income tax tables which are presented in terms of wages, up to £700 per week, in the *Star*, and annual salaries, up to £70 000 per year, in the *Telegraph*.[20]

Other stories are dichotomized between different newspapers in a similar way. Tucked away at the bottom of the page, *The Times*' report about a doctor accused of having an improper relationship[21] connotes objectivity:[22] the business of the news sections of a daily newspaper is to inform in an intellectual and detached manner so that the reader can make her/his own judgement on the facts and significance of the case. The style, devoid of adjectival additives, is centripetal with respect to participation in social philosophizing: there is a clear tension between the caring relationship which is to be expected between a doctor – especially a psychiatrist – and her/his patient, on the one hand, and the requirement that emotional distance must be maintained, if diagnosis and therapy are to be made and prescribed with professional objectivity. This tension is objectified in *The Times'* story, the bland style of which connotes professional objectivity, giving us a clue as to how we should approach the matter. The *Sun's* whole-page presentation, despite its greater length and detail – indeed, partly *because* of this – is centrifugal in this regard. We all know that doctors – especially *woman* doctors – aren't supposed to behave like this, but isn't it good fun when they do. The story connotes not the analytic but the titillating.

Conclusion: school mathematics and social class

The layouts, language and reporting styles, competitions and also the jokes appearing in the 'popular' and 'serious' press are differentiated in a similar way to the textual strategies of the G and Y series of the SMP books, facilitating the connotations: Y → 'serious' press; G → 'popular' press. But the different categories of newspaper also connote different socio-economic groups, as is attested to by their respective readership and advertising .

National newspaper readership

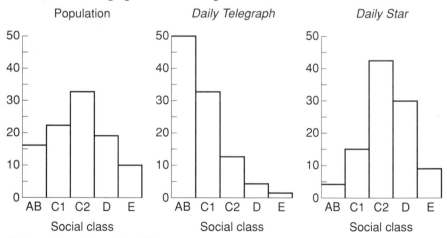

(Adapted from Tunstall, 1983)

As a result, G is able to connote (intertextually) the 'manual', both through the emphasis on physical activities in the G books and through its connotation of the 'popular' press, which itself connotes 'manual labour'[23] and 'working class'. Similarly, Y doubly connotes the 'intellectual' and therefore the 'professional and managerial classes'. A link between curriculum track and socio-economic class is thereby made through intertextual connotations of these curriculum materials: 'working class' is part of what it means to be 'less able'; 'middle class' is part of what it means to be 'more able'. These connotations facilitate the 'recognition' of 'less able' and 'more able' pupils. *SMP 11–16* partitions pupils through a mechanism which is redolent of that of Rist's kindergarten teacher, and the result is much the same. *SMP 11–16* divides and orders pupils precisely on the basis of social class, and labels the resulting hierarchy in terms of 'ability'.

The centripetal strategies of the Y books and of the 'quality' press invite those having an appropriate cultural background to participate in the intellectual activities of mathematics and of high-level analysis and commentary on the world; to explore without, of course, getting one's hands dirty. The connotations of the G series and of the 'popular' press are centrifugal with respect to the rarefied atmosphere of the academic, celebrating the quotidian nature of the here and now and immediately knowable and holding up to ridicule those who would know better: twenty-four volumes of maths exercises, indeed!

The slippage between what the text says and what the text does is not accidental. The social is already (and always already) organized in terms of social class which is thereby encoded into our culture; in the absence of such a social 'text', the connotations described in this chapter could not be read. But this structure is sustained through its realizations in cultural events such as school texts: in reading *SMP 11–16* as constituting equivalences between 'ability' and class positions, we are both making use of and reproducing the social structure – *SMP 11–16* achieves that of which it is itself an achievement.

Like King Midas, the *SMP 11–16* texts have the touch which transmutes – although not everything is turned to *gold*, a 'Platonic touch' might be more appropriate. The texts have the touch because they, themselves, have been touched by an infectious organizing, which relationship is precisely the dialectic of intertextuality. *SMP 11–16*, in my reading, exhibits this structuring in a fairly obvious way, but not all texts need be as brazen: a 'text' comprising the single word 'ability' can be read with precisely the same intertextual connotations, simply because they are there, encoded in our culture. The dismantling of the reproduction of social class might begin less effectively than with a deconstruction of 'ability'. Such a deconstruction will involve the speaking of the unspeakable – the rendering audible of the class–ability relation – and so must be a very public affair. Unfortunately, no one in Ray Rist's kindergarten classroom challenged the assessment procedures or outcomes of the teacher, least of all the teacher herself who, like the *SMP 11–16* texts and quite unbeknown to her, had the touch of class which is education.

Notes

[1] I have no space to give an adequate definition of 'class', but must rely on the *intertextual connotations* of the term and of the content of this chapter, see below.

[2] This is in marked contrast to the interest in the relationship between mathematics and gender: see, for example, Burton (1986), Fennema (1985), Leder (1987), Walden and Walkerdine (1982, 1985) and Walkerdine (1989).

[3] See Halsey *et al.* (1980) for some statistical elaboration.

4   See also Dowling (1990a, b) concerning mathematics and social class, Dowling (1991a) concerning technology and social class, Brown and Dowling (1989) regarding mono-culturalism and able-bodiedness in mathematics, and Dowling (1991b) regarding gender divisions in mathematics texts.

5   I am using the term 'text' very broadly here. It refers to any instance of written or spoken language, or, indeed, any other event which can be interpreted as meaningful; 'intertextuality' cannot be developed adequately here, its use is intended to signify the possibility of a theoretical treatment.

6   That is, taking the scheme itself – including its components – as a text.

7   The difference in binding seems to be a consequence of the relative lengths of the books rather than (or, at least, in addition to) any deliberate decision to produce booklets for the 'less able' and books for the 'more able', since the 'extension book' (YE1) is stapled, having only 64 pages; it is not, however, the authors' *intentions* which are at issue here.

8   Chapter 1 of Book Y1 is 9 pages long and has an average of 218 words ($\sigma = 88.2$) and 2.4 illustrations, diagrams, tables or graphs per page; chapter 1 of G1 is 11 pages long and has an average of 92 words ($\sigma = 37$) and 6 illustrations or diagrams per page.

9   'Exploded diagrams (1)' and 'Exploded diagrams (2)': they are not given chapter numbers.

10   When G materials do involve mathematics which is not contextualized or concretized through reference to the everyday, the mathematical content is most often arithmetic.

11   The illustrations are drawn by David Parkins in both cases.

12   And note the gender division: the 'feminine' character in the front row is reading 'True Stories' and the 'masculine' characters have comics. Note, also, the right-hand hair parting on the otherwise 'masculine' characters.

13   Note the binary spelling of 'blue-tack'/'blu-tack', the latter being a trade name.

14   Terms such as 'money' and 'time' are not here regarded as specifically 'mathematical', and it is clearly possible to interpret words such as 'distance', 'weight' and 'scales' (i.e. for weighing) as 'mathematical'. The selection decision here is of necessity somewhat arbitrary, as there is no space to develop a language of description for 'the mathematical'.

15   We might even note that the letter Y has more obvious mathematical connotations than G.

16   And note the references to 'dwarf' and 'giant' which have distinctly negative connotations.

17   By which I mean they are to be understood in relation to each other and can have no independent meaning, rather as Hegel's 'master' can have no meaning other than through his relationship to his 'slave'. (See Heilbroner, 1980, for a discussion of the dialectic in Marx.)

18   All of the examples from newspapers are taken from those issued on this date.

19   This apparently irresistible joke also appears in the *Daily Telegraph*, but in an advertisement.

[20] Note that social class is not to be interpreted solely on the basis of earnings, but also includes a cultural element: £700 per week is approximately £35 000 per year which is clearly an income which might be envied by most of us. However, the device by which 'middle class' incomes are expressible as annual salaries, while those of the 'working class' are to be given as weekly wages signifies a real cultural division. Furthermore, £35 000 is still only half of £70 000. It is also interesting to note that, while both of the respective terminal books of the Y and G series – Y5 and G8 – include items on income tax, only the Y book makes any mention of tax at above the basic rate.

[21] Both papers use 'woman' as an adjective to describe the doctor – 'woman doc', 'woman doctor' in the *Sun*, 'woman psychiatrist' in *The Times* – the latter, however, uses only the gender-neutral term 'doctor' in the headline.

[22] Which is not to assert that objective reporting, as such, is attainable.

[23] That is, as distinct from the 'intellectual labour' of the professional and managerial classes.

References

Bernstein, B. (1977) *Class, Codes and Control* (vol. 3, 2nd edn), Routledge and Kegan Paul.

Bourdieu, P. and Passeron, J-C. (1977) *Reproduction in Education, Society and Culture*, Sage.

Bowles, S. and Gintis, H. (1976) *Schooling in Capitalist America*, Routledge and Kegan Paul.

Bowles, S. and Gintis, H. (1986) *Democracy and Capitalism: Property, Community, and the Contradictions of Modern Social Thought*, Routledge and Kegan Paul.

Brown, A. and Dowling, P. C. (1989) *A Critical Alternative to Internationalism and Monoculturalism in Mathematics Education*, Centre for Multicultural Education Occasional Paper 10, University of London Institute of Education.

Burton, L. (ed.) (1986) *Girls Into Maths Can Go*, Holt, Rinehart and Winston.

Corran, G. and Walkerdine, V. (1981) *The Practice of Reason, Vol. 1: Reading the Signs of Mathematics* (mimeo), University of London Institute of Education.

Dowling, P. C. (1990a) 'The Shogun's and other curriculum voices' in Dowling, P. C. and Noss, R. (eds), *Mathematics versus the National Curriculum*, Falmer Press, pp. 33–64.

Dowling, P. C. (1990b) 'Some notes towards a theoretical model for reproduction, action and critique' in Noss, R. *et al.* (eds), *Political Dimensions of Mathematics Education: Action and Critique – Proceedings of the First International Conference (revised edition)*, University of London Institute of Education, pp. 76–84.

Dowling, P. C. (1991a) 'The dialectics of determinism: deconstructing information technology' in McKay, H., Young, M. F. D. and Beynon, J. (eds), *Understanding Technology in Education*, Falmer Press.

Dowling, P. C. (1991b) 'Gender, class and subjectivity in mathematics: a critique of Humpty Dumpty', *For the Learning of Mathematics*, **11**(1), pp. 2–8 .

Fennema, E. (ed.) (1985) 'Explaining sex-related differences in mathematics: theoretical models', *Educational Studies in Mathematics*, **16**(3), pp. 303–20.

Halsey, A. H., Heath, A. F. and Ridge, J. M. (1980) *Origins and Destinations: Family, Class, and Education in Modern Britain*, Clarendon Press.

Hammersley, M. (ed.) (1986) *Case Studies in Classroom Research*, Open University Press.

Heath, S. B. (1986) 'Questioning at home and at school: a comparative study' in Hammersley, M. (ed.), *Case Studies in Classroom Research*, Open University Press, pp. 104–32.

Heilbroner, R. L. (1980) *Marxism: For and Against*, Norton.

Leder, G. C. (1987) 'Teacher–student interaction: a case study', *Educational Studies in Mathematics*, **18**(3), pp. 255–71.

Mackenzie, D. A. (1981) *Statistics in Britain: 1865–1930*, Edinburgh University Press.

Rist, R. C. (1970) 'Student social class and teacher expectations: the self-fulfilling prophecy in ghetto education', *Harvard Educational Review*, **40**, pp. 411–51.

Tunstall, J. (1983) *The Media in Britain*, Constable.

Walden, R. and Walkerdine, V. (1982) *Girls and Mathematics: the Early Years*, Bedford Way Paper No. 8, University of London Institute of Education.

Walden, R. and Walkerdine, V. (1985) *Girls and Mathematics: from Primary to Secondary Schools*, Bedford Way Paper No. 24, University of London Institute of Education.

Walkerdine, V. *et al.* (1989) *Counting Girls Out*, Virago.

Willis, P. E. (1977) *Learning to Labour: how Working Class Kids get Working Class Jobs*, Gower.

Acknowledgements

I would like to acknowledge the critical comments made by Parin Bahl, Basil Bernstein and Richard Noss on an earlier version of this chapter.

14 Vision and constraint: politics and mathematics national curricula in a changing South Africa

Jill Adler

Education, as with every other aspect of South African life, has been dramatically affected by the new political climate forged since 2 February 1990. On that date, the government declared a willingness to enter into negotiations over a new constitution with previously banned political organizations. Non-racial state schools, a single education ministry administering a unified education policy and a new curriculum appropriate to the social, political and economic needs of post-apartheid South Africa, are now all possible in the near future.

Change and challenge, however, carry with them the contradiction so wonderfully captured by the ancient Chinese curse, 'May you live in interesting times'. The challenge of a non-racial education system embracing a new curriculum is cursed with the ideological, social, economic and political constraints of 42 years of apartheid education – education that is characterized by pervasive racial inequality and neglect, prescriptive social difference and a highly centralized, authoritarian system that has stifled and disempowered both learners and teachers.[1]

In this chapter, I will consider how, given the legacy of apartheid, the development of a new national mathematics curriculum might inform and interact with the process of change in South Africa. While the focus of the chapter is on South Africa, many of the issues discussed draw on, and are pertinent to, debates on mathematics and national curricula elsewhere, and particularly in the United Kingdom.

I am going to examine two interlocking areas.

- Pervasive inequality and fragmentation demands a coordinated, coherent national reconstruction programme to give content to the call for a single education ministry. *What are the implications for a national mathematics curriculum?*

- The current selection and transmission of school mathematics functions as a critical filter in the interests of a minority and encourages passive, rigid learners. This is clearly not appropriate to the ideals of building democracy. *What forms of selection and transmission would develop mathematical thinking, build skills and encourage critical, participative citizens? How might new ideas take root in classroom practice?*

New ideas and practices are inextricably bound up with the conditions out of which they emerge. While new national mathematics curricula are on the agenda in both the United Kingdom (see Dowling and Noss, 1990) and

South Africa, they are the effects of very different historical conditions and will be influenced by very different political imperatives and contexts. It is important, therefore, that before we examine the two areas given above, I first highlight the practices and effects of school mathematics and curriculum production under apartheid.

Understanding the present

Apartheid's school mathematics – three scenarios

The classrooms described in scenarios 1 and 2 reflect dominant conditions in black and white schools respectively. There are better-equipped and functioning black schools, and more poorly-equipped white schools than these. There are also racially segregated schools where, despite this restriction, educational innovation and good practice is evident. The mathematics classroom described in scenario 3 is one of a tiny number of its kind. It exemplifies, perhaps, what can be. The empirical basis for these scenarios can be found in the statistics contained in the Appendix.

Scenario 1: Quantitative and qualitative neglect

A typical Standard 6 (first-year secondary school) class (Photograph by Justin Sholk)

Teachers gather in a classroom at break for tea and powdered milk. A desperate shortage of finance denies them a separate and permanent staffroom. Burgeoning student numbers and teacher shortages together dictate a teaching load of 50 periods a week to classes of sometimes 50–60 pupils. There are no 'frees' for preparation and marking. There are also no duplicating facilities. Textbooks are the only maths 'resource' and these are sufficient only for one class at a time. Pupils cannot take them home. This school fortunately has mathematics textbooks – many do not. It is also one of a minority that offers mathematics to matriculation level, that is the fifth and final year of secondary school. The mathematics teachers have professional diplomas but limited post-secondary mathematics. Many teaching in the lower secondary school have not themselves passed, that is successfully completed senior secondary mathematics. Pressurized by the state to upgrade their qualifications, overworked, and burdened by heavy-handed, over-controlling subject inspectors, many teachers remain unconfident about their mathematical knowledge and are driven to 'survival teaching'. This consists of some exposition, perhaps some translation and clarification (English, the language of instruction, is a second or third language for most black pupils, and remains a barrier for some), and then rather mindless, rote exercises for the pupils to complete. For many teachers, the prescribed textbook and departmental schemes of work become a lifeline to presenting an abstract and academic syllabus. Paradoxically, for those few confident, more experienced teachers, such prescription is both de-skilling and disempowering.

Overcrowded, under-resourced schools, poor tuition, repressive statutes and the increasing certainty of unemployment for a majority of black school leavers are the perfect ingredients for highly politicized, angry and educationally unmotivated pupils. This picture is further framed by what has been aptly described as 'the destruction of a learning culture' (Samuel, 1990). Since the pupils' revolt of June 1976, continuing political turmoil has ensured that schools have functioned only intermittently. In 1990, compounding factors such as pupil boycotts and a teachers' strike over fundamental issues such as the failure of the authorities to provide sufficient textbooks ensured another lost school year for thousands of black children. For teachers and pupils both, demoralization grows as, year after year, too many students fail the matriculation examination, and mathematics in particular. Such are the conditions in most of the high schools in South Africa's black urban townships. In these schools, over the past decade and a half, the process of schooling has, to all intents and purposes, broken down.

Scenario 2: Limited racial privilege

Across the mine dumps, Johannesburg's 'white' state schools function daily and can boast academically and professionally trained maths teachers, sufficient textbooks for each pupil, tea in established staffrooms, duplicating facilities and perhaps even a computer centre. Certainly, apartheid education has ensured that white schools have the material resources for worthwhile schooling to take place. Such schooling, however, has been warped by the world-view and teaching techniques embedded in a system based on authoritarian, racial hierarchies. Maths classes are largely teacher-centred, with pupil activity restricted to individual practice on exercises from the prescribed textbook. Despite the years of professional and academic training, the transmission approach to the abstract and academic mathematical content of the prescribed syllabus leaves many pupils alienated and anxious. This effect is noticeable in pre-service primary teacher education courses, where, despite a matriculation pass in mathematics, many students are anxious and perceive themselves as failures in mathematics. Until relatively recently, material and political privilege has assured a substantial number of white pupils a matriculation pass in mathematics and a matriculation certificate with exemption. This means they have attained the minimum requirements for entry into tertiary education, and particularly university study. However, the general political climate, demographic change and economic constraints are finally threatening the limited cosiness and viability of a segregated schooling system. White parents and educators too both face an anxious future as the winds of change sweep away decades of comfort.[2]

Scenario 3: A vision of non-racial participatory learning

Situated geographically and, one could argue, metaphorically between white Johannesburg and black Soweto, is a private, *non-racial* secondary school. A decade ago, it, and a small number of similar schools, was born of an alliance between educators with a vision of education unfettered by apartheid, and private sector donors alarmed at the declining ability of both black and white state schools to produce citizens with skill and leadership ability. The staffroom has easy chairs, tea with fresh milk, a stock of local and international teaching journals, a photocopier and personal computer. The classrooms have overhead projectors, whiteboards, and not more than thirty relatively well-motivated learners per class. The mathematics teachers are all fully qualified with tertiary mathematics degrees and professional diplomas. A spirit of enquiry and participation is evident in the school. In a mathematics class, serious teacher-mediated, pupil–pupil discussion and debate about mathematical ideas and concepts is encouraged and developed. Each pupil has her or his own textbook. In addition, the teacher manages, at times, to include sources that provide mathematical exploration, necessary practice and historical and socio-cultural relevance – evidence of both the availability of resources, and the autonomy and flexibility of the teacher in using them to encourage and develop mathematical and critical learning. The school has functioned smoothly all year, and it is reasonable to expect that all these pupils will find their place in both civic and economic life. Some will be suitably armed with a matriculation exemption in mathematics and equipped for further tertiary science study.

Learning environments such as this comprise a minuscule part of educational provision in South Africa. Initially resisted with vigour by the apartheid state, they, together with church-backed private and now desegregated schools, have become examples of what *good, non-racial* education can be.[3] By their very nature, however, they are expensive and élitist facilities with relatively small, selected student-bodies. While many pupils can and do secure bursaries, all private schools administer some kind of scholastic selection test. It is clear that with the financial and skill burdens created under apartheid, the non-racial educational vision of such schools will be become a reality only for the select few.

These scenarios provide a cameo of the three linked faces of apartheid schooling and give a sense of the unequal and diverse contexts in which school mathematics is taught and learned. To complete the picture and context of school mathematics in South Africa, we need an understanding of the current syllabus development process.

Apartheid's 'core syllabus' – school mathematics by and for a few

Despite the obvious fragmentation of seventeen separate provincial, racial, and/or ethnically divided education departments in South Africa, all are bound to a 'core' mathematics syllabus. The core syllabus forms a fundamental part of the curriculum as a whole. The current mathematics curriculum, as pointed to in the scenarios above, fits Connell's (1985, pp. 87–8) description of a typical 'competitive academic curriculum'. The content is hierarchically organized, and derived from (and mainly suited to) university-based mathematics. Teaching is by transmission, learning is organized for individual appropriation of knowledge and assessment is through competitive examinations. This school mathematics curriculum is also 'hegemonic': it is dominant and has come to define what counts as both 'real maths' and 'real learning' – other curricula are marginalized or subordinated (Connell, 1985; Christie, 1990).

How do curricula and their syllabuses come about? Briefly, drafting and revision of the 'core' mathematics syllabus is effectively in the hands of the four provincial 'white' education departments, subject to the guidelines and policy of central government. Syllabus committees for primary and secondary levels are appointed by the departments and comprise (usually): a convener (a departmental official), examiners, subject advisers and mathematics education experts known to and trusted by the convener. The senior secondary syllabus committee lays down the minimum mathematics to be included in the matriculation syllabuses of the country's education departments. While adherence to a 'core' is not required at primary and junior secondary levels, the hegemony is such that the syllabuses from those 'white' departmental committees are usually adopted by the remaining departments, some of whom might make marginal adjustments to accommodate regional and 'cultural' difference (Methula, 1990).

In practice, however, attempts at accommodation reflect the resource base of the departments involved. For example while the mathematical content of the Standard 2 syllabuses[4] across departments is largely the same, extracts from introductory guidelines reflect different material conditions, and qualitatively different perceived and anticipated learning experiences.

> In the study of a new principle, one or more of the following should serve as a starting point:
>
> > ... *experience* with concrete material.
>
> Self activity, which among other things, includes the *handling of apparatus*, observation, discovery, discussion and the *carrying out of assignments*, should be encouraged.
>
> *(Standard 2 syllabus, Transvaal Education Department – for white students (my emphasis))*

And in contrast,

> New concepts should be introduced through and be based on discovery and discussion, and, as far as possible, should be

> proceeded by practical work and explained by *demonstrations* with concrete material.
>
> Self-activity should be encouraged, for instance in the *making up of sums*, in the approach to calculations, and in the collection of material or information.
>
> *(Standard 2 syllabus, Department of Education and Training – for black students (my emphasis))*

In black classrooms, teachers, where possible, demonstrate with concrete apparatus. Pupils' self-activity is limited to making up sums. White children, however, are to experience and handle concrete apparatus themselves. Their self-activity extends to carrying out assignments!

What the above reveals is that syllabus conception is effectively controlled by 'white' education departments and their interests. Furthermore, despite a large common core of mathematical content and skills, the subtly different syllabuses that reach teachers in racially determined departments are powerful reinforcers of the apartheid ideology of racial difference, fragmentation and privilege.[5]

In addition to syllabus conception being racially exclusive, it is also locked into the hands of 'experts'. Mathematics teachers in classrooms have little, if any, say in the syllabus *design* process described above. Furthermore, syllabus *interpretation* occurs partly through departmentally approved textbooks, many of which are of dubious origin and quality,[6] and partly through rather prescriptive schemes of work developed, and more or less enforced, by departmental subject advisers. In short, conceptualization and interpretation are severed from *implementation*. Mathematics teachers are treated as 'knowledge users' (Confrey, 1987), effectively alienated from the design process and left as 'mere technicians' implementing someone else's ideas (Julie, 1990). While the specific processes and contexts might be different, it is interesting that teachers in the UK and the USA face their own alienation from curriculum conceptualization (Ozga, 1988; Apple, 1983).

Building a new and fundamentally different future

Challenge to all facets of apartheid education is neither new nor solely political (Kallaway, 1984). In state schools, many teachers battle creatively with the limits of what is possible. Outside the formal system, innovative responses have gained particular momentum since 1976. The National Education Co-ordinating Committee (NECC – a mass-based educational congress of teachers, parents and students) has sponsored voluntary subject commissions to develop the notion of 'people's education for people's power'.[7] Some desegregated private schools are seriously restructuring their curriculum to meet the challenge of democracy and growth. Despite the horror of a potential civil war, the process of building the future continues.

It is now possible to return to the two areas of discussion that I pinpointed at the beginning of the chapter. Given the legacy of apartheid education, what are the implications for schools of a national mathematics curriculum?

What forms of selection and transmission would develop mathematical thinking, build skills and encourage critical, participative citizens?

As each area is discussed, it is important to recognize that existing government education policy is in disarray. As yet, no firm national education policy proposals for the future have emerged from the liberation movement. This chapter therefore cannot engage with policy. What I will do is present ideas and provoke questions about issues that are likely to impinge on the politics of a national mathematics curriculum in a changing South Africa and have relevance to teachers contending with national curricula elsewhere.

A national curriculum – what implications?

In South Africa, the call for a single, democratically elected education ministry, administering a unified education policy is a call *for* equalizing educational access and *against* apartheid inequality and fragmentation. Extrapolating to the curriculum, this is a call for both a *national* curriculum (centrally administered) and a *core* curriculum (the same foundations for all). A core curriculum is often premised on the broader goals of nation-building and social cohesion. In addition to unity, proponents of a core emphasize commonality, and thus the same set of fundamental learnings for all (Skilbeck, 1988). Underlying such goals are notions of equity and fairness. In some instances, the principle that all citizens have a right to education as a condition for effective civic and economic life is included. In combination, this reflects the increasingly argued position that 'constitutional rights' are necessary but not sufficient for a fully democratic society (Hall and Held, 1989). These political, moral and social justifications for a core thus resonate with the needs and demands for *education for all* under a single education ministry in South Africa.

In the South African context, the need for a national curriculum premised on the arguments for a core above and *legitimized by democratic processes* is not at issue.[8] Years of apartheid have made it politically, ideologically and educationally necessary. What becomes clear is that the demand for a core curriculum does not exist independently of national goals, educational policy and practice.

Mathematics is an undisputed and central element in core proposals. What might be debated is *how much* mathematics should be included as the core and *when* specialization should be introduced. I will not take up this debate. The inclusion of mathematics in the core is often based on either utilitarian (everybody needs mathematical skills to function in the modern technological world) or epistemological assumptions (mathematics is a particular and necessary area of knowledge for foundation learning) (CDC, 1982). Whatever the assumptions, the 'same mathematics for all' in a national curriculum in South Africa (and in any other context too) has challenging implications for pedagogy and control.

Pedagogical implications

As mathematics teachers, we know that all children do not learn in the same way nor at the same rate. Whether to stream or not for mathematics classrooms is an ongoing debate. This foregrounds a fundamental tension in and challenge for a national curriculum in the South African context: how will it simultaneously provide *access* to the *same mathematics for all* and cater for *diverse individual needs* but without any *systematic differentiation* (which might too closely resemble apartheid strategies)? Core proponents maintain that differentiation can and should be provided through classroom organization and teaching (Skilbeck, 1988). Perhaps the ease with which this is asserted reflects the relative homogeneity of both learners and material conditions in those national contexts (for example, Australia, Sweden). Differentiated learning in a primary mathematics class, for instance, requires at the most basic level sufficient space and material resources (workcards, activities, concrete aids, etc.) for different groups of children to do different things at the same time. Sophisticated teaching and organizational skills are also required. The overcrowded, under-resourced conditions and paucity of teaching skills which prevail in South African classrooms hardly facilitate such practice.

Another tension suggested by the phrase 'same mathematics for all' is whether such a curriculum will mean uniformly 'grey', uninterested and conforming learners or whether and how it can encourage diverse interests and individual exploration and autonomy of thought through mathematics and in the mathematics class. Just as dealing with diverse needs in the class has implications for the teacher, so does the encouragement of pupils' mathematical creativity: it requires teachers with sufficient self-confidence in and with mathematics not to be threatened by what their pupils may develop. This invariably entails teachers themselves having experienced autonomous thought in an encouraging and creative learning environment.

In addition to both the above tensions, South African teachers face the challenge of addressing the needs of learners whose histories span widely differential facility in the language of instruction and years of contrasting educational neglect and privilege. This is *within* classrooms. Conditions *across* South African schools, as the three scenarios portray, are starkly different and further determine and limit possibilities for realizing common learnings suggested by a core.

Thus, the potential of a national mathematics curriculum in South Africa, as a contributory mechanism to social cohesion and greater equality, is dependent in the first instance on suitable learning conditions across and within schools. This includes both material resources and teaching skills. While a more equitable allocation of funds and resources across South African schools is obviously essential, it is important to note that simple redistribution of already strained resources across schools, unfortunately, will not result in the conditions pointed to above.

Questions of control

Any suggestion of national redistribution and national administration immediately raises the question of control. Will a national curriculum, because it is centralized and linked to state financing, not breed bureaucratic control and disempowered teachers (Hall and Held, 1989; Hawley, 1985)? It certainly can. The current 'core' in South Africa bears testimony to this. The tendency of a top–down approach, which creates what has amusingly been described as 'apoplexy at the centre and anaemia at the edges' (Rodwin and Sanyal, 1987, p. 13), is accentuated by skills shortages in many situations. The shortage of academic, professional and technical skills in mathematics education, and more generally, loads the responsibility of designing syllabuses, texts, and materials, of training teachers, and of implementing policy, onto the shoulders of an overworked few. In the process, not enough confidence is placed in grassroots initiative and local capacity. The majority yet again have control, initiative and creativity stripped from their lives.

Shortages of human resources and skills in mathematics, and the ideological perception that mathematics is only for the select few, are global, rather than uniquely South African, issues. Overlaid by the apartheid legacy, 'mathematics for all' becomes a double challenge in South Africa, exacerbated by strong tendencies to top–down approaches to the issue of human resources development. In-service mathematics teacher education projects have been criticized precisely on these grounds (Gordon, 1989, p. 81). The challenge for greater democracy, equitable provision and growth is to establish central coordination with decentralized, local autonomy. This, of course, is easier said than done. For some time to come, for example, it is likely that for many mathematics teachers in South Africa, nationally approved textbooks will be a necessary and helpful, if still somewhat controlling, tool/resource (Ball and Feiman-Nemser, 1988).

What is thus needed is a conception which does not conflate a centralized core with control. If a core is a 'set of organizing principles ... providing order, clarity and a central set of meanings ... capable of being communicated and debated in the public domain' (Skilbeck, 1988), then it operates at the level of guiding principles and not prescriptive behaviours. In this way, there is room for local diversity, development and change.

As we have seen, the arguments for any national curriculum need to be placed in context. The South African context suggests that the same set of mathematics learnings for all, and the availability and development of resources and skills are important elements in redressing the apartheid legacy. These, in turn, provoke some complex questions about available resources, pedagogy and control.

Selection, transmission and change

> curriculum ... what is considered appropriate school knowledge and the principles used to select and value it.
>
> (Apple, 1979, p. 156)

The previous section focused on 'the same for all' aspect of any national curriculum. With this focus, what is obscured is the ideology inevitably embedded in the way knowledge is selected and transmitted in the curriculum. What comes to count as school mathematics and how it is learned is ultimately framed by power relations in the society and by broad national goals.

Across many national contexts, school mathematics continues to be the most effective social and educational sieve. Not only is it alienating and exclusive of the majority, it effectively marginalizes as 'other' or 'not real mathematics', the mathematical practices of everyday life. The relationship between school mathematics and the broader social context has been a focus of international debate for some time now. The debate has been taken up in and across contexts ranging from war-torn Mozambique (Gerdes, 1985, 1988) to the streets of Brazil (Carraher *et al.*, 1985; D'Ambrosio, 1985) and to the mathematics classrooms in inner London (Isaacson, 1989; Brown and Dowling, 1989; Abraham and Bibby, 1988) and Norway (Mellin-Olsen, 1986). Much of the debate is pursued in the interests of greater democracy and social equality.

What underlies this debate is an assumption that the nature of mathematical knowledge is contestable. The breadth and depth of debate on 'what is mathematics?' cannot be elaborated here, but an important element is the contrast between the dominant conception of mathematics as idealist, certain/absolute and universal and an argument for a conception of mathematics as a changing, socio-cultural activity.

In this section, I propose, develop and discuss three broad criteria as guidelines for the selection of knowledge for a national mathematics curriculum in South Africa. These criteria are self-consciously responsive to and informed by a concern with building democracy and the common good. They will also provide a useful framework for analysing and evaluating some recent South African initiatives in maths curriculum development.

Selection and transmission for critical citizens

A core maths curriculum should:

    (a) provide all learners with access to a foundation in mathematical knowledge: this includes concepts, content and processes (ways of thinking);

    (b) develop in all learners, mathematical problem-solving skills useful to, and contextualized in, daily life and, ultimately, the work place;

    (c) enhance all learners' critical faculties and hence their effective participation in civic life.

These guidelines and particularly the epistemological and utilitarian thrusts of (a) and (b) are not new. At a global level, it is undisputed that all citizens should have access to fundamental mathematical concepts and skills. But this is also not unproblematic. Which concepts? Which skills? And how much mathematics is essential/fundamental? Who decides? Answers to such questions are both context-bound and political, and I will not attempt to offer my response here. What can be pointed to, though, is that the 'back to basics' movement can be identified through curricula that emphasize skills at the expense of concepts, processes and critical thinking.

In South Africa, emphases on mathematical processes, mathematical thinking and mathematics and work are not part of the current core syllabuses, but they are (particularly the first two) finding their way into draft new syllabuses. They also reflect analyses of the changing workplace (due to technological advances) and the ensuing demands for flexible thinkers, and for school curricula to be less severed from the world of work.

It is the third criterion, the development of critical thinking, that is not commonly found in mathematics syllabus guidelines and thus requires some elaboration. This is not to suggest that it is more important than the first two criteria, but to recognize it is somewhat different, and also controversial.[9] Criterion (c) is premised on the position that the development of a participative democracy entails the development of critical thinkers – people able to reflect critically on the social world. Thus, schooling, and mathematics within it, should not only focus on the learning of systematized knowledge, but also on the development of critical and enquiring minds. This leads to the following two principles for school mathematics.

- Mathematics classes should encourage critical reflection both within mathematics and, using mathematical tools, on the social world; that is, learning should take place in an atmosphere of *enquiry, participation and cooperation*.
- Mathematics learning should be an *empowering* (and not a disabling) process – two corollaries here are that it should harness, rather than destroy, 'street'/'everyday' mathematics and that the contexts in which mathematical ideas are embedded should reflect diverse social interests and practices.

So, how might the three criteria and related principles above inform a future national curriculum and mathematical classroom practice in South Africa? Concern with *access* to school mathematics for the majority (criterion (a)) is not new. The call in 1986 for 'people's education for people's power' gave ongoing work in this area (Adler, 1988a) a new and vigorous impetus, and inserted an explicit political dimension. The myth of the neutrality of school mathematics in apartheid society has subsequently been explored in a series of papers and workshops since 1986 (Taylor *et al.*, 1987; Breen, 1986; Adler, 1988b; MEP, 1989). In particular, race and gender bias in texts have been critically examined. Concurrently, both materials and learning/teaching strategies supportive of change and democratic practice were developed. Breen (1990), for example, advocates reflective writing for learning in mathematics. His premise is that change can only come from 'inner transformation' and he has developed activities that release energy and stimulate pupils' reflection (recorded in their diaries) on their own and others' realities.

Workshops for mathematics teachers held in Johannesburg (MASA, 1990) and Cape Town (MEP, 1989) focused on 'mathematics for empowerment' and a 'changing view of mathematics'. The activities presented were produced by practising teachers and encouraged cooperative learning. They included open-ended mathematical investigations which focused on processes, the teaching of mathematics in its historical context, and the use of mathematics as a tool for reflecting on social issues. The activities in the workshops represent a shift in emphasis from mathematics as universal and absolute to mathematics as a cultural process.

Arising largely in opposition to apartheid education, these strategies reflect the first and third criteria with a focus on the principles outlined above. They challenge the dominant view of mathematics as both neutral and fixed. The contribution to curriculum reconstruction lies in their emphasis on critical participation as a way of concretizing principles of democracy for mathematics learning. While they have been concerned with the development of mathematical thinking and mathematics as tools, the focus has been in a social and civic context.

The more explicit building of skills and the link between school and work, the utilitarian second criterion, has, in the main, been the focus of privately sponsored mathematics and science educational projects. One particularly successful such project works with senior secondary black scholars and has developed materials aimed at encouraging mathematical problem solving, the use of study skills and 'awareness of applications and career relevance of topics' (Kramer, 1990).

How do new ideas become practices?

Despite the resonance of all the above projects with wider socio-political change, dominant practice continues to reflect the hegemony of the competitive academic curriculum and its controlling, centralized matriculation examination (Christie, 1990). These allow little time and space for curriculum experimentation and change. To incorporate greater access, as well as reflective, participatory and investigative mathematical learning requires both a less content-laden syllabus, as well as an epistemological shift to a more interactive approach to constructing knowledge. Resistance to change arises not only from these constraints. Many practising teachers, as well as those previously excluded from school mathematics, view the existing curriculum as the 'real thing', and believe that it is just the conditions, segregation and the lack of resources that need to change. Despite their commitment to a new future, this not-insignificant group construes suggestions involving any pedagogical and content changes as another form of second-best, inferior mathematics.

The cauldron of educational flux is clearly the reflection of a crisis of legitimacy in education. While the old order remains dominant, conflict between competing interests is clearly visible in the educational arena. New draft syllabuses, while positively influenced by pedagogical developments elsewhere, nevertheless disregard changes in the wider society and remain in the hands of 'whites only' education departments. But conflict is a necessary condition for social change and it is not limited to opposing forces: it occurs even where there is a similar commitment to such change (Adler, 1990). What this highlights is that change is ultimately a *process*. The development and implementation of a new national mathematics curriculum will play a role in this process. The extent to which such a curriculum will be 'mathematics for all' on the one hand, and contribute to the development of critical thinking and participative citizens on the other, is not predetermined. It is contingent, I believe, on whether and how it provokes debate on and development around the criteria and principles for selection and transmission proposed above.

What about teachers?

Before concluding, it is important to ask: where do teachers fit in this development and implementation process? It is now generally accepted that effective curriculum change requires widespread participation, particularly of teachers (Samuel, 1990). The question, however, is *how*? How can the production process of a national curriculum be participative and harness rather than disempower teachers and learners? The dilemma of teacher participation in curriculum development is not peculiar to South Africa (Howson *et al.*, 1981, pp. 9–10). There is thus no ready-made formula for ensuring their key role. However, two conditions will go a long way to securing their participation. Firstly, teachers need to organize themselves into effective and democratic trade unions and professional associations. In South Africa at present, a national, progressive, teachers' union, formed in late 1990, is only in embryonic form. Further, while the largest national mathematics association is now constitutionally non-racial, this policy commitment has yet to be effected through its structures.

Secondly, for effective participation, teachers need to develop academic and professional skills and resources (Archer, 1985). In South Africa, the majority of mathematics teachers have been systematically denied these. What is more, caught in the crossfire of student anger directed at government education, the status of the profession is at its lowest ebb ever.[10] Teacher education and organization, and the reconstruction of the status of teaching as a profession, is of crucial importance in South Africa. There can be no effective change without restoring to teaching its status as a professional and a socially, politically and economically valuable activity. Teachers, and teacher organizations, thus emerge as central players in the process of curriculum reconstruction.

It is imperative to add, and emphasize, that curriculum reconstruction is almost meaningless in a context where a culture of learning has all but broken down. Restoring teaching, and restoring school learning as important to intellectual, social and economic development, are two sides of the same coin in South Africa.

Conclusion

In this chapter, I have argued that mathematics national curricula are intensely, but not solely, political products. They both inform and are informed by their contexts. They provoke questions about centralized control, local autonomy, classroom resources, teaching skills, and teacher autonomy and participation. They open debate on the nature of mathematical knowledge and its relationship within school to the development of critical citizens.

In the South African context, the development of a national mathematics curriculum is part of the inexorable drive towards a post-apartheid society. Slowly, some of the ideas and proposals discussed in this chapter are taking root in mathematics classrooms, at teacher conferences and in educational projects outside the official structures. It is important to recognize, however, that these changes occur where conditions are facilitative. These include reasonably sized and resourced classrooms, with teachers who are professionally trained, mathematically confident and semi-autonomous in their work, and an environment that encourages and sanctions progressive change. Thus, the practices forged at present are born in a context of considerable teaching confidence and skill. Unless the inequality in teaching resources and environment is addressed, the emancipatory potential of the practices of teachers described in the previous section may inadvertently breed their own new form of élitism.

Appendix: Mathematics, schooling and apartheid – some statistics

Pertinent comparative figures

	'Whites'	'Black'/ African
(1) *Per capita* expenditure 1990*	R3082 p.a.	R765 p.a.
Ratio	4	1
(2) Pupil–teacher ratios 1989**	16:1	41:1
Schools offering mathematics to matriculation level in 1989**	Over 90%	42%
Teachers who do not have a matriculation certificate*	None	34%
(3) Teacher shortages***	None	6881
Primary	None	5531
Secondary	None	1350

(1) Figures from: *The Star*, 7 September 1990; **Hofmeyr, 1989; ***SAIRR, 1989.

(2) Pupil–teacher ratios obscure actual overcrowding in classrooms. A 60:1 ratio is common in black primary schools (Black Sash education report, February 1990).

(3) It is estimated that teacher shortages will reach 277 000 by the year 2000 (*The Star*, 7 September 1990).

Pass rates

- In 1989, only 20 per cent of black matriculants passed mathematics.
- Of every 100 000 black pupils that enter primary school: only 27 will obtain a matriculation exemption to enter university; only 1 is likely to gain an exemption that includes mathematics and science (Kramer, 1990).

The unschooled

- An estimated 1.5 million black children of school-going age are not attending school (*The Star*, 7 September 1990).

Notes

1   If you are interested in reading further on recent developments in education in South Africa, see Nasson and Samuel (1990).

2   In December 1990, parent bodies of 10 per cent of white schools voted in favour of desegregation. So far (January 1991), approximately 1000 black children have been admitted to these schools.

3   The emphasis here is because non-racial education does not necessarily equate with good practice. This school, and a few others, have consciously developed *both* good educational practice and non-racialism.

4   Standard 2 is the fourth year of primary schooling.

5   Differences in syllabuses for history and English across departments are not so subtle and are more obviously racist in the different selections of historical events and literary works.

6   Currently, departmental officials are being charged with corruption at all levels (*The Star*, 21, 22 September 1990). See also Taylor (1990).

7   This slogan was coined by the NECC in 1986, in an attempt to encourage boycotting students to return to school, and to work to shift control of the schools from the state to the people. Repressive state reaction followed, but debate has continued as to the meaning of the phrase 'people's education' and the implications for the curriculum.

8   While 'national' is distinct from 'core' – for instance, a national curriculum can dictate different streams and thus need not include a core; also, a core is not necessarily centrally administered – in the South African context, they interact inextricably.

9   For arguments for and against the development of critical thinking through mathematics see, for example, Abraham and Bibby (1988) or Pimm (1990).

10   The contradictory position of teachers in volatile township schools has been magnificently captured in Athol Fugard's penetrating play *My Children, My Africa* (Faber and Faber, 1990).

References

Abraham, J. and Bibby, N. (1988) 'Mathematics and society: ethnomathematics and a public education curriculum', *For the Learning of Mathematics*, **8**(2), pp. 2–11.

Adler, J. (1988a) 'Newspaper-based mathematics for adults in South Africa', *Educational Studies in Mathematics*, **19**(1), pp. 59–78.

Adler, J. (1988b) 'Towards democratic mathematics education in South Africa', *Lengwitch*, March, pp. 83–98.

Adler, J. (1990) 'How do you do it? Politics and practice in mathematics education in South Africa', in Noss R. *et al.* (eds), *Political Dimensions of Mathematics Education: Action and Critique* (PDME), Proceedings of the First International Conference, University of London Institute of Education, pp. 5–11.

Apple, M. (1979) *Ideology and the Curriculum*, Routledge and Kegan Paul.

Apple, M. (1983) 'Curricula form and the logic of technical control' in Apple, M. W. and Weis, L. (eds), *Ideology and Practice in Schooling*, Philadelphia University Press.

Archer, M. (1985) 'Educational politics: a model for their analysis' in McNay, I. and Ozga, J. (eds), *Policy-making in Education: the Breakdown of Consensus*, Pergamon Press.

Ball, D. L. and Feiman-Nemser, S. (1988) 'Using textbooks and teachers' guides: a dilemma for beginning teachers and teacher educators', *Curriculum Inquiry*, **18**(4), pp. 401–23.

Breen, C. (1986) 'Alternative mathematics programmes', *Proceedings of the 8th National MASA Congress*, Stellenbosch.

Breen, C. (1990) 'Reflecting on energy activities: an attempt at liberating pre-service mathematics teachers at a South African University' in Noss, R. *et al.* (eds), *Political Dimensions of Mathematics Education: Action and Critique* (PDME), Proceedings of the First International Conference, University of London Institute of Education, pp. 36–45.

Brown, A. and Dowling, P. (1989) *Towards a Critical Alternative to Internationalism and Monoculturalism in Mathematics Education*, Working Paper No. 10, Centre for Multicultural Education, University of London Institute of Education.

Carraher, T. N., Carraher, D. W. and Schliemann, A. D. (1985) 'Mathematics in the street and in the schools', *British Journal of Developmental Psychology*, **3**, pp. 21–9.

CDC (1982) 'Core curriculum for Australian schools', in Horton, T. and Raggatt, P. (eds), *Challenge and Change in the Curriculum*, Hodder and Stoughton.

Christie, P. (1990) 'Reforming the racial curriculum: curriculum change in desegregated schools in South Africa', *British Journal of Sociology of Education*, **11**(1), pp. 37–48.

Confrey, J. (1987) 'Bridging research and practice', *Educational Theory*, **37**(4), pp. 383–94.

Connell, R. W. (1985) *Teachers' Work*, Allen and Unwin.

D'Ambrosio, U. (1985) 'Ethnomathematics and its place in the history and pedagogy of mathematics', *For the Learning of Mathematics*, **5**(1), pp. 44–8.

Department of Education and Training (1983) *Mathematics Syllabus for Std 2*, Government Printers.

Dowling, P. and Noss, R. (eds) (1990) *Mathematics versus the National Curriculum*, Falmer Press.

Gerdes, P. (1985) 'Conditions and strategies for emancipatory mathematics education in undeveloped countries', *For the Learning of Mathematics*, **5**(1), pp. 15–20.

Gerdes, P. (1988) 'On culture, geometrical thinking and mathematics education', *Educational Studies in Mathematics*, **19**(2), pp. 137–62.

Gordon, A. (1989) *The Maths Centre for Primary Teachers: its Impact on Soweto Teachers and their Pupils*, HSRC.

Hall, S. and Held, D. (1989) 'Citizens and citizenship' in Hall, S. and Jaques, N. (eds), *New Times*, Lawrence and Wishart.

Hawley, W. D. (1985) 'The Paideia proposal: noble ambitions, false leads' in Rich, J. M. (ed.), *Innovations in Education: Reformers and their Critics*, Allyn and Bacon.

Hofmeyr, J. (1989) 'Equalising educational opportunities', *South African Journal of Labour Relations*, **13**(2), pp. 20–34.

Howson, A. G., Keitel, C. and Kilpatrick, J. (eds) (1981) *Curriculum Development in Mathematics*, Cambridge University Press.

Isaacson, Z. (1988) 'The marginalisation of girls in mathematics' in Pimm, D. (ed.), *Mathematics, Teachers and Children*, Hodder and Stoughton, pp. 95–108.

Julie, C. (1990) 'Equations of inequality: an overview of mathematics education in South Africa' in Noss, R. *et al.* (eds), *Political Dimensions of Mathematics Education: Action and Critique* (PDME), Proceedings of the First International Conference, University of London Institute of Education, pp. 143–50.

Kallaway, P. (1984) *Apartheid and Education*, Raven Press.

Kramer, D. (1990) *A Profile of the Education Crisis*, PROTEC.

MASA (Mathematics Association of South Africa) (1990) *Day Conference*.

Mellin-Olsen, S. (1986) *The Politics of Mathematics Education*, D. Reidel.

MEP (1989) *Maths as a Cultural Process*, University of Cape Town.

Methula, P. (1990) *The Process of Curriculum Development for Pre-Tertiary Institutions in the Republic of South Africa*, Education Policy Unit, University of the Witwatersrand.

Nasson, B. and Samuel, J. (eds) (1990) *Education: From Poverty to Liberty*, David Philip.

Ozga, J. (ed.) (1988) *Schoolwork: Approaches to the Labour Processes of Teaching*, Open University Press.

Pimm, D. (1990) 'Mathematical versus political awareness: some political dangers inherent in the teaching of mathematics' in Noss, R. *et al.* (eds), *Political Dimensions of Mathematics Education: Action and Critique* (PDME), Proceedings of the First International Conference, University of London Institute of Education, pp. 200–4.

Rodwin, L. and Sanyal, B. (1987) *Shelter, Settlement and Development*, Allen and Unwin.

SAIRR (1990) *Race Relations Survey (1988/89)*, South African Institute of Race Relations, p. 260.

Samuel, J. (1990) 'Education in South Africa: strategic issues for the future', *The Innes Labour Brief*, **2**(1), pp. 53–9.

Skilbeck, M. (1988) 'Core curriculum: old ways and new directions', *Discourse*, **9**(1), pp. 59–71.

Taylor, N., Adler, J., Mazibuko, F. and Magadla, L. (1987) 'People's education and the role of mathematics: a workshop' in Muller, J. (ed.), *Critique–Vision–Strategy: Proceedings of the Kenton Conference*, University of the Witwatersrand.

Taylor, N. (1990) 'Picking up the pieces: mathematics education in a fragmenting world' in Noss, R. *et al.* (eds), *Political Dimensions of Mathematics Education: Action and Critique* (PDME), Proceedings of the First International Conference, University of London Institute of Education, pp. 235–42.

Transvaal Education Department (1978) *Mathematics Syllabus for Std 2*, Government Printers.

Acknowledgements

While I claim full responsibility for the ideas in this paper, they have been shaped and developed with colleagues. In particular, I thank Taffy Adler, Shirley Pendlebury and David Pimm for their insights and assistance.

15 National curricula: paradoxes and dilemmas

Zelda Isaacson and Jane Coombe

In this chapter, we explore arguments put forward by those who espouse national curricula and highlight key issues facing mathematics educators in England. To contextualize the discussion, we look first at different models of the curriculum, and at some of the mechanisms which are employed to narrow the gap between the intentions of curriculum designers and outcomes in mathematics classes. We then use the South African situation (drawing, in particular, on the account by Jill Adler in this volume: all references to her work come from here) as a vehicle for identifying the key arguments in favour of national curricula and discuss these in the context of English mathematics education. We argue that educators wishing to implement national curricula inevitably face a series of paradoxes and dilemmas, and that there are no easy solutions to these difficulties.

Curriculum models

> Don't the Secretaries of State know that schools and teachers seek to realize their aims in all sorts of ways – sometimes via subjects, sometimes via forms of activity in which subject boundaries are deliberately crossed ... sometimes via school ethos and organization ... the list could go on and on.
>
> *(White, 1988, p. 115)*

The curriculum is all too frequently understood as a collection of individual subjects, each of which is based on a recognizable academic discipline history, physics, mathematics, etc. A familiar, contemporary example of this mode of curriculum design is the new national curriculum in England.[1] This consists of ten so-called foundation subjects, each of which has (or will have) its own rationale, attainment targets and statements of attainment.

However, as White indicates, it is possible to begin from entirely different premises. Here are two examples within the context of mathematics education to illustrate this. Subject boundaries are crossed in a secondary school where students and teachers decide to investigate an issue within the school, and tackle this using a multidisciplinary approach. Pupils may decide to investigate the best place for a new pedestrian crossing near their school. This could involve data collection, presentation and analysis, as well as report writing, the development of interview techniques, environmental awareness, and much else. The subject skills serve the research task rather than the task being subordinated to the demands of a subject syllabus. (See Brown and Dowling (1989) for an exploration of research-based curricula.)

The ethos and organization of a typical infant classroom in the United Kingdom in the 1980s provides another example of an alternative curriculum model. Teachers work from a notion of the development of the child as a whole, with schemes of work designed to facilitate each child's growth. Topic and theme-based work provide contexts for the development of mathematical and other concepts and skills. Individual subjects are recognized, but are not the organizing principle – very often, the boundaries between mathematics and science, for example, are blurred. One of the fears of infant teachers currently faced with a national curriculum is that this child-centred approach will be undermined by the need to assess mathematics and other subjects independently of each other.

Whichever model is employed, however, there is the prior question of which knowledge areas are to be chosen and/or emphasized, and what is to be included within each of the selected fields. This applies to choices between subjects (e.g. mathematics or geography), as well as to choices within subjects (e.g. Euclidean geometry or probability). These are value-laden decisions and are based on a range of considerations stemming from political, philosophical, economic and/or pedagogic factors which vary across place and time and in relation to the population groups targeted by the curriculum. In particular, it is interesting to note that mathematics has not always been regarded as an essential feature of the curriculum, nor has the content been constant over time. A few examples from the history of mathematics education in England follow.

While Latin and Greek were deemed essential subjects (Barnard, 1947, pp. 14–15), grammar schools in eighteenth-century England did not necessarily teach mathematics. As Howson comments: 'often boys who wanted to learn some arithmetic or geometry paid for tuition in much the same way that they would now pay in an independent school for music lessons' (Howson, 1982, p. 63). In nineteenth-century elementary schools, working-class children were taught skills considered useful for their roles in life, including arithmetic for boys and needlework for girls. (A further perspective on the changing nature of primary mathematics curricula is provided elsewhere in this volume in the chapter by Eddie Gray.) By the twentieth century, school mathematics courses were generally seen as a preparation for higher education. Although it was recognized that the majority of pupils would not require university entrance-level mathematics, what was offered to those thought to be less capable was often a watered-down version of the highly regarded academic course. This academic emphasis continues to exert a powerful influence on school mathematics, especially at A-level.

Since the introduction of GCSE mathematics, students going on to study at A-level have found that they are inadequately prepared for this highly academic course. A conflict currently exists between the desire to provide a positive mathematical experience for most pupils, the intention of GCSE, and the needs of future A-level mathematics students, previously catered for by O-level. (For a fuller discussion of the contrast between the aims of GCSE and O-level/CSE mathematics, see Isaacson, 1987, p. 8.) At the time of writing, several groups are attempting to address this problem by designing new A-level syllabuses, but it is still unclear how the conflict will be resolved.

The ready availability of calculators and computers is also (too slowly in the view of some people) influencing the content and emphasis of school mathematics. Elsewhere in this volume, Angela Walsh highlights some aspects of the primary school CAN (Calculator-Aware Number) curriculum project. Despite such projects, some of the statements of attainment in the mathematics national curriculum specifically require non-calculator methods of computation. For example, the programme of study for attainment target 2, level 5, states: '… understanding and using non-calculator methods by which … a 3-digit number is divided by a 2-digit number'.[2]

These examples of curricular changes over time in one country are illustrative of the fluid nature of 'school mathematics'. Historical period, gender, class and changing ideas of pedagogy have influenced whether mathematics is taught, to whom it is offered and what is selected for a school mathematics syllabus.

Curriculum implementation

The intentions of curriculum makers do not easily translate into the realities of classroom practices. These practices are mediated by the interpretations of both teachers and pupils and by the material conditions in which the teaching and learning take place. Requiring that mathematics is taught in schools (or that a topic within mathematics, such as algebra, is included) may be necessary, but is never sufficient to ensure that what happens in the classroom matches the hopes of the curriculum designers. It is helpful, for this reason, to distinguish between curricular intentions and outcomes. For example, the intention in introducing investigational work has been to enable pupils to 'become mathematicians', to engage in independent mathematical activity at a level appropriate to their experience. In contrast, the classroom experience of many pupils is to be 'taught' how 'to do' investigations. It is also interesting to note how differently the various GCSE examination boards have interpreted aim 2.13 in the national criteria for mathematics.

> [All courses should enable pupils to] develop their mathematical abilities by considering problems and conducting individual and cooperative enquiry and experiment, including extended pieces of work of a practical and investigative kind

(DES, 1985)

Some boards have required open-ended pieces of work of a pupil's own choice, while others have set structured 'investigations' for all pupils to work through. It is apparent that the intentions of curriculum designers are subject to a great deal of interpretation. (See, also, the chapter by Laurinda Brown in this volume.)

Mechanisms have been developed within education which, whatever their overt purposes, contribute to achieving the desired match between intentions and outcomes. (See Brown (1990) for a discussion of the mechanisms which turn a 'notional' into a 'national' curriculum.) Typical of such mechanisms are syllabuses and textbooks, and, centrally, examinations or other forms of assessment. (Although, as we have seen above, there may be a gap even between the intentions of curriculum designers and of those responsible for setting examinations.) Many countries also have an inspectorate whose brief is to enforce or at least to assist in the implementation of the stated curriculum. In England, in-service training of teachers, often mediated by local education authority staff (mathematics advisers, support teachers, etc.), serves to induct teachers into the curriculum.

We would argue, however, that none of these mechanisms acts in an inevitable or deterministic way to control classroom practices. Teachers interpret the demands of the curriculum in the light of their own understanding of what constitutes appropriate knowledge and pedagogy. This understanding is informed by many factors, such as their own experiences as learners of mathematics in school and higher education (see the chapter by Crook and Briggs in this volume), their study of educational theory and their own political positions. Thus, the degree of consensus among teachers about what a syllabus means or how a textbook should be used will vary greatly in different situations. Whether a consensus is perceived as a democratically achieved general agreement, or as the dead hand of an outdated, dominant ideology, depends on both the situation and the perspective of those concerned.

We now discuss two examples of how a prevailing consensus can impede the implementation of new ideas. The first is the experience of many countries trying to introduce the 'new mathematics' in the 1960s and 1970s. One aim of the curriculum developers was to introduce concepts like sets and functions because of their unifying potential. This ambition was to a large extent not realized, however, because the prevailing understanding of mathematics as being composed of discrete topics, dictated that sets (and functions) were reduced to a new, but separate, section of the syllabus. It is interesting that more recent attempts to change the organizational basis within mathematics have also been perceived as demands for additional content, requiring time for 'investigations lessons' or 'discussion lessons', for example. Everything ends up as content to be taught.

A second, South African, example of a consensus in operation can be found in Jill Adler's chapter. While many teachers reject the control of their teaching practice by the state, they have none the less absorbed some of the traditional views of what constitutes a mathematics curriculum and the best ways to teach it, and are reluctant to see these as issues open to debate.[3]

It is not only teachers who participate in and construct a consensus. Parents and pupils often expect and demand a particular pedagogic style and content. This is partly because they feel they know what employers demand,[4] but their expectations are also shaped by their understanding of what constitutes mathematics. For example, mathematics teachers may wish to encourage pupils to look up answers and correct their own work as part of the learning process, while parents (and pupils) may perceive this as 'cheating'.

In this section, we have argued that there is no straightforward translation of curriculum intentions into outcomes. The key mechanisms by which translation is attempted are syllabuses, textbooks, schemes and examinations. We have also pointed out that these mechanisms cannot fully succeed unless they are backed up by a consensus among all those involved in curriculum design and in the teaching and learning of mathematics. As this consensus patently does not exist in England, and would rarely be found anywhere, the gap between intentions and outcomes is likely to remain an issue for curriculum planners.

Arguments for national curricula

The difficulties of enforcing a curriculum and of creating a consensus to support it become particularly stark when considering the case of a national curriculum. In order for a mathematics curriculum to be applied to all the pupils of a country, with the complexities and scale that this involves, some, at least, of the mechanisms for the enforcement of this curriculum must be under the control of the state. In England, this has taken the form of legislation.

Despite these difficulties, political groups in many countries do wish to have national curricula. In England, the desire for a national curriculum was articulated by the Labour party long before the Conservative party brought in the Education Reform Act of 1988. One way of understanding the drive towards a national curriculum from both left and right in England is to look first at another country (South Africa), where the need to nationalize education seems almost self-evident. We shall then select arguments from the South African case to provide a framework within which to examine the English national curriculum.

First, we look briefly at why groups in South Africa espouse a national curriculum. Interestingly, its advocates have come both from the apartheid government and from progressive, opposition groups. As described by Jill Adler, the apartheid government has controlled education from the centre and has created racially divided but nationally imposed curricula. The differentiated curricula have been intended to serve the changing political and economic needs of the state. The mathematical (and scientific) experience of black pupils has been deliberately limited in order to make it impossible for them to challenge the racially stratified economy. This was true until relatively recently, when the technological needs of the state could no longer be met by white workers only. This resulted in a substantial injection of funds by government and the private sector into, especially, mathematical and technological education for black students. (Despite this, inequities between black and white educational provision remain stark.)

The liberation movement in South Africa is united in its desire to rid education of conservative national control and to abolish the divisive racial categorization within it. It is widely felt that one national curriculum applied to all students is an essential ingredient in the move towards equality and justice. It is also believed that a new government would have the task of healing the wounds created by apartheid and that a national curriculum would contribute towards much-needed nation building. An important feature of this curriculum would be the empowerment of all individuals so as to create critical participants in the new democracy.

In her scenario 1, Jill Adler describes the difficult conditions in mathematics education which result in the belief that strong guidance from the centre is crucial in an expanding education system. Expansion of education is seen as particularly important for the development of the economy. People in the liberation movement are painfully aware that, in order to run their country, they have to be able to control its technology. This requires a massive increase in mathematical, scientific and technological training for black students and also giving priority to these areas within any proposed national curriculum.

This discussion on South Africa enables us to isolate three key arguments in favour of a centrally controlled curriculum, in which mathematics plays a significant role. While it may appear, on the face of it, that the situation in England is very different from that in South Africa, we would claim that the parallels and contrasts illuminate the situation here. The arguments are:

- based on principles of justice, especially in relation to equality of access;
- for educational and/or political control from the centre;
- supporting the technological needs and economic base of the society.

Each of these is discussed below, in the context of the English national curriculum for mathematics.

Justice and equality

Progressive educators in England, like those in South Africa, have argued for a national curriculum because of its potential to contribute to goals of equity. We would claim, however, that the enforcement of a national curriculum is insufficient, in itself, to ensure equality. Inequities in school provision remain regardless of the nominal curriculum. The pupils in a Yorkshire mining village or an inner-city area with a large immigrant population where there is very high unemployment and poor resources cannot be said to have the same access to a set mathematics curriculum as those in a well-to-do, suburban school. Jill Adler's scenarios 1 and 2 (although perhaps less harshly) are echoed, in this way, all over England, while her scenario 3 resonates with the situation in many privileged, independent (private) schools and in the new, foundering CTC programme. Not only does the national curriculum not address inequalities of provision and context, but it has been suggested that it 'provides the government with a fig-leaf for the educational shortcomings of many schools' (Dowling and Noss, 1990, p. 8). A commitment to equity in mathematics education demands far more than the imposition of the same curriculum on all pupils. Minimally, it demands adequate resourcing of all schools, the redressing of existing imbalances, a real investment in teacher education and payment of teachers at appropriate professional levels. (Jill Adler makes a similar point on p. 160.)

The attempt to provide equality of provision through a mathematics national curriculum may also give rise to a paradox. By making mathematics part of the compulsory core curriculum to age 16, and by having common programmes of study, an attempt has been made to provide all pupils with equal access to mathematics. The problem is that entitlement and compulsion are not always clearly distinguished. For instance, if someone is entitled to learn how to solve equations, it does not follow that they must be forced to do this. The paradox arises because the attempt to ensure justice through equality of access may result in the erosion of justice through compulsion. Similarly, the all-pervasiveness of the mathematics programmes of study means that there is little opportunity for teachers to include topics which do not fall within these programmes. In the words of Bruce Douglas (1990), this 'turns entitlement into a strait-jacket'.[5]

The problem is exacerbated by the fact that pupils are generally not in a position to make informed choices about subjects to which they have not had access. In an earlier paper, one of us (Isaacson, 1990) suggests that a possible way to resolve this dilemma is to separate mathematics A, a utilitarian skill (which everyone needs to study), from mathematics B, an aesthetic subject (which need not be compulsory). Pupils would be given enough access to mathematics B in the earlier years of schooling for them to be able to decide whether they wish to continue this to age 16. The argument here is that all pupils are entitled to access to both mathematics A and B, but need not be compelled to study more than a utilitarian minimum in the later years of schooling. This, of course, begs the question of whether even these are real choices (see below, and Isaacson, 1986) and which further choices and opportunities might be impeded by lack of a required, even if not always appropriate, mathematics qualification (see note 4).

There is a further argument related to equality of provision which creates another dilemma for those committed to ideals of justice. The blanket provision of equal access for all students does not take into consideration differences between individuals and groups. Specifically, the national curriculum for mathematics deliberately ignores gender and ethnic differences, despite a sizeable body of research in mathematics education which indicates that many girls and members of ethnic minority communities are marginalized in mathematics classrooms. (For a discussion of this issue and anti-sexist/anti-racist mathematics see, for example, Burton, 1986, 1990; Isaacson, 1988; Joseph, 1990; Singh, 1989.)

These issues will also inevitably face progressive educators in South Africa who, in their desire to see justice done, will come up against the problem of how to balance the imperative of equality with that of freedom. Clearly, in any society with democratic aspirations, a creative tension exists between principles of equality and principles of choice. The task of establishing a weighting between them is both difficult and controversial. There is also a tension between the necessary acknowledgement of differences and the fear of enshrining them in curriculum practice.

Educational and political control from the centre

As we have seen in South Africa, decisions about the mathematics curriculum have always been the prerogative of the state and its 'experts'. In England, a much more fluid system has prevailed. The groups competing for control of the curriculum have included examination boards and universities, professional bodies such as the Mathematical Association and the Association of Teachers of Mathematics, local education authorities and central government. Indeed, the variety which has resulted from this, and the freedom it has given teachers to experiment and innovate, has been seen internationally as one of the great strengths of English mathematics education. However, this diversity in pedagogy and practice has been interpreted by proponents of the national curriculum as weakness, and used as a justification for centralized control.

A key question we wish to address here is: who, in a democratic society, should make decisions about the mathematics curriculum? Do educational professionals have any special rights over these decisions or should they be undertaken by society as a whole? John White (1988) is unambiguously in favour of the latter on the grounds that curricular decisions are decisions about the nature of society: 'in a democracy teachers have no special rights *vis-à-vis* the whole citizenry in helping to decide this' (p. 120). This, however, begs the question of how 'society's' decisions are arrived at, and how they are transmuted into practice in mathematics classrooms. Is 'the whole citizenry' best represented through central government or through local structures, and what part should teachers play in the process? We would argue, with Jill Adler, that the challenge for greater democracy, equitable provision and growth is to establish central coordination with decentralized, local autonomy.

In England, the public acceptance of a national curriculum followed from a growing belief that teachers were both incompetent and politically suspect. The popular press encouraged and propagated these ideas, until there was a sufficient consensus that teachers needed to be controlled both educationally and ideologically. Comments from the political right, such as 'Children who need to be able to count and multiply are learning anti-racist mathematics – whatever that may be', served to fuel the fire (Margaret Thatcher, quoted in *The Times Educational Supplement*, 16 October 1987).

This attack on teacher independence was effective in part because many parents and employers did not feel comfortable with, and even distrusted, new curriculum ideas in mathematics and blamed teachers for the disruption of education as they knew it. ('These calculators are making children lazy. Nobody teaches them their tables any more.') On the other hand, critics of the national curriculum argue that allegations of teacher incompetence served to mask political manoeuvering for ideological control by the right, claiming that what is, in reality, political control is disguised as (legitimate) educational control.

Interestingly, in South Africa, the political left are arguing for a national curriculum, in part because of their concern, which they share with others across the political spectrum, about gross teacher under-qualification (see Adler's scenario 1). Indeed, Jill Adler (p. 155) comments that even under the current system, for mathematics teachers: 'the prescribed textbook and departmental schemes of work become a lifeline'. Paradoxically, direction of teachers can lead (as it has in the past in South Africa) to passive technicians who lack confidence in their own ability to make curricular decisions and to experiment with pedagogy. Critics of the national curriculum in England are concerned about precisely this – will the enforced implementation of other people's ideas lead to the de-professionalization of mathematics teachers?[6]

> The SAT was not adding to their knowledge of the children, and the procedure was making them feel de-skilled. 'I am beginning to feel like a glorified supply teacher', said [infant] teacher Kate Cairns. 'This is not my planning or my organisation. I'm just carrying out someone else's work.'
>
> *(TES, 25 May 1990)*

The problems arising from political and educational control from the centre are highlighted by the dilemmas faced by progressive educators who are committed, for example, to anti-sexist and anti-racist mathematics. Without central control, there is no guarantee that equal opportunities policies will be carried out. At the same time, the imposition of any policy (however just in essence) carries its own dangers. There is the risk that teachers and pupils will fail to internalize the central issues and will do no more than pay lip service to the imposed policies. For example, there is no guarantee that pupils and teachers working within the SMILE mathematics system, where a very strong anti-sexist and anti-racist ideology prevails, will necessarily have made these ideas their own. This disjuncture occurs, despite the exceptionally active involvement of teachers in the development of SMILE materials, and points to the need for the processes of curriculum development to be made visible to other teachers and also to pupils. A further danger is that of over-zealous monitoring of others. In this latter case, paradoxically, the enforcement of justice can lead to its erosion.

Technological and economic needs of society

The necessity for a national curriculum which stresses mathematics and technology is often justified in terms of economic needs. The sometime chairman (*sic*) of the National Curriculum Council commented:

> The pace of change ... is slow when set against the urgency of achieving the goal of a better educated, more highly-skilled nation. Britain's wealth lies in its people; to match our competitors, at least, must be our priority.
>
> *(Graham, 1990)*

It can be argued, though, that only a very small proportion of the population needs high-level mathematical and technological skills, while the real effect of new technology is to de-skill the majority. This idea is expanded upon in the chapter by Richard Noss in this volume. (See also Chevellard, 1989, and Keitel, 1989.) Elsewhere, Noss claims:

> The introduction of new technology has created a need for particular kinds of pedagogic practices – and ... for particular

kinds of socialization within schools; but this has not been in response to a direct need for increased skills. On the contrary, it has resulted in a need to de-skill the curriculum (and teachers) alongside the de-skilling of the labour process.

(Noss, 1990, p. 25)

Other criticisms of the stress on mathematics and technology focus not so much on its inclusion in the national curriculum as on the effects of an imbalance between this and other curriculum areas. This is of particular concern to those who value aesthetic education and the development of critical faculties. Interestingly, critical skills are particularly needed if citizens are to be enabled to assess the use and abuse of technology and to consider whether a particular economic or social problem is appropriately tackled by means of technology.

Our discussions and analysis have brought to light a number of paradoxes and dilemmas facing mathematics educators. Essentially, these are philosophical questions arising from a clash of principles where, inevitably, there are no simple rights or wrongs. Curriculum designers and politicians have to walk a tightrope between the opposing demands of central direction and democratic freedoms. A vital issue here is the extent to which choices remain possible for the educational players in the context of a nationally imposed mathematics curriculum. It is to this that we turn in the next section.

Choices and real choices

It is a feature of nationally imposed mathematics curricula that they tend to limit choices. We would suggest that the extent to which this happens depends on (a) how easy it is to opt out of the system, (b) what proportion of mathematics time must be devoted to the curriculum, (c) the pervasiveness and perceived importance of assessment, and (d) how prescriptive the curriculum is in terms of content, pedagogy and materials.

Within the state system, mathematics is a core subject. While the overall volume of assessment at age seven is being reduced from that originally proposed, assessment in mathematics remains. Recently, further reduction of the statutory demands at key stage 4 of the national curriculum[7] was announced – but mathematics remains a requirement for all pupils to age sixteen. Opting out of the system is possible, but only for those who can afford to pay for private schooling, where, although compulsory mathematics remains the norm, there is a greater degree of flexibility. For pupils within the state system, there is no choice at all. Private schooling appears to offer a choice, but it is not a real choice for the majority of the population.[8]

As previously discussed, the volume of content in the mathematics programmes of study means that the possibility of innovation and experimentation is severely curtailed. When this is combined with assessment at ages 7, 11, 14 and 16, with results to be published and league tables drawn up of schools and local authorities,[9] the effect is a gross reduction of choice. Critics have suggested a sinister underlying motive for over-full curricula and excessive examining, namely as John White (1988) puts it, 'Indoctrination is basically to do with preventing reflection'. He continues, 'by filling school timetables with safe subjects, by determining much of the syllabuses to be covered, and by focusing teachers' attention on getting pupils through national tests, preventing thought about fundamental values is a much more feasible task' (p. 121).

Jill Adler proposes (p. 162) that a core mathematics curriculum should 'enhance all learners' critical faculties and hence their effective participation in civic life'. There is a growing international debate about the use of mathematics as one vehicle for enabling pupils to develop the critical abilities necessary for full participation in the political life of their society. (See, for example, the writings of Frankenstein, 1989; Evans, 1990; Lee, 1990.) We would argue that 'mathematics for critical citizenship' has little chance of being developed and debated under the circumstances of the English national curriculum.

Although the curriculum is clearly prescriptive in terms of content, it appears to be less so in terms of pedagogy and curriculum materials. On further examination, however, it becomes clear that pedagogy will inevitably be restricted by the demands of assessment and by the time available to teachers in which to explore new ideas and approaches. The requirements of assessment will also drive the development of curriculum materials. The apparent variety of materials on the market may, on analysis, be found to mask a growing uniformity.[10]

In this section, we have shown that there are few real choices for mathematics educators and pupils under the national curriculum for England. It is very difficult to opt out of the system or to include any curriculum content other than that prescribed. The demands of assessment also constrain both pedagogy and curriculum materials, thus further limiting the autonomy of individual schools and teachers.

Concluding remarks

We have seen how the desire for a national curriculum can arise from groups both on the political left and the political right, and have drawn out three key arguments employed by those who espouse a national curriculum. These are arguments based on justice and equality, educational and political control from the centre, and the technological and economic needs of society. While we acknowledge the very real motivations underlying the drive towards national curricula in particular contexts, we believe it crucially important also to emphasize the equally real problems associated with their implementation.

A frank analysis of the issues surrounding national curricula inevitably throws up a series of dilemmas and paradoxes. We have highlighted and discussed some of these in the context of mathematics education. We would argue that there is no easy resolution of these difficulties and that, as Isaiah Berlin (1969) comments, when situations result in a 'clash of values at once absolute and incommensurable, it is better to face this intellectually uncomfortable fact than to ignore it' (pp. xlix-l). Our discussions in this chapter show that it is vital to uncover the implications of a national curriculum and to provide a forum for open and thorough debate, if democratically acceptable compromises are to be found.

Notes

1 Interestingly, the national curriculum for England also applies (with differences relating to the Welsh language) to Wales, but not to Scotland or Northern Ireland, each of which have, none the less, introduced their own. Nor does it have effect in private schools. This has raised many questions about how 'national' the national curriculum really is.

2 Noss (1990, p. 24) comments: '… long division has not been imposed because anybody thinks it is useful … it certainly will not be of assistance in the dole queue but it might just help the pupil to know his or her place. Divide and rule indeed.'

3 Note that Adler's use of the Gramscian term 'hegemony' (p. 157) is very close to our 'consensus'.

4 It is often claimed that the skills employers say they need, or the standard of education they demand, are badly matched to the realities of jobs. A similar claim can be made about the qualifications required as entry to courses in further and higher education. Mathematics often acts as a 'critical filter' in this context, even though the level of mathematics demanded may not, in reality, be needed for a particular course.

5 In general, the all-pervasiveness of the demands of the national curriculum in England, both in terms of the proportion of school time absorbed by national curriculum subjects and in terms of subject prescriptiveness, acts to limit freedoms. Can a right be said to be a right if it cannot be waived? This dilemma is parallel to, but arguably less easily resolved, than that which emerges in debates about compulsory schooling.

6 Carlson (1988) develops this idea when he refers to the de-professionalization of teachers as 'proletarianisation'.

7 Key stage 4 describes the last two years of compulsory schooling (ages 14 to 16, approximately).

8 We need to distinguish between 'opting out' of local education authority control by becoming a grant maintained school, still subject to the national curriculum, and opting out of the constraints of the national curriculum completely, which is only possible for independent (private) schools. (The law also allows for the national curriculum partially to be waived in the case of children with specific learning difficulties.)

9 Teachers', schools' and authorities' success will be measured by the outcome of the assessment procedures. Noss (1990) has argued that the national curriculum 'is about a centrally imposed and nationally validated system of grading children, schools and teachers' (p. 28).

10 Control of curriculum materials, with concomitant loss of choice, can of course occur in other ways, such as through market forces. Even before the advent of the national curriculum, one particular mathematics scheme, SMP 11–16, was being used in approximately 60–70 per cent of secondary schools despite having been initially designed by university and private school groups for high-ability and middle-class children. (See also the chapter by Paul Dowling elsewhere in this volume for a discussion of certain aspects of the SMP 11–16 mathematics scheme.)

References

Aldrich, R. (1988) 'The National Curriculum: an historical perspective' in Lawton, D. and Chitty, C. (eds), *The National Curriculum*, Bedford Way Papers No. 33, University of London Institute of Education.

Barnard, H. C. (1947) *A History of English Education*, University of London Press.

Berlin, I. (1969) *Four Essays on Liberty*, Oxford University Press.

Brown, A. and Dowling, P. C. (1989) *Towards a Critical Alternative to Internationalism and Monoculturalism in Mathematics Education*, Centre for Multicultural Education, University of London Institute of Education, Working Paper 10.

Brown, A. (1990) 'From notional to national curriculum: the search for a mechanism' in Dowling, P. C. and Noss, R. (eds), *Mathematics versus the National Curriculum*, Falmer Press, pp. 195–215.

Burton, L. (ed.) (1986) *Girls Into Maths Can Go*, Holt, Rinehart and Winston.

Burton, L. (ed.) (1990) *Gender and Mathematics: an International Perspective*, Cassell.

Carlson, D. (1988) 'Beyond the reproductive theory of teaching' in Cole, M. (ed.), *Bowles and Gintis Revisited*, Falmer Press.

Chevellard, Y. (1989) 'Implicit mathematics: its impact on societal needs and demands' in Malone J. *et al.* (eds), *The Mathematics Curriculum: Towards the Year 2000*, Curtin University of Technology, pp. 49–57.

DES (1985) *General Certificate of Secondary Education: the National Criteria – Mathematics*, HMSO.

Douglas, B. (1990) 'Tightening a strait-jacket', *The Times Educational Supplement*, 30 November 1990.

Dowling, P. C. and Noss, R. (eds) (1990) *Mathematics versus the National Curriculum*, Falmer Press.

Evans, J. (1990) 'Mathematics learning and the discourses of "critical citizenship"' in Noss, R. *et al.* (eds), *Political Dimensions of Mathematics Education: Action and Critique*, Proceedings of the First International Conference, University of London Institute of Education, pp. 93–5.

Frankenstein, M. (1989) *Relearning Mathematics: A Different Third R – Radical Maths*, Free Association Books.

Graham, D. (1990) 'The wealth of the nation', *The Times Educational Supplement*, 16 November.

Howson, A. G. (1982) *A History of Mathematics Education in England*, Cambridge University Press.

Isaacson, Z. (1986) 'Freedom and girls' education: a philosophical discussion with particular reference to mathematics' in Burton, L. (ed.), *Girls Into Maths Can Go*, Holt, Rinehart and Winston, pp. 223–40.

Isaacson, Z. (1987) *Teaching GCSE Mathematics*, Hodder and Stoughton.

Isaacson, Z. (1988) 'The marginalisation of girls in mathematics: some causes and some remedies' in Pimm, D. (ed.), *Mathematics, Teachers and Children*, Hodder and Stoughton, pp. 95–108.

Isaacson, Z. (1990) 'Is there more than one math?' in Noss, R. *et al.* (eds), *Political Dimensions of Mathematics Education: Action and Critique*, Proceedings of the First International Conference, University of London Institute of Education, pp. 127–33.

Joseph, G. (1990) 'The politics of anti-racist mathematics' in Noss, R. *et al.* (eds), *Political Dimensions of Mathematics Education: Action and Critique*, Proceedings of the First International Conference, University of London Institute of Education, pp. 134–42.

Keitel, C. (1989) 'Mathematics education and technology', *For the Learning of Mathematics*, 9(1), pp. 7–13.

Lawton, D. and Chitty, C. (eds) (1988) *The National Curriculum*, Bedford Way Papers No. 33, University of London Institute of Education.

Lee, L. (1990) 'Radical practice', *Mathematics Teaching*, **133**, pp. 55–8 (a review of Frankenstein, *op. cit.*).

Molteno, F. (1984) 'The historical foundations of the schooling of black South Africans' in Kallaway, P. (ed.), *Apartheid and Education: The Education of Black South Africans*, Raven Press.

Noss, R. *et al.* (eds) (1990) *Political Dimensions of Mathematics Education: Action and Critique*, Proceedings of the First International Conference, University of London Institute of Education.

Noss, R. (1990) 'The National Curriculum and mathematics: a case of divide and rule?' in Dowling, P. and Noss, R. (eds), *Mathematics* versus *the National Curriculum*, Falmer Press, pp. 13–32.

Singh, E. (1989) 'The secondary years: mathematics and science' in Cole, M. (ed.), *Education for Equality*, Routledge.

The Times Educational Supplement Editorial (1990) 'Let them all settle for a new set of initials', 21 December.

White, J. (1988) 'An unconstitutional national curriculum' in Lawton, D. and Chitty, C. (eds), *The National Curriculum*, Bedford Way Papers No. 33, University of London Institute of Education.

Section IV

Reflections

Section introduction

A key focus for reflection is the language we use in our field. The language used within mathematics education has both broad historical roots and is strongly related to descriptions of current practice. Fay Weldon, in *Letters to Alice*, writes of the importance of a sensitivity to words and an awareness of the historical resonances intertwined with their contemporary senses.

> You will just have to take my word for it, that the words a writer uses, even now, go back and back into a written history. Words are not simple things: they take unto themselves, as they have through time, power and meaning: they did so then, they do so now.

One commonality among all the pieces in this section is an attention to language. Geoffrey Faux offers a metaphor for thinking about the roles of teacher and curriculum coordinator – whether in a primary or a secondary school – in interpreting a national curriculum and placing it in relation to other ways of describing what it is a teacher does and might do in the classroom. Sandy Dawson, drawing particularly on the work of Imre Lakatos, offers three classroom scenarios exploring the possibility of mathematics teaching in schools proceeding by cycles of claim, justification and counter-example. Richard Noss examines the role of social forces in helping determine what place computing may take within mathematics education. He looks at why so much change has been superficial and yet sees the radical developments in technology as being likely to have a dramatic effect. Dick Tahta offers a penetrating analysis of some current practices in primary schools, drawing on historical images and calculating practices as well as the discourse and concerns of linguistics and psycho-analysis. This piece develops an entire area of important work in mathematics education between inner and outer meanings and signals how language mediates crucially between the two.

The piece by John Dewey, written in the 1930s, indicates that such reflective concerns about language in use have always played a part of thoughtful analyses of philosophical issues. He explores the possible *educational* sense of a common piece of educational folklore, 'proceed from the concrete to the abstract'. Finally, Eric Love and Dick Tahta explore some of the various senses and uses of terms employed when discussing mathematics education, attempting a version of the enterprise initiated by Raymond Williams in his book *Keywords*. Williams traced some of the shifts, interconnections and clashes of meaning among various words which partake of discussions of social concerns. Love and Tahta show some of the changing mathematical and ideological philosophies at work in the persisting discourse of teachers and mathematics educators.

16 The keeper of the map

Geoffrey Faux

I would like to start by thinking back to 1982 and the publication of the Cockcroft report (DES, 1982). The report made a considerable case for the appointment of a mathematics coordinator in each primary school. Paragraph 354, reads:

> The effectiveness of the mathematics teaching in a primary school can be considerably enhanced if one teacher is given responsibility for the planning, co-ordination and oversight of work in mathematics throughout the school. We shall refer to such a teacher as the 'mathematics co-ordinator'.

The next paragraph then lists seven large tasks which should be part of the duties of the school's mathematics coordinator. By paragraph 356, the authors are remarking that: 'It would not have been difficult to extend this list further …'. Indeed, and that is a real trap for all of us.

The Cockcroft list is included in an appendix at the end of this chapter. The trouble with any such list is that it is just too easy to get sucked into a debate about the importance of one particular item or even into reconstructing the fine detail of that item. An altogether more difficult, but worthwhile, task is to work with the essence of the job of being a mathematics coordinator, both for the person doing it and from the point of view of the other teachers in the school.

In Cumbria, the publication of the Cockcroft report was used as a springboard to appoint a team of three primary mathematics advisory teachers. In the early stages, they worked across groups of schools, teaching alongside a class teacher, introducing a variety of different mathematical activities. The concerns in the schools were often different from the concerns that the advisory teachers saw might be productive to work with. One of the most frequent traps for the advisory teachers was that of being 'the expert'. All of them had been class teachers the previous July, with all the variety and complexity that that implies. Now, at the beginning of September, they were mathematics advisory teachers and being asked, 'Which is the best scheme?' Or more bluntly, 'What do you think of Peak?', 'Can you bring in a test for my worst six?', 'What should I do about time/pounds and kilograms/ Logo?' And perhaps worst of all, they were starting to feel pressurized by me, as their mathematics adviser, saying that being an advisory teacher was not really about classroom activities – that was only the medium – the message was about working collaboratively.

Only a short time into working with the new team, we had a long and very complex team meeting when a lot of the conflicting emotions created by existing in the no man's land between the advisory service and the schools were brought out and examined. A central problem for all three Cumbrian advisory teachers seemed to be the unwritten and unspecified nature of the job. I hit on the lucky metaphor 'mathematics advisory teacher as keeper of the map'. This enabled us to share a whole range of worries and concerns linking in a host of similar statements. The map is not the territory. There are maps of mathematics, there are maps of mathematics schemes, there are maps about learning and teaching. Some of them are about *mathematics* learning and teaching. Teaching and looking at a map about teaching are complementary and worthwhile activities. And so on.

I have to confess an interest. All maps fascinate me. I will spend time with a map before going to a place and then more time with it after I come back. I think one of my fascinations is the very nature of maps. However good they are, there is always an element of surprise when faced with the real thing. It is easy to say, 'Oh, the fault is mine, I mis-read the map', and, often on a second look, 'Yes, I can see how it really is now'. But this is only part of the story. I have also got to come to terms with the limitations of a map as an instrument to describe reality.

I try hard to hang on to the idea that the map is not really what it is about, but then I suddenly notice a geological map: how does it connect under the surface? Or a nautical chart: how does it appear from out at sea where other concerns are uppermost? Or a set of historical maps comparing 1945, 1919 and 1900: when was it real? It all depends upon what we want to move to next, a stressing and ignoring of information. So I justify my passion for maps by trying to suggest that it is a way of engaging in mathematical activity. Working with maps is, for me, a very seductive activity. Maps are important, but they are only an approximation to reality. How much easier they are to work with than the real thing. This truanting from the main task may be something shared by those of us who were attracted to mathematics as an interest when we were at secondary school.

Through the advisory teachers, I suggested to a number of schools that not only should they see the mathematics advisory teachers as keepers of the map, but that it might be a very useful overall description for the job of school mathematics coordinator. This has an immediate consequence of releasing the mathematics coordinator from being the resident expert in schemes of work, working with colleagues, organizing and buying mathematics equipment, monitoring assessment and record keeping, diagnosing children's difficulties, arranging whole-staff in-service and liaising with neighbouring schools. This last list is a paraphrase of the seven items given by Cockcroft. With the idea of a keeper of maps, the list now feels to me to be a more human-sized task.

It may not yet be clear what the job of a map keeper is. Museums have jobs with titles like 'Keeper of Oriental Manuscripts', 'Keeper of Victorian China'. These are senior and important positions. The people appointed not only have knowledge and interest in their particular field, but by the way in which they develop the job, they exert considerable influence on the direction of enquiry and interest in that field.

How can this idea translate into primary school? There seem to me to be a number of parallels. Firstly, the map keeper needs to have some enthusiasm and curiosity for the territory about which she is collecting maps. Secondly, she requires enough familiarity with using a variety of maps as aids to exploring the territory to be able to offer a choice of usable maps to fellow travellers. Thirdly, she needs to exhibit a wish to be involved in determining the future direction of mathematics education (the particular territory of this set of maps), and to see that this can continue to be worked on as a local problem.

Does this idea, map keeper, have any resonance with the role of a head of department in a secondary school? My feeling is that, when I was a head of department, map keeping was not a metaphor that I would have found useful in helping me to take a look at my job 'through a different pair of glasses'. I have struggled a bit to recollect how it was. Now, with the benefit of hindsight, the best I can suggest is a group of robber barons, each protecting their own territory with an occasional sortie to conquer some that belonged to another department. I am not proud of that; that is how it was for me.

Things have moved on: secondary teachers also need metaphors to help them see the necessary division of their energies into, on one side, leading curriculum change and development and, on the other, working within the hierarchical structure of the school on behalf of their department. Something that I have found helps me with the second task of working within and around a departmental team is the idea of the *wills*, the *wants* and the *won'ts* (Faux, 1987; ATM, 1987, p. 74). What I said in the former piece was:

> There are people around who desperately *want* to be involved in change and development work; there are people around who *will* be involved given the chance; and there are people around who *won't* be involved, almost whatever you do. That is an instrument for the here and now. It is certainly not something that I would wish to write down or show anyone. I find it helpful when deciding how to use my limited energies – I work mostly with the wants and use any spare energy with the wills.

This does not, however, help me to see my role with respect to mathematics and mathematics education within the secondary school. Mathematics is a central concern of secondary mathematics teachers: perhaps what this writing offers to a secondary teacher is a view that the rest of the world (primary teachers, parents, pupils, etc.) will not be as involved in things mathematical as they are, and this is not only how it is, but how it must be.

The national curriculum as a map

A current concern of teachers in England and Wales is to implement the national curriculum (and similar items in Scotland and Northern Ireland: for the rest of this chapter, I shall refer to the one for England and Wales). It has been left unclear, some might say deliberately so, whether the national curriculum is a map or the territory. The national curriculum can only be a map; it cannot even be The Map. The trouble with this map is that hardly any teachers have any experience of either making or using a map constructed with this particular set of conventional signs.

There are clearly some much more useful maps so far as teachers are concerned. However, it is not going to be seen as a helpful response if, when asked for assistance with the national curriculum, the school coordinator offers a publisher's guide or a book of investigations. The task in hand was, after all, seen not as an exploration of the territory, mathematics education, but as a request for help in becoming familiar with a particular map, the national curriculum. It is possible to look at the introduction of the national curriculum from the point of view of the publication of a new and esoteric set of maps, not the standard Ordnance Survey ones that we are all used to and have used.

The national curriculum was developed within the structure of the TGAT report (DES/WO, 1988), which required the curriculum to be specified into ten levels in a number of distinct attainment targets. When it was published, there was both confusion and protest from the teaching profession. Some of this was based on an assumption that the map was the territory. Other, and more direct, disquiet came from people who were rightly concerned that a map that had been conceived as a structure to develop an assessment scheme was being presented as if it were a suitable map to use in describing a complete curriculum.

The underlying and not well-articulated protest was about the discrepancy between teachers' views of the land of mathematics education and this division into strip-field cultivation: ten levels in an attainment target; six or eight attainment targets in a profile component; two or three or four profile components in a subject. A good number of the teaching force were old enough to remember yards, chains and furlongs, but this did not seem the moment to mention anything so trivial. Acres of tests? Where did that idea come from?

No, the ostensible task was to become very familiar as fast as possible with this new way of mapping the curriculum and, of course, to decide during this familiarization where this particular map was going to be a help and where it was going to be a hindrance.

Advice was offered to schools about how to familiarize themselves with national curriculum documents. However, a major difficulty was the different frameworks within which the advice-givers and the advice-receivers existed. Advice was given by people who had some familiarity with the TGAT report and who had also been privy to much of the debate as the national curriculum attainment target structure was being formed. Advice was received in 1989 and 1990 by infant and secondary teachers lacking this background, but with an understanding of the structure of their classroom operation and an overview of the territory based on their use of other maps.

It is easy using the map metaphor to see now more productive ways of overcoming this particular difficulty. The curriculum ground changes slowly all the time. It always has and it always will. The national curriculum is a new map hurriedly constructed with new and untried map-making tools. If you start to use it, there will be both surprises and disappointments. There will be areas where it offers illumination, like any map, and other places where previously unmapped and difficult areas are still unmapped and still just as difficult. But notice as well those knolls, those places where distant views are now possible, where you see things that you had not noticed before. If it had been taken in this spirit, a number of useful advances could have been made. A principal one of these might have been the acknowledgement of the folly of sticking with a printed map as if it were the territory.

Looking at some specific detail of the first (1989) national curriculum map, what do we see? Attainment targets 2 and 3 are specified separately in the document. Attainment target 2 states: 'Pupils should understand number and number notation'; attainment target 3 states: 'Pupils should understand number operations (addition, subtraction, multiplication and division) and make use of appropriate methods of calculation'. What is this really about? What are the differences and samenesses here? For me, attainment target 2 is about structure, symbols and place value, while attainment target 3 is about sums and arithmetic. The Nuffield Project had made this distinction in their *Computation and Structure* books twenty-five years earlier but, perhaps because at that time much of the in-service stress was laid on the structure side of the title, Nuffield came to be seen as standing for a strong emphasis on structure and a disregard for computational competence.

The Nuffield map set out to indicate computation and structure as two complementary attributes, each working and supporting the learner's growing mastery of number. Both were valid, both necessary. The debate was and still is about whether the principal reason for teaching number is because it gives entry to a useful field, getting your sums right, or whether it gives entry to an exciting mental space where difficult questions about infinity, continuity, and symbolizing can be worked on.

It is not surprising that the national curriculum should still be hedging around and not coming down in favour of either of these camps. It is one of the comforting indicators I see that the ground that we are trying to map is only shifting very slowly. For instance, imagine what different messages would have been given if attainment targets 2 and 3 had been placed in the reverse order, computation then structure. Hidden messages are buried within the order of the attainment targets. In 1965, Nuffield judged it important to indicate that computation by itself was an insufficient basis for school number work. By 1989, the national curriculum had reversed the order and also started to indicate that structure has a much more all-permeating role by including, in the first version, an attainment target that made a direct link between number, structure and algebra. This happens just thirty years after the three separate subjects of arithmetic, algebra and geometry were pulled together to form one subject: mathematics. That lag feels comfortable in terms of the shift of the curriculum over time.

Computation or sums have to be about something. The first set of attainment targets made this more specifically part of the agenda than ever before by including attainment target 4 – 'able to estimate and approximate in number' – and attainment target 8 – 'should estimate and measure quantities, and appreciate the approximate nature of measurement'. This introduces a disturbance. Measurement has, since the 1960s, been seen as part of the infant mathematics curriculum, while at the secondary stage, there has been a prevalent feeling of 'that's all science; we can leave the messy, inaccurate stuff to the scientists'. The national curriculum map, by its layout, starts to indicate an area where there is work to do, where discontinuities exist. What happens about measurement in junior classrooms, and how will each phase respond through the nineties to the joint pressures from the science and the mathematics national curriculum documents? (See also the article by Janet Ainley in this volume.)

All the places that I have drawn attention to so far have been ones where the working party took existing practice and, by classifying it, perhaps a little differently, drew attention to what is already being taught. However, they also used the opportunity to introduce two ideas that were being worked on in some schools, but not by any means in all. These are Logo and data handling. It is an open question as to whether this technique of inserting a piece of content by drawing it in on the map will or will not be successful. Part of me wants to remark that, at the end of the story about the Emperor's new clothes, everyone noticed that the Emperor was without; but another part of me says that progress sometimes comes because we have been prepared to suspend judgement while working with new and exciting material.

Other maps

What then are some of the maps that are available to every mathematics coordinator in every school? And what could be her specific tasks as a keeper?

First, here is a list of some maps.

> **Maps for everyone** (this list changes with time)
>
> DES (1982) *Mathematics Counts*, HMSO
>
> National curriculum (mathematics, science, technology)
>
> Textbook scheme(s) and teachers' guide(s)
>
> School schemes of work
>
> **More esoteric maps** (my current list)
>
> Martin Hughes (1984) *Children and Number*, Blackwell
>
> Margaret Donaldson (1978) *Children's Minds*, Fontana
>
> Michael Armstrong (1980) *Closely-observed Children*, Chameleon
>
> ATM publications (Discussion series, Activity series, Readings)
>
> Caleb Gattegno (1987, 1988) *The Science of Education: parts 1 and 2B*, Educational Solutions
>
> Videos of children working
>
> **Boring maps** (they are seldom what they seem)
>
> Assessment – a quick guide for beginners
>
> How to remove bias from your teaching once and for all
>
> A new method in instant arithmetic

Remedial teaching: breaking your work into really small steps

Record keeping made simple

Stretching exercises for the gifted.

The classification of this list into the three categories that I have chosen is, of course, arbitrary. What one person sees as an esoteric map will be mainstream and in daily use by another. Much of teaching consists of moving forward without lengthy map-reading stops, and that is just how it should be. After all, we know the ground pretty well. As Eric Love has remarked, we deal with the samenesses in children's responses and adjust to the differences, not when they occur, but when we notice them occurring. It may be worthwhile, as an exercise, making a list of the maps that you see as essential and those that appear to be completely esoteric in nature. Then put it away somewhere, and look again in one year's time. How will you feel if there are changes? How will you feel if there are no changes?

Maps, then, are what we reach for when the going gets a bit tougher, when the ground becomes unfamiliar. This might happen when I move to teach a different age group, when the school changes its scheme, or the national curriculum asks me to report assessment in a way that is not familiar to me. The first map I want in such a situation must be good on relevant detail and not include much else. I need to re-establish my position and get my bearings. Before too long, I want to explore further, initially perhaps on my own, but quickly I want to start referring to a map with a bit more detail. Not so much as a constraint, more as a comfort that other people have been into this country before me, and that if there are any sheer drops around the corner, I have a little advance notice.

The map metaphor taken this far suggests that the keeper of the map is a job requiring a great deal of sensitivity. Most of the time, other teachers just won't need or use your maps, nor will they thank you for offering them. There will, however, be moments when they want a map and *now*! And at that point, it has to be both relevant and readable.

Appendix (reprinted from the Cockcroft report)

355　In our view it should be part of the duties of the mathematics co-ordinator to:

- prepare a scheme of work for the school in consultation with the head teacher and staff and, where possible, with schools from which the children come and to which they go (we discuss this further in paragraph 363);

- provide guidance and support to other members of staff in implementing the scheme of work, both by means of meetings and by working alongside individual teachers;

- organise, and be responsible for procuring, within the funds made available, the necessary teaching resources for mathematics, maintain an up-to-date inventory and ensure that members of staff are aware of how to use the resources which are available;

- monitor work in mathematics throughout the school, including methods of assessment and record keeping;
- assist with the diagnosis of children's learning difficulties and with their remediation;
- arrange school based in-service training for members of staff as appropriate;
- maintain liaison with schools from which children come and to which they go, and also with LEA advisory staff.

References

ATM (1987) *Co-ordinating Maths in Primary and Middle Schools: Strategies for Change*, Association of Teachers of Mathematics.

DES (1982) *Mathematics Counts* (the Cockcroft report), HMSO.

DES/WO (1988) *National Curriculum Task Group on Assessment and Testing: a Report*, Department of Education and Science and the Welsh Office.

Geoffrey Faux (1987) 'Doing nothing', *Mathematics Teaching*, **119**, pp. 2–7.

17 Learning mathematics *does not (necessarily) mean* constructing the right knowledge

Sandy Dawson

Let us eavesdrop on a classroom of eleven-year-olds. The teacher, Mr Lakatos, has the children trying to find the next number in a sequence. They are trying to find a pattern, to come up with a conjecture about how the sequence is created. They will then test their conjectures by predicting what the next number in the sequence would be, and Mr Lakatos will confirm or refute each guess, because he is currently acting as the keeper of the sequence-generating rule. The children all have calculators which they use regularly to do their maths, so the guesses they make about the sequence come in rapid fire succession.

MR LAKATOS: Can anyone guess what the next number in the sequence would be? How am I producing the sequence? 4, 16, 37, ...

JAMIE: I think the next number is 1369.

MR LAKATOS: Anyone agree with Jamie's guess? Anyone want to challenge it?

SCOTT: That can't work, because 16 squared isn't 37.

[It seems that Scott is assuming that Jamie (a) looked at only the first two numbers of the sequence, (b) decided that squaring would get the next number, and hence (c) squared 37 to get the answer 1369. So Scott provides Jamie with a counter-example to what he assumes is Jamie's hypothesis.]

MR LAKATOS: Any reaction, Jamie?

JAMIE: Not that I can say out loud!

[Titters of laughter are heard throughout the class.]

SCOTT: Is the next number 49?

[Scott seems to have focused on the difference between 16 and 4, namely 12, and the difference between 37 and 16, namely 21. He is perhaps guessing that these differences alternate. Hence, 37 + 12 = 49.]

MR LAKATOS: No!

SCOTT: Then how about 58?

[It seems that Scott *is* focusing on differences. Hence, 58 would be his next guess because 37 + 21 = 58.]

MR LAKATOS: Yes, that's right, Scott. And what would the number after 58 be?

[The sequence is now 4, 16, 37, 58, …]

SUSIE: Well, the gaps now are 12, 21 and 21. Is the next number either – let's see – 70 or 79?

[Susie is not assuming that the difference will now stay at 21. She seems to be covering her bets, as it were, perhaps by reasoning that the pattern of differences might be 12, 21, 21, 12 or that it might be 12, 21, 21, 21.]

MR LAKATOS: No, neither of those is the next number. Should I give you the next number?

JAMIE: Yeah, because I agree with Susie. I think it has to be either 70 or 79. What could it be if it isn't one of those?

MR LAKATOS: Well, it could be that the next number is 89, and it is!

[General puzzlement follows. The sequence so far is 4, 16, 37, 58, and 89. Susie, who had made a plausible case for the next number being 70 or 79, has had her pattern refuted.]

JEFF: Does it [the pattern of numbers in the sequence] have anything to do with the squaring of the numbers?

[Jeff, like Susie, is looking for patterns, not just the next correct number. The guessing of an actual number serves only to test the pattern. The pattern is the real guess, the real conjecture.]

MR LAKATOS: Perhaps!

[Mr Lakatos is not too helpful, or is he?]

SUSIE: Is the next number 120 or 102?

[Susie has many conjectures, but she is apparently remaining focused on differences between numbers in the sequence. In the case of 120, she seems to be guessing that the pattern of differences is 12, 21, 21, 31 and 31. In the case of 102, her hypothesizing appears to be 12, 21, 21, 31, 13.]

MR LAKATOS: No, neither of those is the next number. Actually, the next number is 145.[1]

[The sequence is now 4, 16, 37, 58, 89, 145, …]

The children described here are now more than twenty years old. Though Mr Lakatos was not their real teacher, I chose to give the actual teacher that name because the sessions occurred about five years after the writings of Imre Lakatos first appeared (Lakatos, 1963–4, 1976). It was from ideas contained in Lakatos' articles and book that an alternative way of working in mathematics classrooms developed. The lesson above was an early attempt to teach in this way, the so-called fallibilistic way of teaching, which has gradually gained recognition during the intervening two decades (Dawson, 1969, 1971; Lampert, 1990). The children above made conjectures, that is, reasoned guesses, and then subjected these to the test of (in this case) whether their conjectures accurately predict the next number in the sequence. Lakatos claimed that the creation of mathematics comes about as the result of a process of proofs and refutations, a process in which a conjecture is created, tested and proved, or refuted and modified, or rejected outright. A classroom environment designed to provide opportunities for pupils to operate in a fallibilistic fashion would provide pupils with a problem, a problem about which they could make conjectures as to its solution. The pupils must be allowed to guess the solution and to evaluate their proposed solutions. Opportunities to test and examine critically each conjecture must also be provided. This last provision does raise the issue of how and when guessing is a valid strategy in mathematics classrooms.

Some teachers have worried, for example, that the pupils' 'reasoned' guesses may actually be nothing more than thinly veiled, wild guesses, and that to let pupils guess in this way would be disruptive of the classroom situation, thereby making management difficult. However, this need not be the case, if the pupils are provided with the means to test their guesses. If testing procedures are available to the pupils, they are not as likely to guess in a vacuum, as it were, but will be more likely to make guesses appropriate to the testing procedure. Consequently, the testing procedure acts as a control mechanism which does not require the teacher to be the classroom disciplinarian. By the way, it is important to note that a guess is usually called 'wild' if it fails; if it succeeds, it is called 'daring'. Hence, as teachers, we must be cautious in labelling a wrong guess as being 'wild'. The pupil making the guess may have had strong grounds for making that particular guess, such as Susie had when making the guesses of 70 and 79 above, and it would be a great disservice to the pupil to be criticized unjustly for making what outwardly appeared to be a wild guess, but which actually was not. It is important to elicit reasons, that is, for pupils to offer justifications for their claims.

The fallibilistically-oriented teacher's broad curricular and instructional viewpoint is one which is concerned with pupils learning how to learn rather than with pupils learning specific material. The end result of any mathematics course should not be, according to this view, the acquisition by pupils of the ability to memorize and produce on demand a great number of facts, results, definitions and theorems. Rather, pupils should develop the skills and attitudes for attacking problems in a rational and critical fashion. A teacher who is functioning fallibilistically, like Mr Lakatos was above, establishes a classroom climate in which an atmosphere of guessing and testing prevails, where the guesses are subjected to severe testing on a cognitive rather than an affective level, and where the pupils' goal is to expand their awareness of mathematical relationships and of themselves in a situation where knowledge is treated as being provisional. Because of the provisional nature of knowledge, pupils are encouraged to confront the mathematics, their peer group, and, where appropriate mathematically, even their teacher. In this climate, there are no wrong answers, only refuted conjectures, a subtle but crucial distinction. As we saw with Mr Lakatos, the fallibilistic teacher confirms or refutes guesses, but as Ms Watt will demonstrate below, the teacher can also provide counter-examples to conjectures which pupils feel with great confidence they have already proven!

Ms Watt is working with a group of fourteen-year-old girls who are sitting around a table on which sits one computer. These pupils started using Logo a couple of weeks previously. They have made squares, rectangles and triangles. They know how to use the REPEAT command, so that the instructions of how to draw a triangle, say, can be written in one line. However, the pupils have not yet learned how to write procedures. They are working in immediate mode: when they type an instruction and hit the return key, the turtle performs it immediately, tracing the path it was directed to by the instruction the pupils typed into the computer. The pupils have been exploring the question: when the turtle goes on a trip, how much turning must it do in order to come back to its original starting position?[2] They have just drawn an equilateral triangle using the command: REPEAT 3 [FORWARD 50 RIGHT 120]. It is at that point we pick up the conversation Ms Watt is having with the girls, who have adopted the group name of the Gang of Five.

MS WATT: So, Gang of Five, how much did the turtle turn to get back where it started from?

JANICE: It turned a total of 360° – three times 120°.

MS WATT: Anyone want to challenge Janice's conclusion?

SHERRY: No, I agree with it. The turtle turns a full circle, so it has to be 360°. It doesn't matter which way the turtle is pointing when it starts, it still has to turn a full circle to get back to where it started from.

MS WATT: Okay! If it turns 120° at each corner, what is the angle inside the triangle? Not how much the turtle turns, but the size of the angle which is made when the turtle turns and makes a new side for the triangle.

DEIDRE: I don't get it! What are you asking?

MS WATT: Well, the turtle is heading in one direction for 50 steps, and then it turns 120°, and heads off in this new direction. Type this instruction for the turtle, Deidre: FORWARD 50, RIGHT 120, FORWARD 50. What do you see?

DEIDRE: Oh, I see. It's an angle.

MS WATT: And what would the size of that angle be?

DEIDRE: Let's see. The turtle heads one way, and almost turns completely around in the opposite direction. It turns 120°, so what's left?

SUE: Wouldn't it be 60°?

DEIDRE: Why is that?

SUE:	Because if it turned completely back in the opposite direction, it would have turned 180°. But since it only turned 120°, that must leave 180° − 120°, which is 60°.
DEIDRE:	Right! I get it now.
MS WATT:	So if we added up the three angles of the triangle, what would be the sum?
JEAN:	That's easy! It's three times 60°. That's 180°.
MS WATT:	Do you think that would be true of all triangles: that the sum of the interior angles of a triangle is 180°?
JANICE:	It might be true just for the triangles that have all the same angles and the same length of sides.
SHERRY:	No, it can too be true for all triangles. Look, I can prove it!
MS WATT:	Show us, Sherry.
	[Sherry draws a collection of different triangles on the chalkboard. Using a pointer placed along one side of a triangle, she shows how the pointer makes a complete rotation as she moves it around the sides of the triangle. Sherry does this for several of the triangles she has drawn, to the point that the other members of the Gang of Five tell her that enough is enough!]
JANICE:	So it doesn't matter what size the angles are – so long as they are less than 180° – the sum will still be 180°. Brill!
MS WATT:	Yes, it would seem so, wouldn't it? But imagine this. Suppose the turtle were sitting at the North Pole, and it headed off towards the Equator travelling along a line of longitude. Deidre, get the globe, will you please, and use Sherry's pointer as the turtle.
	[Deidre gets the globe, places the pointer at the North Pole directed down one of the meridians. She slides the pointer down to the Equator.]
MS WATT:	Good, now turn the pointer to the right so that it is lying along the Equator. How much of a turn is that?
SUE:	It would have to be 90°, wouldn't it? Doesn't the Equator and any line of longitude make a right angle?
MS WATT:	Do you all agree? [Heads nod in agreement.]
MS WATT:	Okay, Deidre, slide the pointer along the Equator, and then turn right back up a different line of longitude.
DEIDRE:	That would be another 90° turn?
JEAN:	I don't like the look of this!

MS WATT:	Wait a minute, Jean. Now, Deidre, slide the pointer back up to the North Pole. When you get there, turn it right again so that it is pointing back down the meridian you started down before.
JANICE:	But she has traced out a triangle ...
JEAN:	Yes, and that triangle has two right angles, two angles of 90°, and another angle of – I don't know – it looks about 30°. So the sum of this triangle's interior angles is, uh, 210°, and not 180°. I don't get this. I thought Sherry's rule worked for all triangles.
DEIDRE:	But the path I traced is not really a triangle, is it? I mean, the globe is curved.
MS WATT:	But didn't the path you traced have three sides, and three angles, and didn't you get back to where you started from?
DEIDRE:	Well, yes, but if that's true, then the total turtle trip must have been greater than 360°. But I thought you said that it was always 360°, so long as the turtle got back to where it started from – that it closed its path?
MS WATT:	Oh, yes, well Gang of Five, that is a problem, isn't it.

Central to Lakatos' view of the growth of mathematical knowledge was his contention that there are no immutable truths in mathematics, and that even mathematical proofs can be challenged, and counter-examples found for valid, deductively derived results. Sometimes, these counter-examples arise because of a change of focus, a different realm of application, such as was the case above when Ms Watt introduced a non-Euclidean triangle. She is attempting to expand the pupils' conception of triangles, and acquaint them with spherical geometry. The pupils are excited and animated in response to Ms Watt's ploy and seek to discredit the situation she has put forward as a purported example. On the other hand, they also seem to realize that the path which Deidre followed does, in fact, generate a triangle in some sense, and hence they have a dilemma. In his work on the foundations of mathematics, Lakatos cites many instances where the growth of mathematical knowledge was fostered by mathematicians coming up against just such dilemmas. The behaviour of the Gang of Five, then, is very mathematical in nature, and totally consistent with how mathematicians challenge and expand their own mathematical understandings.

Teaching mathematics in a fallibilistic way is, therefore, derived from the contention that there are no immutable truths in mathematics. Consequently, pupils learn how to investigate unknown terrain in mathematics, not with the goal of finding truth, but with the desire of obtaining an ever-improved map of the terrain. In attempting to chart the unknown terrain, pupils may be guided by their teacher, but they are not given the complete map. Indeed, from a fallibilistic orientation, such a map[3] is not available, not even to the teacher. A teacher working in this Lakatosian tradition allows pupils to create, revise and expand their own mathematical maps. This teacher aids pupils by putting forth conjectures and counter-examples which focus their attention on specific points of the map. This is contrary to what happens all too often in maths lessons where the teacher attempts to give a complete map of the mathematical terrain to all pupils, and then gets upset when the pupils do not 'learn it'. Each pupil's map of the mathematical terrain is incomplete and basically idiosyncratic. After all, any map is incomplete, and is not and cannot be the terrain! Learning mathematics does not mean constructing the right knowledge, as no one is sure what that knowledge is.

Finally, join me in watching as a visitor, Dr G, to a primary school classroom works with a group of children seated around a table (Gattegno, 1970, 1974). There are three nine-year-old boys (Marty, Arthur and Dick), and two ten-year-old girls (Janet and Cecelia). Dr G has told the classroom teacher that he wants to try something out with the children; namely, he wants to see if they can find the difference between two eighteen-digit numbers, if they can do this entirely as a mental calculation, and if they can write the answer down from left to right and not right to left as is usually done. The lesson begins with the children using Cuisenaire rods to make trains as per instructions given by Dr G. Let us listen in on the ensuing conversation.

DR G: Make one train composed of a pink rod and a blue rod, and a second train of just a dark green rod, like this.

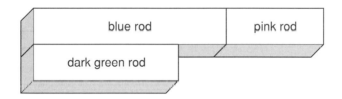

DR G: Which rod would fit onto the end of the dark green train, so that the two trains become the same length?

MARTY: Well, it sure ain't the white rod! Nor is it the orange rod.

CECELIA: Be serious, Marty! I think it is the brown rod.

MARTY: I am being serious! What I said is true, isn't it? Anyway, I don't think the brown rod will work. It's too long – try it!

[Cecelia tries the brown rod, and finds that indeed Marty is right – the brown rod is too long.]

JANET: The black rod will fit exactly. It is a white rod shorter than the brown one, and that is how much too long the brown rod was.

[Janet tries it, and the black rod is, in fact, the one which fits.]

DR G: Now watch what I am going to do.

[He places a yellow rod on the end of each train, so the trains now look like this.]

yellow rod	blue rod	pink rod
yellow rod	dark green rod	

DR G: Which rod would fit onto the end of the yellow plus dark green train, so that the two trains become the same length?

DICK: It hasn't changed. It will still be the black rod.

ARTHUR: That's right. You can keep adding as many rods as you want to the left end of the two trains, so long as they are both the same colour, and it'll still be the black rod which makes the shorter train the same length as the longer train.

DR G: If that is true of trains of rods, is it also true of numbers?

JANET: I don't understand what you mean?

DR G: Pick two numbers. Find the difference between your numbers. Keep that in your mind. Have you got it? [There are nods of agreement from the children.] Now, add seven to each of the two numbers you started with, and find the difference between these new numbers. Is this difference the same as the one previously?

JANET: Yes, right! I get it. Do you get it, Marty?

DR G: What if we were taking coaches off the trains instead of adding them on? Would the difference in the length of the two trains still be the same?

CECELIA: Yes, that wouldn't make any difference to the difference! And the same would be true for numbers.

JANET: Oh, I get it. Look, I can write something like this.

24 –	subtract 5 gives	19 –	subtract 7 gives	12 –
20	subtract 5 gives	15	subtract 7 gives	8

In all cases, 24 – 20, 19 – 15, 12 – 8, the difference between the two numbers is 4.

DR G: Look at these differences.

40 –	$\rightarrow$	39 –		400 –	$\rightarrow$	399 –		4000 –	$\rightarrow$	3999–
26	$\rightarrow$	25		268	$\rightarrow$	267		2674	$\rightarrow$	2673
14		14		132		132		1326		1326

MARTY: So?

DR G: So, can you subtract 678456234123 from 800000000000 in your head and write the answer down from left to right?

DICK: Eh! That's too hard! You'd have to do all that borrowing, and you have to start on the right, not the left.

ARTHUR: Wait a minute! I'm not so sure. Let me write it down.

800000000000–
678456234123

If we subtract one from each of these numbers, we can write them as

799999999999–
678456234122

and hence we can write down the answer from left to right.

121543765877

JANET: So, we *could* do it without writing it down. Just think of it as subtracting one from each number. All the zeros change to nines, except the leftmost digit of the top number. And the rightmost digit of the bottom number decreases by one. Now, we subtract the bottom numbers from all those nines … it's easy!

DICK: Yeah, right, so if we start with something like five followed by a bunch of zeros, and subtract 234345456567678789, we'd get …

CECELIA,
MARTY: (together) 265654543432321210. Hooray! We couldn't do that on our calculators!

JANET: But what happens if the one number isn't composed of all zeros? Would we still be able to find the difference and write in down in this way?

DR G: Try it and see, Janet. Can you find a counter-example which would refute the pattern we have here?

Janet is fallibilistic to the end, is she not? Of course, Dr G has led the pupils along a particular path, in a quasi-deductive fashion in order to lead them to a certain conclusion. In a Lakatosian sense, the result obtained in this example is deductively generated; that is, the pupils made a series of observations and drew conclusions from them with the result that they could eventually generalize the pattern which allowed them to find the difference successfully between the two eighteen-digit numbers. Though one may not wish to call such a derivation a proof, it certainly falls into the classification of convincing argument. (For further discussion of what thirteen-year-old pupils think proofs are, see Balacheff, 1988.) However, Janet is ever ready to challenge this result, and Dr G encourages her to attempt to find a counter-example. This epitomizes fallibilistic teaching writ large!

So I invite you to try a few fallibilistic lessons of your own. The sources listed in the references all give examples of mathematical topics which can be approached fallibilistically. Try being Mr Lakatos, or Ms Watt, or Dr G, and see whether the pupils in your mathematics class become as excited and animated as the children described above.

And, oh yes, do try to find the difference between a couple of twenty-digit numbers tonight before you doze off. Do it in your head, and when you get up in the morning, write the answer down from left to right! Or if you prefer, take a flight on a globe like Deidre's, but start on the Equator. Can you fly around a rectangle? Start by flying north on a line of longitude, but stop short of the North Pole. Make a 90° right turn onto another great circle. Fly on again and then make another 90° right turn onto a third great circle and fly on. Can you make a 90° turn at some point and still be heading home, back to where you started? If so, study the fourth angle you get on returning to your starting-point. Is it also 90°? Or is it less than 90°? Or greater than 90°? And what is the sum of the interior angles of this quadrilateral?

Sweet dreams!

Notes

[1] For those readers who have not already *guessed* the pattern which creates the sequence, the complete sequence is 4, 16, 37, 58, 89, 145, 42, 20, 4, and then the sequence repeats. Each term is obtained by summing the square of the digits of the previous number; thus 145 produces 42 because $1 + 16 + 25 = 42$.

[2] This question gives rise to the 'total turtle trip theorem', or the enclosed path theorem, which states that the total amount of turning the turtle does in travelling along a closed path back to its original starting-point is a multiple of 360°.

[3] This imagery is explored further in the chapter by Geoffrey Faux in this volume, entitled 'The keeper of the map'.

References

Nicholas Balacheff (1988) 'Aspects of proof in pupils' practice of school mathematics' in Pimm, D. (ed.), *Mathematics, Teachers and Children*, Hodder and Stoughton, pp. 216–35.

Sandy Dawson (1969) 'The implications of the work of Popper, Polya and Lakatos for a model of mathematics instruction', unpublished doctoral dissertation, University of Alberta, Edmonton, Canada.

Sandy Dawson (1971) 'A fallibilistic model for instruction', *Journal of Structural Learning*, **3**(1), pp. 1–18.

Caleb Gattegno (1970) *What We Owe Children: the Subordination of Teaching to Learning*, Outerbridge and Dienstfrey.

Caleb Gattegno (1974) *The Common Sense of Teaching Mathematics*, Educational Solutions Inc.

Imre Lakatos (1963–4) 'Proofs and refutations', *The British Journal for the Philosophy of Science*, **14**, pp. 1–25, 120–39, 221–45, 296–342.

Imre Lakatos (1976) *Proofs and Refutations: The Logic of Mathematical Discovery*, Cambridge University Press.

Margaret Lampert (1990) 'When the problem is not the question and the solution is not the answer: mathematical knowing and teaching', *American Educational Research Journal*, **27**(1), pp. 29–63.

18 The social shaping of computing in mathematics education

Richard Noss

In his book *Mindstorms*, Seymour Papert (1980) points to a future in which the 'computer presence' will act in such a way that schools 'as we know them today' will have no place. His rationale is essentially psychological: in Papert's view, the 'artificial' and 'inefficient' learning environment of the school is a response to the impoverishment of informal (extra-school) environments. Papert's vision is of a world where much of the formal instruction which takes place within school will be accomplished 'painlessly', and 'without organized instruction' through interaction with suitably designed computer environments.

It is a mere ten years since Papert proposed his vision, a period which is, in my view, much too short to determine whether his revolutionary predictions are likely to be realized. In mathematics education, and on a more modest scale, there is evidence that understandings of some formal mathematical notions such as ratio or algebraic variable *are* influenced in quite fundamental ways by interaction with the kinds of computational environments envisaged by Papert. This work has spanned a decade of research, and has employed a variety of methodologies from within a broadly psychological perspective. As an example, a recent study (Hoyles, Noss and Sutherland, 1991) clearly indicates that experience within a carefully constructed 'microworld' can reveal and build pupils' mathematical intuitions, as well as develop a language for representing these intuitions. In addition, it appears that when pupils approach mathematical problems which they express in computational terms (in this case, using Logo), they develop strategies which differ significantly from those employed in a paper-and-pencil setting.

More generally, I claim that computer-based environments potentially offer pupils the opportunity to test out and make robust intuitive mathematical ideas: my image of the computer[1] is as an intellectual resource for encouraging pupils to express mathematical ideas (not necessarily 'correct' ones), to explore problems and make explicit existing and implicit intuitions of the mathematics embedded in situations. The computer can mediate between two distinct discourses: *everyday* activity, where mathematical fragments are *used*, and *school mathematics*, where the emphasis is on reflection and *understanding* of formal relationships. Evidence for these assertions, as well as a reasonably comprehensive overview of the state of play in relation to research, can be found in Hoyles and Noss (1991).

My approach in this article is other than psychological. I would like to explain why, despite the large-scale introduction of the computer into many (though far from all) classrooms in the 'developed' world, schools show little sign of withering away as a result of the computer's entry onto the educational stage. From a mathematical perspective, there are few indications of any serious reappraisal of the content, rationale or methodologies involved in mathematical education as a result of the computer's introduction. In fact, there are signs – especially in the US – that the computer as an educational device is seen as having run its course, much like the video recorder or the overhead projector.

In order to make sense of this relative lack of impact on the educational scene, I need to draw on sociological analyses of technological change, and to examine the specificities of mathematical learning from a perspective which ranges beyond the strictly mathematical domain: in doing so, I raise some broad questions about the nature of mathematics and its relation to technology.

I begin by briefly outlining the position in UK schools as I see it. Essentially, the situation in general is little different from that characterized by Pam Linn a few years ago: 'as currently used, the microcomputer in school is nothing but an electronic workcard, blackboard, calculator or drawing block '(Linn, 1987, p. 313). This depressing picture might be thought too pessimistic, especially as the intervening years have at least witnessed the introduction of a small number of potentially interesting programs into the educational domain. Yet primary schools certainly contain a considerable number of computers which remain largely (or even totally) unused. Those that are used are employed in a variety of roles which include 'computer literacy', games, drill, and 'problem solving'. Mathematical uses incorporate most, if not all of these; in addition, a substantial number of classrooms use Logo as an elementary geometrical program, or simply as an exercise in enjoyable computer interaction. In secondary schools, the situation is complicated by the tendency to ghettoize machines into laboratories where they are used for 'computer studies', and by the widespread use of limited 'packages' for the teaching of specific curricular content. Only a minority of mathematics classes have routine access to a computer, and only a tiny fraction to more than one.

I am aware that I have grossly oversimplified the position, and have ignored some of the interesting and innovative work currently taking place by individual teachers. (See, for example, some of the thoughtful snapshots of mathematical classrooms reported in *Micromath*.[2]) Nevertheless, whatever the exact situation, it is clear that the reality of computer use in schools and in mathematics classrooms is seriously adrift from the vision which Papert proposed.

Before I go any further, I should like to lay to rest one possible (and popular) attempt at explaining this state of affairs: namely, that it is all 'the fault' of teachers. Suppose, for a moment, that this were true – what would it mean? It would mean that a 'pure' innovation – the computer – had been 'perverted' (either intentionally or unintentionally) by the practitioners who used it. Even if this view could be sustained, we would still need to know how and why this perversion had taken place, unless we were content simply to blame teachers' general incompetence (even then there would be something to explain). The point is simply that the 'teachers' fault' view is totally lacking in explanatory power. (Other, more fundamental, criticisms of this view will become apparent later.)

In fact, the ways in which teachers, computers and mathematical learning interrelate are extremely complex. For example, in a recent study with a number of secondary school mathematics teachers, Noss, Hoyles and Sutherland (1991) showed that teachers' attitudes and approaches to using computers constructively were shaped by an intricate web of interacting themes, which included a tendency to project personal learning styles onto their pupils, a range of sometimes conflicting motivations, disparate views of mathematics and subtle distinctions in their approach to mathematical pedagogy. I will return to the teacher's role below.

An outline framework for conceptualizing technological change

I will outline three strands of thought which set out to conceptualize technological change, as I need a more general theoretical framework for understanding what is actually happening (or not happening) in mathematics classrooms, and my analysis of the computer's role is in the context of the relationship between mathematics and technology in general (see the next section).

The first strand attributes to technological artefacts some degree of autonomy in the process of educational change. For the optimists, technology is seen as solving all educational problems, and the evidence is there, residing on the disc, or in the resolution of the screen. For the pessimists, there is simply not *enough* technology: it is too expensive, it is too primitive. This *technological determinist* view is routinely deployed to explain processes (which range far beyond those in education) with which to theorize changes in society, and forms the basis for many 'popular' accounts of history. For example, when I was training to be a teacher, a nameless tutor asserted that the collapse of the Roman Empire was due to the Romans' failure to develop a number system based on place value! By suggesting that the computer *itself* may have the power to revolutionize education and/or society, technological determinists propose that the technology is constituted independently of those who use it. In mathematical education, it is routine to encounter findings which claim to have observed 'effects' of 'the computer' on children's learning; such accounts almost always ignore the settings in which the computer is employed, the social interactions among children, computer and teacher, and broader questions of the nature and purpose of the computer's presence in the educational arena. (See, for example, Pea and Kurland, 1984.)

A second way of thinking about technological change involves a focus on the *distribution* of technology. For example, as far as educational computing is concerned, Michael Apple (1987) has demonstrated a clear link (in the US) between social class, gender and race and how computers are used in schools: he shows that the number of computers is substantially greater in middle-class schools than in working-class schools. Paul Olson (1987) points to a marked tendency (again in the US) for the children of the middle class to use open-ended applications and to learn programming, while schools in working-class areas tend to rely on mechanical drill programs and games. I am unaware of any studies which have investigated the position specifically in relation to mathematics education, but it is not too far-fetched to speculate the existence of a corresponding pattern.

The third approach derives from a perspective which suggests that the very notion of 'the technology' is problematic. In an educational setting, the challenge is to examine how the notion of, say, *the computer* is constructed by teachers and learners, to focus on the meanings evoked by it and the ways in which it functions as a set of *cultural symbols*. More generally, viewed from this perspective, the individual 'user' of a technology is seen as socially constructed: actual use is governed by the ways in which the user 'reads' the set of cultural signs which constitute the technology. This approach – that technology is socially rather than technically *shaped* – provides a helpful way of thinking about computers in (mathematics) education, and I return to it below.

My purpose in outlining these three strands of thought is to transform elements of them into a discussion of a specific curricular area – that of mathematics. More precisely, I want to consider how the specific technology of the computer enters into the teaching and learning of mathematics in schools. So I will begin by specifying those elements which I want to preserve in my transformation.

It seems to me reasonably clear that something like the same divisions which Apple and Olson discuss exist in the UK. Not surprisingly, the specificities of these divisions are likely to be different: after all, the educational systems of the UK and the US are not equivalent (for example, some of the best-equipped schools in the UK were, at least until recently, in inner London – hardly an area noted for its affluence). However, I am concerned to look beyond questions of what or how much hardware or software children use.[3] My interest centres on *how* software is used, the relationship between the computer (simplistically considered as the sum of hardware and software[4]) and the mathematical learning which is (or is not) taking place. Consequently, I have little alternative but to focus on the nature of the computational technology itself, how and why it is designed, and how it is produced: I want to emphasize *production* rather than *distribution*.

I therefore suggest that the ways in which the computer is deployed in mathematics classrooms is important, but this should not obscure our interest in the ways in which the computer is shaped, and the forms and functions which the computer is made to assume in practice. Saying this lays me open to the charge of technological determinism, and it is certainly the case that discussion of the design and nature of the computer runs the risk of focusing on technology at the expense of the social issues involved. Nevertheless, technological determinism implies more than simply 'concentrating on technology'. It implies first that technological change takes place autonomously, outside of the intricate networks of social relationships, and second, that it is change in technology that determines social or educational change.

This last element is crucial: there is no sense in which I am arguing that any particular form of hardware or software will determine the way in which mathematical learning and teaching develops. But, at the same time, it is equally futile to suggest that the unfolding of educational innovation is independent of that technology. Without the introduction of mass printing, western education systems would necessarily look very different. That is not to say that mass printing determined the form or content of education: only that its role can fruitfully be examined as an element in the educational system, and that it makes sense to ask questions about the role it played in influencing the nature of what is taught and how.

The mathematical–technological relationship

I have argued elsewhere that the relationship between mathematics and computing is potentially special (Noss and Hoyles, 1991): that is not to say it demands privileged status, only that there are specific and interesting questions to be asked about the relationship. It will help to consider the relationship between mathematics and technology in general as well as that between mathematics and the computer seen as a particular form of technology. Two questions which emerge are:

- How is mathematics incorporated into technology in general, and into computer software in particular?
- To what extent can mathematics be usefully distinguished and accessed from the technology into which it is inserted?

The answers to these two questions will, I hope, allow me to consider what pedagogical implications follow for the uses of computers in mathematics education.

Conventional wisdom asserts that as mathematics enters increasingly into the objects and relationships of everyday life, the amount of mathematical (and technological) knowledge needed by children in general will increase. In fact, the reverse is true. I take it as axiomatic that almost nobody uses mathematics beyond elementary arithmetic in their daily lives; and, at the same time, as mathematics 'enters' into daily use through technology, the need for individuals to gain access to that mathematics – or indeed the ease with which they can do so – diminishes (see Chevellard, 1989; Keitel, 1989). More and more people will need less and less mathematical/technological know-how: fewer and fewer will need more and more.[5] This analysis relies heavily on the work of Harry Braverman (1974), who amply demonstrates the critical role that technology has played in the de-skilling of the labour process (particularly since the second world war): I have outlined some of the implications of this analysis for mathematics education in Noss (1989).

The drive towards technological sophistication is essentially a drive to substitute human labour power by machines. This is not, of course, unique to the technological 'revolution' of the post-war era; it is a fundamental tendency of our economic system, and one which was pointed out and analysed in considerable detail over a century ago by Karl Marx. In Marx's terminology, machines embody dead labour – in contrast with the living labour which the worker brings to the production process. The introduction of technology is the substitution of living by dead labour, thus increasing the productivity of the workers who remain. It is the need for ever-increasing productivity which drives the system towards higher and higher levels of technology.

Marx's distinction between dead and living labour has been fruitfully explored in the context of computers in education by Linn (1987), and by Dowling (1991) who extends the distinction to include dead *mathematical* labour. Following Chevellard (1989), I want to harness this metaphor to discuss the ways in which mathematics is incorporated into computational media.[6] There are two definitions which will help. First, I define the *density*[7] of mathematics incorporated within a technology – a measure of how much of the dead labour it embodies is mathematized: *mathematics per unit of dead labour*. Consider, for example, a chip. The process by which the chip is programmed is essentially mathematical, so much so that we might say that *all* of the programming is constituted by mathematical labour power. But the chip is made from (among other things) silicon; silicon has to be obtained and purified using machines, some of which themselves incorporate dead mathematical labour. These machines are, in turn, created using a variety of technologies. This process is, in theory if not for practical analytical purposes, infinite, and (as Chevellard points out) recursive. Whatever the exact proportion, we can see that the density of dead mathematical labour in a chip is high: for a pen, it is relatively low.

It should be clear that the density of mathematics within a technology is *socially* – not just technically – determined: that is, the ways in which mathematics is deployed in the construction of a new technology is largely tied to choices and decisions which involve social and historical, not just technical, issues. However, the notion of density is not sufficient to provide any answers to the second question I posed above: once the mathematics is 'in' a technology (or program), how easy is it to gain access to it?

It will help to define a second construct, the *depth*[8] of mathematics within a technology – a measure of how near the surface of that technology the mathematics is. How easily may the mathematics within it be uncovered, reflected upon and interpreted? How effectively can it be – to use Gerdes' (1986) rather different metaphor – unfrozen? A washing machine incorporates within its chips a surprising amount of mathematics. It is mathematically dense. But that mathematics is also deeply buried: to view that mathematics would be extremely difficult, even supposing that one had access to other technologies which would permit any kind of access to it at all.

The depth of mathematics is similarly socially determined. Mathematics is not a fluid which can be poured into a technology in a unique way. It is perfectly feasible to postulate – somewhat schematically – that the same quantity and quality of dead mathematical labour can make up a technology in ways which substantially differ in terms of their depth. As far as mathematics education is concerned, I will argue below that the question of how deeply mathematics is buried in computers has critical implications for pedagogy.

There are two general corollaries which follow from this analysis and which I will briefly consider before returning to the theme of mathematics education. In the first place, it allows us to make some sense of claims that 'technology is increasing' or that the (first) world is becoming 'increasingly mathematized'. It is. But that does not of itself tell us much about how that mathematics enters directly into social relations. In fact, I postulate an inverse relationship – in general – between density and depth. This relationship – which I will call the *invisibility principle* – is a corollary of the drive to replace humans by machines in the productive process, to de-skill and routinize the jobs which remain in order to bring them into line with the increasingly demanding economic and ideological needs of the productive system.[9] In this scenario, density without depth not only poses an expensive option, it poses an option which fundamentally cuts across the intentions behind the introduction of the technology itself.[10] Thus, dead mathematical labour can be used to *control* living labour: as Joseph Weizenbaum (1984) points out, calculation – especially hidden, inaccessible, buried calculation – can be used to replace judgement and control.

Second, it allows us to consider the structure and use of computer software *without* lapsing into the view that the computer – by its very nature – carries with it particular (and undesirable) pedagogic practices. As an instance, consider the following claim.

> Implicit in the microelectronic technology of computers is a particular form of education and a specific set of educational objectives. This educational package only appears to be a 'program', to be used or dispensed with at will. In fact, under the surface of the computing device, it is wired in as surely as are the microchips, formatted into the actual disks, motivated by the actual drives. It is a function of the very *microelectronicity* of the computer, carrying all of the thickness of connotation acquired through word and deed over the centuries by the physical, mathematical, and engineering sciences.
>
> (Broughton, 1984, p. 115)

This is primarily a failure to distinguish between the way the computer works and the way it is used. From the perspective I have outlined, Broughton fails to distinguish between the dead labour encapsulated within the computer, and the living labour which – to borrow Marx's phrase *breathes life* into the centuries of physical, mathematical, and engineering sciences.[11] Broughton correctly locates the mathematically dense nature of the computer. He would be right, in some sense, to talk of mathematics being 'wired in' to the chips, discs and drives. But paradoxically, and this is where the confusion lies, that mathematics is very deep. It is not the mathematics we encounter when we routinely interact with a computer.[12] The mathematical or quasi-mathematical material we interact with is precisely *not* that which is put there by the programmer, but derives from the user's interactions with it.

The social shaping of technology

I will remain a little longer at the general level of technology, before I attempt to draw the implications for mathematics pedagogy in the next section, and consider the balance between living and dead mathematical labour 'within' computers. This balance is not arbitrarily defined and so I need first to consider how technologies are shaped, how social forces interact with their evolution.

I begin with an example. While writing this article, I discovered to my cost (literally) that monochrome film now costs almost twice as much to be developed commercially as colour. When I asked for an explanation, I was told that this was because 'the machine has to be set up specially'. This is despite the considerably simpler process and cheaper chemicals involved in monochrome processing. Presumably, this technological change signals the end of mass black-and-white photography. Moral: the ways in which technologies develop have comparatively little to do with the inner logic of that technology and are much more related to the social forces under-pinning the production (and distribution) process.

But that is not all: such changes reinforce the view that photography is 'about' reproducing reality as 'faithfully' as possible. From this perspective, colour is *better*, because it is closer to reality, a more faithful representation of what is photographed. (I do not discuss the truth of this assertion, I only claim that it is one among many possible views of photography.) And so there is a dialectical relationship between the way in which the technology evolves and the ideas (or ideologies) which it gives rise to (and which in turn shape the technology). The social and economic spheres shape the development of the technology, and *simultaneously* legitimize particular views of what the technology is about.

This perspective is a variant of what has become known as the 'social shaping of technology' perspective. This approach focuses on the construction, design and development of technologies from the perspective of the network of social forces and interactions on which design is based, and which crucially shape the invention/production process.

There are numerous debates and issues which arise from this perspective (see, for example, the collection by Mackenzie and Wajcman (1985) and the helpful review by Mackay and Gillespie, 1989). From my point of view, the most important element of the argument is the possibility it opens for *alternatives*. Monochrome photography does not *have* to go out of existence; computers in schools do not *have* to become tools for developing managerial skills in the few; mathematics education is not doomed to an endless diet of increasingly (un)intelligent tutorial systems (in various guises) or well-intentioned 'investigations' which result in the further fission of an already fragmented learning domain. Of course, changing such patterns of development involves all kinds of difficult social, economic and political dimensions which are beyond the scope of this chapter. Nevertheless, it is to the potential for change that I now turn.

The computer in mathematics education

The development of programming languages is an interesting instance of social shaping. There are several hundred programming languages in existence, each formally equivalent to any other (in the sense that each can be reduced to the native machine code of the computer on which it runs). But this formal equivalence masks considerable disparities in the ideologies surrounding each language (or its 'culture'), and these are in no small part related to the purposes for which they were *designed*. For example, Ada is a computer programming language developed and used for missile guidance. There are, as the reader can imagine, some rather stringent requirements for such a language, not least that programs can be *proved* mathematically to be correct before they are run. This is an extreme example of a language developed for a specific function, which has given rise to associated *computational ideologies* involving planning, structure and proof.

But this kind of intentionality is not essential. The story of BASIC, for example, is a supreme example of a programming language whose associated computational and mathematical ideologies developed unintentionally – though none the less strongly.[13] I have pointed to some of the specificities and effects of these ideologies elsewhere (see Noss, 1986) and I do no more than simply list some of their elements: the view that programming is linear, and has to be planned in advance;[14] that elegance can be legitimately sacrificed for efficiency;[15] that programming is essentially numerical; that it is an individual rather than collaborative task. Reciprocally, these ideologies feed back into the language itself: through the ways BASIC 'does things', the kinds of programs which are shared (and not shared) and the culture which is propagated through magazines and books.

The point is that programming languages are structured in particular ways which shape and are shaped by particular ideologies and cultures. In fact, this is a feature of computer software in general, although the case of languages is particularly clear as they provide an expressive medium which offers a broad canvas on which ideologies can be painted. In order to home in on the point at issue – the computer in mathematics education – I now return to the programming language Logo.

Logo is mathematically dense. In this, it is not unique. But it is an interesting observation in two distinct yet related aspects. In the first place, some (but not all) of that mathematics is buried relatively near the surface. For example, consider the way in which the elements of differential geometry have been incorporated into the turtle's behaviour. Second, the pupil is able to add to the mathematical density of the software (by writing his or her own programs), *without* a corresponding increase in depth. I will examine these claims a little more carefully.

There are two types of dead mathematical labour embedded in Logo considered as a piece of software. Type 1 labour consists of the programming language itself, the code which makes FD 50 move the turtle forward 50 steps: this is essentially uninteresting from our point of view. Type 2 labour consists of the mathematical structure of the language, for example, the differential geometry of the turtle and the functional programming structure it inherits from LISP, which views a program as a collection of mathematical functions which can be applied to arguments and composed with other functions. But, just like any device, this dead mathematics needs to be brought to life by living, 'type 3' mathematical labour – the commands and programs (I shall not distinguish between them) which 'activate' the type 1 and 2 mathematical labour in the system.

Logo is mathematical because mathematical objects can be captured in symbolic form (by living mathematical labour) and thus be reflected upon (see Noss and Hoyles, 1991, for an argument that Logo programming is essentially a mathematical activity). But this is not an arbitrary event. It arises because of the way that living mathematical labour 'breathes life' into the (type 2) dead mathematical labour embodied in the language. When a pupil enters the classic program for a square (REPEAT 4, etc.), she or he is able to add mathematics to the system in a way which mirrors the mathematical structure of the square, and in a way which is directly accessible to manipulation and generalization. This is why, incidentally, it is simply too easy to argue, as many writers have, that 'children can do wonderful mathematics with the worst software'. The dead mathematical labour cannot be activated by itself, but its design crucially shapes the living activities that can be undertaken with it.

But the converse is also true: the mathematics embedded 'in Logo' needs living mathematical labour (pupils in mathematics classrooms, perhaps) expressing mathematical ideas. Thus, we are led inevitably to consider the classrooms in which Logo is used, and the teachers who use it. And from the analysis I have outlined above, it is clear that we can have few expectations about what 'Logo' or 'the computer' might do or not do in such situations. The computer (I am deliberately slipping from 'Logo' to 'the computer' as I see the former as very much a paradigm for the latter) offers something mathematical only in so far as pupils express themselves mathematically with the language. The point is that this kind of activity is determined by what counts as mathematics in the classroom – it is *not* determined by the structure of the Logo system itself.

Let me give an example. In our research on mathematics teachers' attitudes towards curricular change with the computer (Noss, Hoyles and Sutherland, 1991), we report the case of Bob, a teacher[16] who saw his role as a mathematics teacher predominantly as a deliverer of the curriculum: he was happy to subordinate his own personal mathematical preferences to the constraints of the mathematics scheme he was using. Bob became committed to new ideas he encountered while working with us in strictly *personal* and *utilitarian* terms (for example, on being introduced to the idea of recursion, he commented that it was 'quick and simple' – but did not then or subsequently draw any pedagogical implications or possibilities for the classroom). For Bob, the computer was – indeed it *had* to be – a means to an existing end. And this, of course, implied that he was unwilling to cede serious control to his pupils, to engage them with new possibilities for mathematical expression which the computer might offer.

The point here is that the computer had to fit into Bob's practice. He constructed it as a device that matched his own culture – it is unrealistic to think that the computer could have reshaped or determined it. That is not to say that such radical reshaping is impossible: the mathematics embedded as dead mathematical labour in the computer *might* act as a catalyst for change, but only if the main focus of attention is on the kind of (living) mathematical activity which it is appropriate for pupils to undertake and how that mathematics forms part of the social and pedagogical priorities of the classroom, the school, and the (national) curriculum.[17]

Let me conclude by returning to the main question of the article, to try to explain how events are unfolding in relation to Papert's vision. From the educational point of view, software allows knowledge to be encapsulated directly into the device,[18] and (potentially, at least) to allow it to be brought back to the surface. I speculate that the interesting computer applications for mathematics education are precisely those which, while being mathematically dense, allow the learner to *add* density in a shallow way (sticking with Marx's metaphor, we might say that the learner constructs his or her own *mathematical capital*).

What do such computer environments look like? We have a few to use as pointers, and as I have said, Logo is perhaps a paradigmatic example. I think that they are *informal* in the sense that they allow, even encourage, playful and goal-less activity (in this, they differ substantially from 'tools'). They allow a medium for articulating half-formed fragments of ideas which can be cohered into concepts (a good, non-mathematical example would be a word processor). They allow access to different representations (like the visual and symbolic representations in turtle graphics). They allow entrance to a range of cognitive styles.

If, as I suggest, the most interesting educational potentialities of the computer in mathematics education (and beyond) are characterized by their capacity to *informalize the formal*, they stand in essential opposition to the social objectives of schooling, which are precisely to privilege formal discourses at the expense of informal ones. Thus, if we attempt to construct the computer as a malleable, expressive medium in mathematics (or elsewhere) within the curriculum, we run into a difficulty. Those practices which fit most readily into the school setting are formal, hierarchical and subject-bound. In contrast, the educational power of the computer lies in its potential for environments which are informal, richly interconnected and which blur subject boundaries. It is not surprising, therefore, that one resolution of the difficulty is precisely to (re)construct the computer as a mechanism which is little more than a delivery system for existing pedagogic practices; we should not be surprised to discover that the computer is routinely used to formalize rather than informalize children's learning.

Is there, then, any hope for change? I have made it clear that change is dependent on the social and pedagogical, rather than the technical. But the technical does not emerge from thin air, and educators have as much right as any to attempt to influence the course of (educational) technological development. The industrial sociologist, John Mathews (1989), has suggested that certain sections of industry are moving towards a 'post-Fordist' view which challenges the assumption that 'it is most productive to vest intelligence and control in technical systems, and treat workers like donkeys'. He suggests that the notion of computers acting on behalf of workers is being superseded by the construction of computer systems which work alongside them, allowing the latter to exercise traditional craft skills and to exercise certain (restricted) forms of control over their working practices.[19] In pointing to the contradictions in the process of de-skilling demonstrated by Braverman, Mathews argues that the social shaping of technology may be beginning to change the relationship between humans and machines in the workplace.

Might there be implications in the educational domain and in particular for the teaching of mathematics? One example is a shift in some ways congruent with the contradiction outlined by Mathews, the recognition by researchers in artificial intelligence that it is much easier to get a computer to play chess, than to recognize the faces of a solid object. I am referring to the process described by Marvin Minsky who asserts that the things that people find easiest are precisely the things that they have forgotten how to do. Thus, the project of AI to deliver 'intelligent tutoring systems' is constrained by the difficulty of getting the technology to work, as much as by the fundamental limitations of thinking of sophisticated learning as if it can be 'tutored'.

Working through the implications of this and similar shifts seems to me to be a major project for research in the coming period. There are, however, two which I can outline here. First, serious attempts are being made to develop computational media which transcend the notion of application programs (or even 'user interfaces'), and which are specifically designed for educational use (see, for example, the work on BOXER by diSessa, 1988). For mathematics, these might begin to move us into the arena of expressive media which can genuinely allow learners to use the computer as a writer uses a word processor; as media which can express and build mathematical and trans-mathematical ideas.

Second, there are hardware considerations. We should not underestimate how far our current conception of the computer's mathematical role is determined by the sheer unwieldiness and immobility of the machine; just how much of our thinking about the computer is overshadowed by the apparent 'need' for networks, computer 'labs', network 'managers', etc.? The demise of the plug[20] will allow us (*allow*, not *force*) to re-evaluate the relationship between pupil(s) and computer, and to restructure the way we conceive of this relationship in the educational setting.

By suggesting that change is possible in education, that new software and hardware can be designed which will map alternative futures for mathematics education, I know that I have run the risk of being accused of technological determinism. But I argue that the computer is not 'just another technology'; we can reject technological determinism, without lapsing into the view that the computer is incapable of bringing anything radical (or progressive) to the educational setting, or that technological change will necessarily engender pedagogical change. I do not want to suggest that any of these alternative futures would solve, or necessarily even raise, the crucial range of social, political or pedagogical issues which will need continually to be addressed. But it might at least be a start.

Notes

1 I am slipping into the inevitable shorthand which suggests that 'the computer' – by itself – has its own effects. I hope to redress this in this chapter.

2 *Micromath* is a journal of the Association of Teachers of Mathematics.

3 This does not mean that such disparities are not interesting. A recent article in *The Times Educational Supplement* (1 February 1991), discussing a new governmental report (*Technologies for Teaching*, by the Parliamentary Office of Science and Technology), reveals that there is a '10-fold variation in the number of computers available per pupil in schools, even within the same LEA'. Typically, the article, headed 'Britain "loses world lead" in computers', only discusses the number of machines available (in comparison with, for example, the US), not what they are used for.

4 This distinction is rapidly outliving its usefulness.

5 I am grateful to Michael Young for pointing out that this remark is more contentious now than it once was, as some writers have forwarded the thesis that there is a 'high-tech' future for the capitalist system. I touch on this possibility in discussing the work of John Mathews later.

6 The following paragraph owes much to Chevellard's (1989) formulation, which I read after I had begun to draft this article. His reference to Marx's distinction between living and dead labour is largely implicit, and the language I employ is slightly different.

7 Chevellard calls this the *grade* of the device.

8 This is more or less what Chevellard refers to as *visibility*. The difficulty with his term is that mathematics is *never* visible, it never exists independently of reflective thought. On the other hand, I am aware that 'depth' connotes something more than distance below the surface. This connotation is not altogether unfortunate: *deep* mathematics is, apart from anything else, always difficult to uncover. (Interestingly, this is often so when the result is 'obvious': for example, every closed curve in the plane partitions the plane into three distinct regions – an inside, an outside and the curve itself.)

9 The invisibility principle helps to explain why workers in the field of 'ethnomathematics' exclusively deal with unsophisticated technologies, such as the construction of fishing nets. This is *not* to debase such activities: on the contrary, I think it is a mistake to assign value to such activities on the basis of their mathematical density. The point is that these kinds of 'unsophisticated' technologies generally incorporate mathematics – however dense – in a shallow way, near the surface of the technology, where it is relatively straightforward to gain access – a point of considerable educational importance.

10 *Intentionality* does not imply some kind of overarching conspiracy. On the contrary, I would argue that this process has its own dynamic drawn from the nature of economic and social demands of the system(s) which gives rise to it.

11 It is also a mistake of *level*. To argue the inevitable connotations evoked by the computer of 'hard', 'scientific' 'microelectronicity', is to argue that the playing of a violin evokes the connotations of the farmyard – connotations evoked by the horses who donated their hairs to the bow and the cats who offered their guts to the strings. The issue is how the form and function of technology are moulded by the social interactions that give birth to them.

12 Of course it might be, if our routine interaction included assembler or systems programming.

[13] Interestingly, BASIC was at the time conceived as the 'people's language' in contradistinction to FORTRAN.

[14] My favourite example is a sign I once saw hanging in a school 'computer lab' which read: ALL PROGRAMS MUST BE WRITTEN OUT ON PAPER BEFORE USING THE COMPUTER.

[15] A nice example of this is a teacher who took great pride in inserting comments into his programs, and took care to program in what passes (in BASIC) for a modular style, but who admitted: 'I always strip all that stuff out before I actually run it!'

[16] In fact, this was a *composite* character based on a cluster of teachers with similar attitudes (see the final report of the project).

[17] For more on the national curriculum and its constraining influence on the learning and teaching of mathematics, see Dowling and Noss (1990).

[18] Morris-Suzuki (1984) refers to software as 'the ultimate commodification of knowledge'.

[19] An example: something like 70 per cent of plane crashes are directly attributable to pilot error. This is in no small part due to the fact that, for example, on a flight from London to Bangkok, the pilot is in control of the plane for something like eight minutes. Most of this eight minutes is spent just so that the pilot can keep in practice, rather than being demanded by the technology which can also control take-off and landing automatically. Apparently, aeroplanes are often flying with their entire flight crew asleep, and it is not uncommon for planes to overshoot their destination in this state.

[20] Just before writing this, I was amazed to read of a *portable* SUN 'sparc' workstation. This may not be surprising when this volume is published!

References

Apple, M. (1987) 'Mandating computers: the impact of the new technology on the labour process, students and teachers' in Walker, S. and Barton, L. (eds), *Changing Policies, Changing Teachers*, Open University Press.

Braverman, H. (1974) *Labor and Monopoly Capital*, Monthly Review Press.

Broughton, J. M. (1984) 'The surrender of control: computer literacy as political socialization of the child' in Sloan, D. (ed.), *The Computer in Education*, Teachers College Press, pp. 102–22.

Chevellard, Y. (1989) 'Implicit mathematics: its impact on societal needs and demands' in Malone, J., Burkhardt, H. and Keitel, C. (eds), *The Mathematics Curriculum: Towards the Year 2000*, Science and Mathematics Education Centre, Curtin University.

diSessa, A. (1988) 'Social niches for future software' in diSessa, A., Gardener, M., Greeno, J., Reif, F., Schoenfeld, A. and Stage, E. (eds), *Towards a Scientific Practice of Science Education*, Lawrence Erlbaum Associates.

Dowling, P. and Noss, R. (1990) *Mathematics versus the National Curriculum*, Falmer Press.

Dowling, P. (1991) 'A dialectics of determinism: deconstructing Information Technology' in McKay, H. Young, M. and Beynon, J. (eds), *Understanding Technology in Education*, Falmer Press.

Gerdes, P. (1986) 'On culture, mathematics and curriculum development in Mozambique' in Hoines, M. J. and Mellin-Olsen, S. (eds), *Mathematics and Culture*, Caspar Forlag, pp. 15–41.

Hoyles, C. and Noss, R. (eds) (1991) *Learning Mathematics and Logo*, MIT Press.

Hoyles, C., Noss, R. and Sutherland, R. (1991) *The Ratio and Proportion Microworld*: report of the *Microworlds* project (vol. 3), University of London Institute of Education.

Keitel, C. (1989) 'Mathematics education and technology', *For the Learning of Mathematics*, **9**(1), pp. 7–13.

Linn, P. (1987) 'Microcomputers in education: living and dead labour' in Scanlon, E. and O'Shea, T. (eds), *Educational Computing*, John Wiley.

Mackay, H. and Gillespie, G. (1989) 'Extending the social shaping of technology approach: ideology and appropriation', available from the Dept of Behavioural and Communication Studies, Polytechnic of Wales.

Mackenzie, D. and Wajcman, J. (eds) (1985) *The Social Shaping of Technology*, Open University Press.

Mathews, J. (1989) *Tools of Change: New Technology and the Democratisation of Work*, Pluto Press.

Morris-Suzuki, T. (1984) 'Robots and capitalism', *New Left Review*, **147**, pp. 109–21.

Noss, R. (1986) 'Programming and mathematics – is small really beautiful?', *Micromath*, **2**(1), pp. 26–9.

Noss, R. (1989) 'Just testing: a critical view of recent change in the UK mathematics curriculum' in Clements, K. and Ellerton, N. (eds), *School Mathematics: the Challenge to Change*, Deakin University Press.

Noss, R., Hoyles, C. and Sutherland, R. (1991) *Teacher Attitudes and Interactions*: report of the *Microworlds* project (vol. 2), University of London Institute of Education.

Noss, R. and Hoyles, C. (1991) 'Looking back and looking forward' in Hoyles, C. and Noss, R. (eds), *Learning Mathematics and Logo*, MIT Press.

Olson, P. (1987) 'Who computes?' in Livingstone, D. et al. (eds), *Critical Pedagogy and Cultural Power*, Macmillan.

Papert, S. (1980) *Mindstorms*, Basic Books.

Pea, R. and Kurland, M. (1984) 'On the cognitive effects of learning computer programming', *New Ideas in Psychology*, **2**(2), pp. 137–68.

Weizenbaum, J. (1984) *Computer Power and Human Reason: from Judgement to Calculation*, Penguin.

Acknowledgements

I would like to thank Paul Dowling, Celia Hoyles, David Pimm and Michael Young for their comments on earlier drafts of this paper.

19 Understanding and desire

Dick Tahta

You may have glanced at the picture on the opposite page as you began to read this chapter. It is worth looking at again now, for I want to offer various ways of interpreting it before I come eventually – after some lengthy digressions – to make some comments about the learning and teaching of mathematics at the present time.

The picture is often used in histories of mathematics to illustrate the spreading use of Indian–Arabic numerals in medieval Europe. It comes from a woodcut in one of the earliest printed books, the *Margarita Philosophicae* – 'The Pearl of Philosophy' – by Gregor Reisch. First published in 1503, this book was a popular encyclopedia of arithmetic, geometry and astronomy which had run into sixteen editions by the end of the century. The three characters shown in the picture are conveniently labelled, so that it is easy to start interpreting the scene. The presiding woman is *Typus Arithmeticae* – 'The Spirit of Arithmetic' – representing one of the seven liberal arts of the classical curriculum. Below her, on her left, is Pythagoras, performing some calculation by manipulating counters on a board marked with lines. The other figure, at whom she appears to be looking, is Boethius, a sixth-century Roman philosopher, who is writing out a calculation in the 'new' numerals.

It is tempting to interpret the scene as a contest between old and new methods of calculating; and this is the way the picture is usually presented. Some commentators have even taken Pythagoras to be frowning as Arithmetic casts her favourable glance at his seemingly triumphant rival. But, as I shall try to show, there are some ambiguities in the picture that suggest something more complicated than just a simple binary opposition between successful innovation and defeated tradition. Moreover, as I shall suggest later, these ambiguities seem to me to be still at the heart of current problems in the teaching of mathematics.

Pythagoras as abacist

Like any text, Reisch's picture can yield many rich layers of meaning as you study the details and look at some of the context. It is worth focusing on each of the characters in turn: I shall start with Pythagoras. Schoolchildren now know this legendary Greek mathematician's name for the geometrical theorem usually ascribed to him. But in classical and medieval times, he was known mainly for his theories about number, and for having found how musical notes are related by whole-number ratios.[1]

The theoretical arithmetic of the Pythagorean tradition had nothing to do with the numerical calculation that might be required in daily life. It was concerned with the nature of number. Thus, numbers could be even or odd, they could be prime or composite, they could be triangular, square, or some other shape. These properties could be illustrated figuratively by representing the numbers by piles of stones, but it was not the material content (*hyle*)

221

of the pile that was important, but rather its quality or form (*eidos*). In contrast, what the Greeks called *logistic* was usually said to be concerned with actual things being counted and with the ways numbers of things are combined.[2] In this context, numbers were more 'concrete' than the abstracted entities we usually consider them to be today, even though in daily usage, people still operate with numbers as amounts of different units – 'two' may be at one moment two knives and at the next two pennies.

Medieval thought preserved some of these distinctions – as indeed we still do today. On the one hand, there was the Pythagorean tradition of arithmetic, with its later accretions of numerology and magic, and of schoolroom exercises. On the other, there were the actual calculations required in the home and the market-place. These were carried out, as they had been in classical times, with counters arranged on rows drawn or carved on a counting board or table (Greek *abakion*, whence 'abacus', now usually just referring to a small, hand-held version). A person skilled in the use of the counting board – the abacus – was called an *abacist*. Use of the board became widespread in Europe; it remained a standard feature of commercial offices for some centuries, and shops still sell goods 'over the counter'.

It is not clear why Reisch cast Pythagoras as an abacist. The intellectual and artistic traditions referred to Pythagorean arithmetic, which was far removed from the bank clerk's logistic. It may be that the link was made through the arrangements of pebbles said to have been made by the Pythagoreans to illustrate the *eidos* of a number, whether it is even or odd, or square, and so on. It may even be that a more sophisticated scholastic point was being made. The rows of the counting board embody the notion of place value in a concrete form. A counter is a thing, but number is a concept – or what was classically called a 'universal'. But the nominalists – followers of the fourteenth-century thinker, William of Occam – had argued that whereas some words refer to objects, universals were 'terms of second intention' that pointed to other terms and not to things.[3] The new numerals were, for nominalists, like the word 'unicorn': that there was such a word did not mean that there was a corresponding thing. Perhaps Pythagoras was being invoked in a traditionalist defence against what was perceived to be a nominalist heresy lurking behind the new numerals.

This speculation may be merely fanciful. But the activity of the abacist certainly raises some crucial questions about meaning and reference. We are so used to conjuring up numerals when we think of numbers that it is difficult to know what might have gone on in the mind of the abacist. The problem here is not unlike that of trying to imagine what it was like before people learned to read silently. To do this, you have to repress the sound while internalizing its meaning. The abacist had no need to repress the action of combining things and did not need to internalize any numerals. The manipulation of counters on the board could be fairly 'mechanical', until the final interpretative act of saying the result, or writing it down in whatever numeration system was being used.

It was, of course, a more sophisticated procedure than herding cows together or sweeping pebbles into a single pile. The counters were already 'signifiers', able to 'stand for' different amounts. The same counter placed on one row 'signified' ten, on another a hundred, and so on. Thus, in the picture, the abacist is about to bring together a group of counters that may be read as one thousand, two hundreds, four tens, and one unit, whether these are taken separately or thought of as a single collection (1241 in our notation). This group is perhaps about to be combined with the second group which may be read as one fifty – the counter in the space below the hundreds row – three tens, and two units (corresponding to the LXXXII of Roman notation). It is simplest to assume that the two amounts are about to be added or subtracted. But abacists had developed rapid and accurate ways of multiplying and dividing as well.

The problem – as anxious merchants or, later, fussy pedagogues pointed out – was that you were left with no record of the actual calculation. There was no way of finding and correcting any mistakes, other than repeating the whole thing. This was perhaps the main reason why the use of the Indian–Arabic numerals, which had appeared in Europe much earlier, spread very rapidly after the invention of printing in the fifteenth century. Reisch's book had sections on calculations with the new numerals as well as with counters. These numerals had already arrived in Europe by the tenth century when Gerbert – later Pope Sylvester II – used a form of them to label counters of the abacus which he was held to have invented. These marked counters – known as *apices* were then taken to represent that number of counters with which they were marked. Though the method was cumbrous – since counters were not now interchangeable and 'carrying' was not automatic – it was an early attempt to turn the new numerals into objects.

Boethius as algorist

Meanwhile, the Arabs had developed various ways of calculating directly with numerals and these were described by Leonardo Pisano (called Fibonacci) in his *Liber Abaci*, published in 1202. This book was enormously influential; over the following two centuries, it set the style and content for most of the practical textbooks describing the new methods of calculating. These methods were called *algorisms*, or *algorithms*, and a person who calculated directly with these new numerals in the manner recommended by Fibonacci was called an *algorist*.[4]

It took many years for the methods of the algorists to be widely accepted. People were very suspicious of these 'transparent symbols', particularly of the zero, for which there had been no need before and which was easily mistaken for a 6 or a 9. A Florentine statute of 1299 decreed it illegal to enter amounts of money in the new numerals, requiring them instead to be written out 'in letters'. Even in the fifteenth century, a French writer was still grumbling about the zero: 'Just as the rag-doll wants to be an eagle, the donkey a lion, and the monkey a queen, [the zero] puts on airs and pretends to be a digit'.[5] At one level, the zero is a 'signifier' that points to an absence – of coins, counters or whatever. At another, it is a nominalist 'term of second intention', pointing to other signifiers, giving them a value – as in 1200, for example – different from that which they have on their own.

It is just as difficult to get a feeling for the mental state of the algorist as it was in the case of the abacist. How to work with written numerals is still a difficult problem for pupils, and indeed for those who try to teach them. We can only speculate what it must have been like for people in earlier centuries. It must have been very difficult to break from the habit of manipulating objects and then labelling the outcome. On the other hand, there had been some tradition of working with written numerals, in that there were times when Roman numerals could be deployed directly in a way that directly mimicked the manipulation of counters. Thus, you can process the sum of MCCXLI and LXXXII directly without laying them out with counters. The letters have a physical individuality and can be concatenated directly with some replacements for 'subtractive' forms like XL and some simple substitutions such as C for LL, and so on.

It is possible that the new numerals were seen as vivid images that 'stood for' amounts of counters, coins, or whatever, but which could be worked on – 'manipulated' – in a direct way. This work had to be internalized. But the algorist still made marks on paper that echoed previous methods. For example, removal of counters would be replaced by the crossing out of numerals and the writing in of others above them. The resulting array was often embellished in a fanciful way, as in the first example from a sixteenth-century manuscript. 'Scratch' methods continued to be used for a long time.

The second example (on the previous page) of a scratch division comes from an eighteenth-century textbook. Here, the intermediate steps in calculation have more of a physical 'presence' than in present-day condensed methods.

A scratch method seems to be being used by the algorist in Reisch's picture, but it is not clear what calculation is being carried out.[6] It seems equally mysterious – or arbitrary – that Reisch cast Boethius in the role of an algorist. For apart from his stoical philosophy written while he was in prison, this Roman was mainly known for his transmission of the Pythagorean theory of proportions, in particular its use in music theory. His attitude to music was highly theoretical: the real musician knew the harmony of the celestial spheres, the mere performer was a servant. As he put it: 'Physical skill obeys like a handmaid, while reason rules like a mistress.'[7]

Boethius was the main source for the medieval accounts of the theoretical Pythagorean tradition. His unexpected and unlikely role as an algorist in Reisch's illustration is ignored in the text, which presents arithmetic in two parts. These were the so-called 'speculative' arithmetic, which was a direct summary of Boethius, and a separate section on 'practical' arithmetic, which included a brief account of the new methods of the algorists as well as a traditional treatment of computation using counters. Speculative arithmetic was of no interest to merchants and bankers. But practical arithmetic, whether carried out with counters or pen, was of no interest to Greek or Roman philosophers, and it remains surprising that Pythagoras and Boethius were cast as practitioners, and supposedly opposing ones at that.

The Spirit of Arithmetic

What about the third character in Reisch's tableau? Does the personification of Arithmetic also turn out to have ambiguous characteristics? If you suppose that she favours the algorist, there is certainly a curious inconsistency with her appearance on the title page (below), where she is seated in the front between Grammar and Music and identified by a counting board!

But it is more interesting to consider the numbers seemingly embroidered on her skirt; note the rotated forms for 4 and for the 7 in 27.

This arrangement of the powers of 2 and 3 was known as a *lambda* figure, after the Greek letter Λ. It was derived from a passage in Plato's *Timaeus*, describing the creation of the 'soul of the world' by a separation of the series 1, 2, 3, 4, 8, 9, 27 into two branches and the insertion of means in the resulting intervals. This had been linked with Pythagorean arithmetic and music theory by a first-century writer, Nicomachus. Renaissance writers derived the details from Boethius whose influential and widely read work was largely a transcription of Nicomachus; the lambda figure appeared in various contexts.[8]

The figures of Pythagoras, Plato, Nicomachus and Boethius were often portrayed together, as in the illustration from a medieval manuscript (shown below). The Pythagorean tradition is invoked by each of the three figures in Reisch's illustration, which could be seen as a disguised index to the contents of the book. Though the *Margarita Philosophicae* was a practical compendium with, for instance, a detailed discussion of various contemporary weights and measures, it does seem that its author allowed himself the occasional hidden message for those in the know. The educated cognoscenti would easily recognize that the classical philosophers and Arithmetic with her platonically embroidered skirt were really all of the same mind – one of pure reason and of intellectual insight uncluttered by actual physical objects or indeed by mental images. The musical harmony of numbers was not meant actually to be played but rather contemplated. The cultivation of pure reason required the suppression – indeed, the repression – of earthly desires and connections.

The new numerals were associated with the market place and remained mainly the concern of merchants and bankers for some time. But they were at least a step away from the material reality of counters, coins and the actual material goods and physical labour that lay behind them. This distancing – a shift of the signifier away from the signified – is a characteristic feature of the subsequent development of mathematics. Meanwhile, if the algorist were competing with the abacist, it was for the favours of commerce; Arithmetic loitered in the cloisters for some time. It was under the patronage of capitalism that the new arts of practical arithmetic flourished. By the fifteenth century, there was a stream of printed textbooks spreading the new techniques to all the rapidly growing commercial centres of Europe.

The new numeration system, with its seemingly mysterious zero, meant that you could keep accounts in tidy and manageable columns, even when you may have still preferred to process them with counter rather than pen. The rivalry between algorist and abacist was not so much about notation as about how you calculated – and whether you could get more students to attend your classes and buy your textbooks.

Numerals

At the start, the new numerals must have felt very much like the old Roman numerals that had been used to label collections of counters or coins. For Fibonacci, '25' was not all that different from XXV; both replaced – 'stood in for' – five single strokes together with two bundles containing ten strokes. The Roman numerals were more or less abbreviations of tally marks. They invoked a specific number of specific things – gold coins, bales of wool, bags of spices, and so on. But like the bills of exchange and the promissory notes that soon began to supplement – and sometimes replace – coinage, the new numerals began to take on an abstracted life of their own. Numbers were now no longer the classical 'multitudes'. They were more general and began to include elements – such as the unit or the negative – that had previously been excluded. There is no such thing as number as such – only number worlds. And the 'number world' of the sixteenth century was quite different from that of medieval and classical times.[9]

Numerals were – and often still are – held to 'represent' numbers that are supposed to have some reality independent of their representation. This distinction between numeral and number is unfortunate, and can often be the source of much confusion in the teaching of arithmetic. Access to the 'numbers' supposedly represented by the new numerals can only be through symbolic operations on paper. Unless, that is, substitutes are offered like the counters, blocks or rods provided in classrooms. But in this case, of course, the access is to the number world of the abacist and the problems of the algorist may still have to be tackled.

T: But what does it mean this five? [long pause – then picks up matchstick] Is this five?

R: No, it's a matchstick.

T: Well, what's five then?

R: [takes five matchsticks and makes a numeral 5]

Even though the new numerals might have been processed at first almost as if they were counters, they soon developed a less tangible meaning of their own in the world of the algorist. What does '25' mean? According to Wittgenstein, words gain meaning by the ways they are used in relation to other words. 'Twenty-five' is not just a name like 'Fido'; it does not refer to some platonic object, but takes its meaning from its use in language. In the same way, the meanings of mathematical signs – like 25 – need to be found in the way they are used and not in some supposed 'essence' that they might be thought to represent.[10]

A similar shift of awareness may be found in art. The classical theory of representation held that pictures were copies – Wordsworth's 'mimic sights that ape / The absolute presence of reality'. This was attacked in a vigorous and amusing way by the surrealist painter Magritte. The pictures shown below speak for themselves – it is worth lingering over them a while.[11] 'Ceci n'est pas une pipe', says the caption to the painting of a pipe. And '1 is not One', adds the Platonist. But if there are many number worlds, there are various ones, and one (!) of these social, cultural artefacts may indeed be 1. As has been already suggested, this 1 gains its meaning and significance from its relation with the other digits and from the rules that govern its use in a particular social practice.

228

Metaphor and metonymy

Discussion of the relation between words and things, or words and concepts, has been taken up in modern linguistics in various ways. As with any specialized discipline, this work has its particular technical language in which it is easy to drown. But there are some notions that can be particularly useful when considering some of the issues about meaning and reference that have, I hope, been raised by the historical digression into medieval arithmetic. Thus, the contrast between the abacist and the algorist corresponds in a very informal way to the two dimensions of language that were described by Ferdinand de Saussure earlier this century, and taken up later by Roman Jakobson.[12] These have been named after certain figures of speech in classical rhetoric, namely *metaphor* and *metonymy*. I propose linking these with the abacist and the algorist respectively, and will consider these two dimensions briefly in turn with this association in mind.

Metaphor is defined in grammar as the figure of speech in which a name or description is transferred (Greek *metapherein*, 'to carry across') to something to which it is not usually applied. In contemporary linguistic terms, it creates meaning by substituting new descriptions that have been selected through some link of similarity. When you 'balance' both sides of an equation or 'manipulate' one, and when you 'carry' a digit in an addition, you use physical actions as metaphors for what you do with strokes of the pen. Metaphor is intrinsic to any communication of meaning. It pervades our language and thought, so much so that it can soon become automatic and unnoticed like the spatial metaphors that lie 'behind' most of our thinking – as in this very sentence. Another example of such a 'frozen' metaphor is the equal sign '=' chosen by the sixteenth-century mathematician, Robert Record, because 'no 2 thynges can be moare equalle'. Various metaphoric connections are implied when numbers are substituted for counters, counters for coins, or coins for labour. In particular, numbers are *like* counters in some ways. Counters can become metaphors for numbers; the abacist – who is after all the 'counter' – may be associated with metaphor.

Jakobson described metaphor as a 'vertical' axis or plane of language. Part of this spatial metaphor (for metaphor!) came from Saussure who had expressed the signified/signifier pair as a fraction. The bar of the fraction provided an image for the separation between the components that Saussure wanted to emphasize; in general, signifiers are arbitrary and only function within certain agreed social practices. But the substitution of signifiers through some perceived similarity of meaning invokes a 'vertical' crossing of the bar of the fraction. This vertical axis has also been linked with Freud's notion of *condensation*. This mechanism of the unconscious refers to the way in which our dreams, for example, are shorter and more compressed than their verbal descriptions. In psychoanalysis, symbols – such as the Phallus or the Breast – are condensations of very much more extensive thoughts and feelings; for example, the first symbol may condense – according to context – such elements as father, law, dominion, power, mastery, hardness, rigidity, independence, separation; while the second symbol may condense mother, nourishment, container, withholder, power, oppression, softness, dependence, merging, and so on.

In mathematics, symbols such as $\sqrt{2}$ and $\sqrt{-1}$ can also be powerful condensations of some primitive feelings: they are called 'irrational' and 'imaginary', and these names are significant despite denials by mathematicians that the ordinary meanings of these words are relevant. But – more straightforwardly – to call either square root a number is to make – metaphorically – a condensation of a lengthy chapter of mathematical history.

Metonymy is a more elusive figure of speech, in which something is referred to by the name of some aspect or attribute; literally, it means a change of name. Some typical examples of metonymy are found in phrases like 'pass me Shakespeare' (the author for the work), 'I'd like a glass' (the container for the contained), 'serve the Crown' (the symbol for what is symbolized), and perhaps most universally in the various ways in which people are referred to by their genital parts (part for whole). Linguists have described the common element in these various usages as substitutions of words linked by contiguity. This link may be an actual 'neighbourhood', as in the phrase 'a bottle of Bordeaux', where the wine is named by the district in which it is made. Or it may be contextual in the literal sense, as when a note follows another in music, a shape lies beside another in abstract art, or when mathematical symbols are brought together in equations. In effect, the equivalence notion in mathematics is metonymic when it is interpreted as 'is another name for'. The algorist manipulating numerals in the course of a calculation may be seen to be making a sequence of metonymic substitutions. But notice the frozen metaphor in the use of the word 'manipulating' which will be referred to again.

$$123-45-67+89$$

$$=98-76+54+3+21$$

$$=1+23-4+5+6+78-9$$

The contiguity of context in metonymy implies that it operates 'horizontally' across adjacent signifiers; one obvious example is the left to right sequence of letters you are at this moment reading. This axis has also been linked with the psychoanalytic notion of *displacement* – another mechanism of the unconscious producing verbal diversions, 'disavowals' and indirect representations by metonymic substitution. Examples include so-called slips of the tongue: 'in loving memory of Mother who has departed this life and left us in everlasting peace'; the *double entendre*: Hamlet's 'May I lie in your lap … do you think I meant country matters?'; and schizophrenic speech: 'suicide is jumping to a conclusion'. Similar shifts occur in dreams; the image or word that appears in a dream may arise from a sequence of metonymic substitutions. But some of these may have been repressed, so that it is not always easy to uncover the unconscious wish that may be the latent content of the dream. What does the dream 'really' mean? As in the case of numerals and numbers, the issue is again whether 'essence' can be knowable. According to the psychoanalyst Jacques Lacan, there is a 'metonymic residue which runs under the chain of signifiers, an indeterminate element, which is at once absolute, but untenable, a necessary and misunderstood element called Desire'.[13]

This language might be baffling at first, but bear with it a while. Lacan, who took up and developed the two polarities of language described by the linguists, has been an important influence in literary criticism and in psychology; and I believe his ideas have some relevance for mathematics education.[14] Lacan inverted Saussure's fraction; he placed the signifier as the numerator 'on top', thereby asserting its primacy. All discourse, he claimed, is a metonymic chain which leads us along an endless path, in which reference to 'reality' becomes increasingly problematical. The word becomes 'the murder of the thing'.[15] This is the sense in which mathematics tends towards the metonymic pole. As a practitioner develops a particular mathematical skill, the metaphor that at first sustains the activity becomes more frozen. The more skilled the algorist, the more metonymic is the algorithm.

It is always dangerous to describe polarities, because they cannot be described simultaneously and so run the risk of seeming to be exclusive. 'Metaphor and metonymy are not entities', as Anthony Wilden reminds us, 'they are categories of distinction, not bags to put things in … this polar distinction itself has a signification only in a context, and since everything has everything else as its context, it is up to the commentator to define the context he is talking about.'[16] The number worlds of the algorist and abacist are both contexts in which it can be helpful to invoke the axes of language that have been described. The number world of the contemporary classroom is another. But before considering that, you are invited to look at the reproduction of a further pair of paintings by Magritte. One can be read as a metaphor, the other a metonymy. Or is it the other way round?[17]

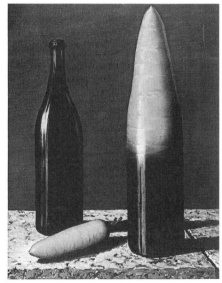

Mathematical practices

A preference for metaphor rather than metonymy – using these terms in the extended senses described – may be observed in the early development of mathematics, whether this be that of a society or of an individual. The Greeks conceived the notions of even and odd through spatial metaphors derived from arrangements of pebbles. This led to a verbal definition such as the following quoted by Nicomachus: 'An even number is that which admits of being divided, by one and the same operation, into the greatest and the least parts, greatest in size but least in number ...'.[18] This invokes the image of an actual physical separation of a pile of stones into two parts (the least number of parts you could have), each containing half the stones (both parts being the largest possible). Eventually, division loses some of its metaphoric content and becomes a virtual operation in the mind. An even number may then be defined as a number that can be divided by two 'exactly'. In this case, the division may now be understood purely as an operation on written numerals – the thing you do in response to a division sign. A further shift in meaning of the concept occurs when even numbers are simply defined as multiples of 2: attention is now drawn to which numbers are even, rather than what evenness is. This also shifts from the inverse operation – actual or virtual – of division to the direct one of multiplication. But it does not invoke the multiplying so much as the results of doing so – a lingering trace in the memory of a chanted chain of signifiers: 'two, four, six, eight, ...'.

Teachers in primary schools often introduce division with the metaphor of sharing. That such metaphors can be taken in other ways than intended is illustrated in the case of a girl, reported by Valerie Walkerdine, giving 15 as an example of an even number, because it was the number of her house and 'we share it with the people upstairs'.[19] Mathematicians have often been led astray by metaphors in the same sort of way. A famous example is the notion of a function which was originally conceived as a continuous curve. When this graphical metaphor became too problematic, it was replaced by a sort of culinary metaphor – a function was defined by a single recipe or rule. Eventually, that too had to be discarded, and a function had to be defined 'extensionally' – or, as I am tempted to say, metonymically – by listing its values: 2, 4, 6, 8, ...

Mathematicians seem to need to get away from metaphors as soon as they can; many nineteenth-century mathematicians were quite explicit about this.[20] As William Frend fulminated: 'When a person cannot explain the principles of a science without reference to metaphor, the probability is that he has never thought accurately upon the subject.' His son-in-law, Augustus de Morgan, used a striking metaphor to express a similar view: 'metaphor and paranomasia [a play on words] can draw the car of piety, but they tumble the waggon of geometry into the ditch'. These remarks may seem aggressive enough, but Gottlob Frege's spluttering criticism of the metaphorically based 'pebble arithmetic' offered by the empiricist philosopher John Stuart Mill can only be described as pathological. Frege's work has been described recently – by David Bloor – as being 'steeped in the rhetoric of purity and danger, and full of the imagery of invasion, penetration, disparagement, contempt and the threat of ruin'. Such pathology is an uncomfortable reminder of the nature of the repression that mathematics may sometimes demand. It suggests a way in which we might make some sense of Lacan's linking of metonymy and desire.

Whatever the reason why mathematics tends towards metonymy, it is well known that this has the effect of inhibiting access to its formal texts. Most teachers come across the muddles caused by unattached metonymies in students' work. Here is an example from a six-year-old's description of her work: 'You have to colour all the evil numbers in. First you have to write it up to a hundred and then you colour all the evil numbers in.'[21] This example is also taken from the work of Walkerdine, who has very powerfully exposed some of the paradoxes found in the teaching of mathematics in contemporary primary classrooms. According to her analysis, these paradoxes – muddles would be a deservedly harsher term – can be seen in terms of a tension between metaphoric and metonymic interpretations of mathematics and approaches to mathematics teaching.

For some decades now, teachers have been encouraged in their training to think in terms of children passing through various stages of 'concrete' thought and not coming until early adolescence to the sort of formal 'abstract' thinking that mathematics is assumed to demand. These notions derived from the developmental psychology of Jean Piaget; and they were welcomed by sensitive and concerned teachers who had despaired of the difficulties that otherwise obviously intelligent pupils seemed to have with mathematics. But almost all pupils can move counters around – like the abacist – and they are always eager to grab hold of the rules of anything that is presented to them as a game. Well designed and carefully planned classroom activities offer children metaphoric access to arithmetic in its classical 'logistic' sense, that is where numbers are still attached to objects, be these counters, coins, rods, or mental images of these.

This logistic is not unlike that which is naturally encountered at home or in the streets and shops. Except for the fact that the classroom activities are inevitably artificial and not only do not really matter, but are to be explicitly understood as not really mattering. Thus, Walkerdine quotes an incident when the infant teacher joins a group engaged in a prescribed 'shopping' activity, and asks a boy to buy a dolly for her. He says he has only one penny left. Another child points to a pile of coins, but the boy says that he had already spent those. The teacher then comments: 'Oh, I see what you are doing. No, it's all right, you … each time, you get another ten pence to go shopping with.'[22] Part of the case presented by Walkerdine is that different children will have different attitudes to money. 'Counting pennies' may have different meanings – for some a grim reality, for others a casual game of let's pretend. Using money as a metaphor for number in classrooms may be sometimes more problematic than is supposed.

The paradox is that those children who understand about money precisely because lack of it is important in their family life may not find it easy, when money is invoked in the classroom, to take in only those aspects of the metaphor that are relevant for the transition to the more 'abstract' – metonymic – thinking that is the teacher's ultimate goal. It is ironic that this transition is likely to be smoother for those children who already have a more abstract notion of money – one which is not linked so closely in their lives to rent, food, labour, and so on. When you stay on one side of the paradox, you may deplore the irrelevance of school subjects like mathematics to ordinary daily life. You may feel that mathematics has become a political and social tool in a patriarchal order dominated by people with a tremendous investment in the education of the intellect and a denial of other – repressed – possibilities. On the other side of the paradox, you may be perturbed by yet another example of the way in which some children might be disadvantaged in their schooling. You may feel that such children deserve access to tools which may be empowering, and that more successful ways of doing this need to be devised.

Both sides of the paradox have been explored by Walkerdine in various articles, research reports and in her book, *The Mastery of Reason*, which contains a devastating criticism of some current orthodoxies in mathematics education.[23] In particular, Walkerdine and her colleagues have criticized some of the pedagogical assumptions ostensibly derived from Piaget's developmental psychology. Thus, the construction of concepts through perception and action is often interpreted as an individual matter in which the relation of knower to known is taken to be more or less straightforward. But, as Walkerdine and others have emphasized, this is always problematic, and is always mediated by particular social practices.

Numeration and place value

Whether to emphasize metaphor or metonymy is not just a theoretical issue. Consider, for example, the notion of place value, which does take up a considerable amount of teachers' attention in present-day classrooms. A standard recommendation is that children should be provided with an eclectic range of experiences with blocks, rods, coins, rulers, balances. Activities with each of these are carefully designed in order to force a grouping of the elements involved in a way that corresponds to the grouping into tens of our numeration system. After the objects are manipulated in this way, the resulting groups are labelled with numerals. Numerals then directly name a particular arrangement of particular objects – which may be different objects on different days. The emphasis is highly metaphoric. But the eventual aim of this work is to achieve metonymic fluency, in which the blocks, rods and so on can be dispensed with. Walkerdine has given an intriguing account of a seven-year-old discarding the matchsticks with which he is supposed to be working to add 20 + 44, and then 48 + 48, working from left to right directly with the numerals. He has difficulties in the second case and has to defer to his partner, Tony, who has been using the matchsticks. The teacher is reported as making the following comment after reading the transcript of the dialogue between Michael and Tony: 'I'll have to take him back. He obviously hasn't got it. I'll have to take him back and give him experience ... He shouldn't really be trying to do that yet.'[24]

It is, of course, too easy to misinterpret and misuse such anecdotes. But there is no doubt that place value is taken very seriously by teachers and that it is taught carefully and in well prepared detail. Teachers are concerned that children should understand what they are doing. But the understanding of number that they have in mind is, more often than not, a Piagetian construction in which the notion of place value is a prominent, metaphoric feature. Is there a metonymic alternative through which the use of the numerical signifiers can be explored directly, as Michael in the above account tried to do? For many teachers, such a question might conjure up rejected, old-fashioned methods: formal teaching, rote learning, mindless mind training, and all the other bogeys of yesteryear. But there are other ways of offering children entry into metonymic procedures that are not meaningless and destructive, and some of these may need to be considered more seriously if mathematics education is to meet the criticism of some current practice that has been presented by Walkerdine.

A pedagogical treatment of number that might be described as having a metonymic emphasis has been described by Caleb Gattegno, in particular in his posthumous work, *The Awareness of Mathematization*.[25] One feature of Gattegno's approach is the association of mathematical signifiers with positions in an array, with number-names, with folded fingers, and so on. Such images are linked with numerals in a vivid way that recovers the frozen metaphor in the description of the action of the algorist as manipulation of numerals. The approach is that of a language-game in Wittgenstein's sense – the participant gains meaning by being immersed in the usages of a particular discourse. In this treatment, 'place value' becomes a totally unnecessary concept as far as teaching it is concerned; it can be dispensed with completely in classrooms!

The customary treatment of place value is also put into question by the development of small, hand-held electronic calculators (see the article by Angela Walsh, in this volume). In fact, the arguments for and against calculators are not unlike those that were made for and against the Indian–Arabic numerals when they were first introduced into Europe. Surely, said the abacists, people will not *understand* what they are doing with this new-fangled notion which has no tangible reference. It is ironic that it is now the skilled algorist who claims that people will not understand what they are doing when they merely push buttons on a calculator. Both then and now, the innovators claim that the new technique offers greater accuracy and that understanding will develop from confident and successful use. The issues continue to be discussed in schools and in the market-place.

An amusing version of Reisch's original illustration appeared in a 1979 issue of *The Economist* (see opposite). The abacist is still named as Pythagoras, who appears as a somewhat baffled senior manager; the algorist is an anonymous and self-satisfied yuppy. Significantly enough, Arithmetic is now male – a bowler-hatted, pinstriped City gent with a rolled umbrella, who is here giving neither of the others a glance, but seems to be using some sort of sextant. The moral of the picture is as ambiguous as the original version.

Counting and cardinality

Another redundant notion that has played a dominating but quite unnecessary role in the early stages of teaching number is 'matching', or the one one correspondence of sets. This is taken, in most textbooks and manuals for teachers, to be a fundamental aspect of number. Yet this has only happened relatively recently. How did the notion arise? It seems to have first appeared in the work of philosophers; David Hume, for example, observed that numbers, as collections of units, could be said to be equal when 'the one always has a unit answering to every unit of the other'.[26] Galileo had noted earlier that the set of counting numbers could be matched with the seemingly 'smaller' subset of square numbers. This seemed to contradict the usual assumption that the whole was greater than any of its parts. Later – in the nineteenth century – it was realized that this apparent paradox could be used to characterize the infinite. Georg Cantor defined the 'numerosity' of an infinite set by metaphoric analogy with that of finite sets.[27] This introduced an emphasis on 'cardinality' into mathematics *for the first time*. In creating a theory of transfinite numbers, Cantor found that he had to make a clear distinction between cardinal and ordinal numbers. Until then, it had only been of grammatical interest; as far as mathematicians were concerned, finite cardinal and ordinal were the same. But Cantor provided the tools for making more careful definitions of number; and those that were then made by Frege and Russell had a cardinal bias that required the notion of set and of one–one correspondence.[28]

These were taken over by Piaget when he sought to establish 'foundations' for arithmetic in another sense.[29] The various practical experiments he undertook to explore children's understanding were adapted by teachers as activities in which children could acquire ('get', 'own', 'have', ... – the implicit metaphors are revealing) the supposedly required concepts. But there are alternative approaches which make these totally unnecessary. The fact that one particular 'foundation' has been proposed and developed does not mean that others are not possible. Many critics have now realized that it is more useful to see the early stages of learning number as like learning language. Such an approach places a greater emphasis on ordinality. Learning the numeration system becomes an initiation into ordinal counting practice through a series of language-games: for example, rhymes like 'One, two, three, four, five, Once I caught a fish alive' or 'Two, four six, eight, ...', followed by invented spoken or written sequences like 3, 6, 9, 12, 15, ... or 317, 318, 319, ... or 10, 100, 1000, 10 000, ..., and so on.

Teachers steeped in the Piagetian tradition are sometimes appalled by programmes of this sort which seem to revert to old-fashioned habits such as the meaningless chanting of multiplication tables. Apart from the fact that chanting is never meaningless – it does, after all, play an important role in all rites, whether religious or secular – direct entry into the essentially *metonymic* activity of counting can be achieved by using triggers like number rhymes or 'visual dictation' from a table of numerals recommended by Gattegno.[30] This does, of course, emphasize the *use* of numerals as opposed to a supposed meaning of number.

It is often generally assumed that knowing numerals is a rather unimportant, even though necessary, prerequisite for a proper understanding of number. So that, for instance, time will be spent counting collections of up to ten or twenty objects before counting up to a hundred. This indeed is explicitly recommended in the current (1991) national curriculum for England and Wales, where we are told, in all seriousness, that the treatment of whole numbers requires carefully graded steps: to at least 10 by level 1, at least 100 by level 2, at least 1000 by level 3, culminating in all whole numbers by level 4.

An alternative curriculum that emphasized ordinality would postpone the issue of being able to count things correctly, an issue which takes up an enormous amount of both teachers' and children's time in primary schools. Counting things correctly could perhaps be more usefully considered as a regularly encountered social practice which does not need to be taught in the broken-up and conceptually analysed, step-by-step manner that fascinates pedagogues. So-called 'conservation of number' is yet another redundant notion which can be cheerfully discarded.

An amusing case of 'failure to conserve' is said to have occurred when the bishops assembled for the Council of Nicaea in the year AD 325. People wanted to know how many had turned up. It is said that there were 318: but 'when they rose up to be called over, it appeared that they were 319; so that they never could make the number come right, and whenever they approached the last of the series, he immediately turned into the likeness of his next neighbour'.[31] Later, people were to ascribe the varying total to the wayward presence of the Holy Ghost. Such an explanation might be useful next time someone seems to count something wrongly. For it cannot be more strange than some that tend to be made. Here is a transcript of a conversation between an adult (A) and Patrick (P), aged four.

A: How many is two and one more?

P: Four.

A: Well, how many is two lollipops and one more?

P: Three.

A: How many is two elephants and one more?

P: Three.

A: How many is two giraffes and one more?

P: Three.

A: So how many is two and one more?

P: [looking adult straight in the eyes] Six.

The researcher's comment here is that Patrick has 'just failed to make a crucial leap in his understanding of number'.[32] Many might agree with this; but note again the significant 'so' in the adult's last sentence. Why should we assume Patrick shares this sense of a deduction? What if he reckons 'four' was the right answer to the first question? So that, as this was apparently not acceptable, he might as well say anything next time. Perhaps his four was 'two and one more [two]'. We shall never know, of course, what Patrick meant. But then nor can the researcher. We have been easily persuaded by researchers to think in terms of what children can or cannot do at certain ages or stages. This can lead all too easily into preconceived explanations of events which could be interpreted, more fruitfully, otherwise.

Understanding and desire

A numeration system permits people to write numerals that name 'numbers' that they could not actually count up to. It also achieves a reality of its own, independent of any physical reality from which it may have arisen, or to which it may now be applied. For Wittgenstein, to understand such a system means to be able to master a technique. But people often find it difficult to learn some techniques. In the case of arithmetic, teachers have supposed that learning may be eased when there is understanding. But this understanding has then to be taken to mean something other than the mastery of the technique to which it is supposed to lead. This then means that a double understanding is required of student – of usage and of a supposedly distinct meaning.

What is understanding? How do I recognize that I have understood something? Can I ever *really* understand? Such questions seem to expect answers in terms of 'essence'; they often betray a desire for underlying certainty. A useful interpretation has been proposed recently by Julian Jaynes: understanding involves arriving at a familiar metaphor. 'The feeling of familiarity is the feeling of understanding.'[33] In this sense, I begin to feel I understand negative numbers as I notice ways in which they are like temperatures. But, of course, for someone else it might have been debts; and later for both of us it might be directions. Metaphors for understanding may be relative, temporary and personal. The various – and often very different – metaphors invoked by individual teachers are not necessarily helpful to some learners.

The word 'understanding' and various related words do themselves contain some interesting metaphors. The latinate equivalents – 'comprehend', 'apprehend' – invoke a metaphor of possession: I *grasp* your meaning, I *seize* upon an idea, I *grab* you. But there is also the metaphor of perception: you *see* what I mean, you are *enlightened*, you have had an *illumination*. Such metaphors indicate how it is that understanding can sometimes be interpreted unfortunately as an all-or-nothing affair, a matter of 'getting hold of' or 'seeing' independent and discrete ideas. There is also, of course, the more passive metaphor of position in the notion of standing under, suggesting supporting foundations, first principles or 'basics'; this may be contrasted with, say, the German word *verstehen* which suggests more of a standing away from, a standing back, in effect a standing over or 'seeing the wood for the trees'. These connections indicate some of the importance that can be attached to the notion of understanding.

There is a deeper commitment that is linked by psychoanalysts with our earliest emotional experiences. Putting it very briefly, the baby's first experience of satisfaction derives from identification with the mother. Inevitably, the baby then has to come to terms with absence, with loss. Fantasy offers a way of 'filling the gap' and language provides control over the loss. Increasing fluency with words – or other symbols – distances the infant from the sense of loss, from the original fantasy, and from the original lost object – the mother; every word learned is a step away from her. But the control is only a symbolic one and has to be continually maintained. Seeking understanding is one way of doing this; and sometimes, especially for those that teach, the need to understand is also accompanied by the need to get others to understand.[34]

Lacan referred to the baby's pre-verbal identification with the mother as being of the Imaginary order. What he called the Symbolic order occurs after the intervention of the father – or whoever makes the two become three – and the consequent development of language. In his condensed formulations, the Imaginary is replaced by the Symbolic behind which remains Desire for the Other. The capitalized words are condensations; they can be interpreted in various ways. According to Brian Rotman, the mathematician sees the object of Desire as 'a pure timeless discourse, where assertions proved stay proved forever ... where all the questions are determinate, and all the answers totally certain'.[35] Such a discourse offers mastery and control; but the real Desire – for the repressed Other – remains unfulfilled. For Valerie Walkerdine, the Other of mathematics is 'uncertainty, irrationality, lack of control, madness, and so on'.

From this point of view, mathematical practice involves considerable repression. This is both painful and powerful. The pain is manifest in the continuing anxiety and despair that many people still undergo in their encounters with mathematics. The power is manifest in the more arrogant claims that are sometimes made on behalf of a mathematical education and in what Walkerdine refers to as the 'government of reason, the bourgeois and patriarchal rule of science'. Rationality is valued in education in so far as it enables the ruled to understand the rules – so 'rendering the governed governable'.

It is possible to interpret the situation more optimistically, though I am aware that in wanting to do so, I can be taken merely to be defending a lifetime's interest in mathematics teaching. As signifiers become more detached from their original meanings, there may indeed be a suppression. But there could also be a possible liberation, offering 'unlimited possibilities of discourse'. Mathematics is not disembodied knowledge. What sort of knowledge it is is a matter of much discussion and argument. But whatever else it may be, it has roots in the unconscious. This then means that creative mathematical activity has unconscious components. But, as Sherry Turkle observes in commenting on the work of Lacan, it also means that 'mathematics repays its debt by giving us a window back to the unconscious'.[36] In displaying, and sometimes revealing directly or indirectly, some of the workings of the unconscious, mathematics can be healing in the sense that it may assist the symbolic resolution of certain emotional conflicts. Signs may become Symbols: and the Symbolic need not necessarily always be destructive.

The etymology of the word 'symbol' offers interesting overtones that may still be relevant: the word derives from the Greek prefix *sym* (meaning 'together') and *bolos*, a throw; 'simbolon' was a mark or token, and 'simbole' was a putting together, a contribution – properly to a feast or picnic. Sometimes, the symbol may contribute its healing work unseen.[37]

> Hail, the spirit able to unite!
> For we truly live our lives in symbol,
> and with tiny paces move our nimble
> clocks beside our real day and night.

> Still we somehow act in true relation,
> we find that ourselves we know not where.
> Distant station feels for distant station –
> ...

Perhaps some final summarizing interpretations of the Reisch illustration can now be made. Pythagorean arithmetic was as metaphor-bound as the logistic of the abacists. Metaphors provide a sense of understanding. But as the mathematician Herman Weyl pointed out, this sort of understanding – rich in connections and associations – is 'concrete and full [and] lacks the freedom of the hollow symbol'.[38] The arithmetic of the algorist is a metonymic discourse which may contain its own meaning within its signifiers. Entry into this discourse was perhaps originally in terms derived from previous practice: so that the signifiers were in some sense not arbitrary – they were 'iconic' representations pointing to themselves. Then algorists broke free of their past and developed a practice in which signifiers were processed according to certain context-free rules. This eventually became associated with formal and authoritarian 'drilling' methods of teaching. In recent years, entry into mathematics has been effected through a metaphoric introduction, with an emphasis on an understanding of concepts rather than operational fluency. An alternative, metonymic approach offers a direct entry through 'language-games', in which signifiers are associated with purely sensory images; in this case, understanding becomes operational fluency with the signifiers.

In any case, the brooding, compassionate face of Arithmetic presides over the Symbolic order, perpetually reminding us of the Desire for the Other and the painful, but seemingly inevitable, payments exacted by control of it. Can that ever be worth the price? Can her followers *bring back body* to 'the cold, dry fruits of the Pythagorean tree'?

> Fishes are dumb, ... so one imagines. Who knows?
> May there not be some place where, *without* them,
> the dwellers are able to speak what would be the language of fish?

Notes and references

[1] This is confirmed, for example, by the illustration (below) from the title page of a 1480 text on musical theory by Franchino Gafurio. It portrays the sequence 4, 6, 8, 9, 12, written in the 'new' numerals. These yield the ratios that define the intervals of the harmonic scale: *tone*, *diatessaron* (3:4, in current terms, a fourth), *diapente* (2:3, a fifth) and *diapason* (1:2, an octave). Renaissance architects often used these ratios to determine the proportions of their buildings.

2   A more theoretical form of logistic was also described – somewhat obscurely – by Plato. This has been identified with the theory of ratio and proportion; the origins of this theory in the practical activity of tuning strings might explain its classification as a theoretical counterpart to the more common practical logistic. See D. Fowler (1989) *The Mathematics of Plato's Academy*, Oxford University Press, pp. 108–17.

3   On the other hand, 'terms of first intention' point to objects. Science was held to be concerned with these, whereas logic was concerned with 'second intentions', such as universals. This neat division was upset by the development of mathematical symbols which started as terms of second intention, but soon came to be treated as objects in themselves. See J. Klein (1968) *Greek Mathematical Thought and the Origins of Algebra*, MIT Press, p. 208.

4   The word 'algorism' was a latinization of the name of the ninth-century Arabic mathematician, al-Khwarismi, who was named – like Pisano – after the place he came from, in this case the district of Khwarism – the present-day Khoremskaya in Uzbekistan. His books on computation and 'algebra' were beginning to be known in Europe during the twelfth century. The more common form, 'algorithm', is an artificial version, probably invoked by an echo of 'arithmetic'.

5   Cited in K. Menninger (1969) *Number Words and Number Symbols*, MIT Press, p. 422.

6   In Boethius' written calculations, the numerals 6 and 7 appear in rotated form – variations which might have derived from the different ways *apices* (the marked counters) could be laid down. Calculations were performed column by column, from left to right. The crossings-out are, at first, consistent with a subtraction of 970 from 1234: the 9 from the 12 leaves 3, written above the 2; this then reads with the existing 3 as 33; subtracting 7 leaves 26 – usually, the 2 would have been placed above the first crossed-out 3; the remainder would then be read as 264, but it now seems that the 4 is about to be crossed out, having been replaced – mysteriously – by a 5.

7   Cited in E. Helm (1967) 'The vibrating string of the Pythagoreans', *Scientific American*, December 1967, p. 95. Boethius was more interested in ratios than in scales; he classified and named various ratios in great detail; for example, the ratio 2:3 – corresponding to the musical interval of a fifth – was *sesquialtera*, while 7:100 would have been expressed in his system as *subquatuordecupla subsuperbipartiens septimes*.

8   Powers of 2 are even numbers yielding octaves, while powers of 3 are odd and yield fifths. Nicomachus inserted mean proportionals within the lambda, thus creating a triangular array with 4, 6, 9 in one row and 8, 12, 18, 27 in the next. This revealed the numbers used in the Pythagorean music scale. The sixteenth-century architect, di Giorgio, presented a version (overleaf) with inserted means – multiplied by 6 – along the arms of the lambda. The resulting proportions were recommended for buildings. Other examples of the lambda figure appear in the fanciful drawings of the seventeenth-century writer, Robert Fludd. See J. Godwin (1979) *Robert Fludd*, Thames and Hudson, pp. 79, 45.

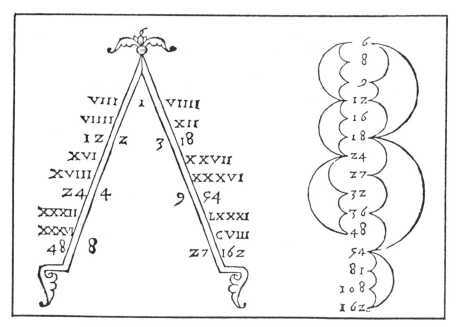

9   The notion that different cultures produce different number worlds – and that these are incommensurable – was suggested by the historian Oswald Spengler earlier this century: 'We find an Indian, an Arabian, a classical, a Western type of mathematical thought and, corresponding to each, a type of number – each type fundamentally peculiar and unique.' Spengler's view of mathematics is discussed in S. Restivo (1983) *The Social Relations of Physics, Mysticism and Mathematics*, Reidel, chapter 12. For a discussion of 'family resemblances' that cause different things to be called number, see L. Wittgenstein (1953) *Philosophical Investigations*, Blackwell, book 1, paragraph 67.

10   'For a large class of cases – though not for all – in which we employ the word "meaning", it can be defined thus: the meaning of a word is its use in language.' L. Wittgenstein, *op. cit.* (previous note), book 1: paragraph 43.

11   The pictures shown here, by the Belgian surrealist painter René Magritte (1898–1967), are *L'usage de la parole* (1928/29) and *Les promenades d'Euclide* (1955).

12   Ferdinand de Saussure (1857–1913), a Swiss linguist, was one of the founders of modern linguistics. Roman Jakobson (1896–1982) a founder-member of the so-called Prague school of linguistics, was later an influential teacher in the USA.

13   J. Lacan (1973) *Le seminaire*, volume XI, Editions de Seuil, p. 141. This volume has been translated into English (J. Lacan (1977) *The Four Fundamental Concepts of Psychoanalysis*, Penguin), but the translation used here comes from a passage in R. Coward and J. Ellis (1973) *Language and Materialism*, Routledge and Kegan Paul, p. 120.

14 The work of Jacques Lacan (1901–81) has been enormously influential in a variety of disciplines. His ideas are complex, and expressed in an unfamiliar way; they are perhaps best approached at first through commentaries. See, for example, B. Benvenuto and R. Kennedy (1986) *The Work of Jacques Lacan*, Free Association; S. Felman (1987) *Jacques Lacan and the Adventure of Insight*, Harvester; M. Bowie (1991) *Lacan*, Fontana. See also the works cited in notes 16 and 35. Some of Lacan's writings have been translated into English – these are cited in notes 13 and 15.

15 'The symbol manifests itself first of all as the murder of the thing and this death constitutes in the subject the eternalisation of his desire.' (J. Lacan (1977) *Ecrits – a Selection*, Tavistock, p. 104.)

16 A. Wilden (1980) *System and Structure*, Tavistock, p. 58. Various authors describe these polarities in different ways and it is perhaps worth emphasizing that 'metaphor' and 'metonymy' should be considered to be very general place-holders for specific meanings in specific contexts.

17 The Magritte pictures shown here are *L'explication* (1952) and *Le modèle rouge* (1935).

18 T. Heath (1981) *A History of Greek Mathematics*, Dover, p. 70. Nicomachus ascribes the given definition of even numbers to the early Pythagoreans.

19 V. Walkerdine (1981) *Reading the Signs of Mathematics*, Leverhulme Trust Project Report, volume 1, mimeo, University of London.

20 Various mathematicians are quoted in this paragraph. The first is William Frend (1757–1841): the quoted passage is from the preface to his *Principles of Algebra* (1796). Augustus de Morgan (1806–71) married Frend's daughter, Sophia; his words are quoted from a book review in *The Athuneum*, 18 July 1868, p. 72. (There is an interesting account of these two non-conformists in A. G. Howson (1982) *A History of Mathematics Education in England*, Cambridge University Press, chapter 5.) Gottlob Frege (1848–1925) was a German logician who strongly criticized J. S. Mill's empiricist foundation of mathematics; the comment on his work is from D. Bloor (1976) *Knowledge and Social Imagery*, Routledge and Kegan Paul, p. 83.

21 V. Walkerdine (1982) 'From context to text – a psychosemiotic approach to abstract thought' in M. Beveridge (ed.), *Children Thinking Through Language*, Arnold, p. 154.

22 V. Walkerdine, *op. cit.* (note 21), p. 156.

23 V. Walkerdine (1988) *The Mastery of Reason*, Routledge (paperback 1990). See also her chapter cited in note 21, and a chapter, 'Developmental psychology and the child-centred pedagogy' in J. Henriques *et al.* (1984) *Changing the Subject*, Methuen.

24 V. Walkerdine, *op. cit.* (first item, note 23), p. 178.

25 See C. Gattegno (1988) *The Awareness of Mathematization*, Educational Solutions. See, also, this author's (1974) *The Common Sense of Teaching Mathematics*, Educational Solutions; and various articles in the journal *Mathematics Teaching*, in particular, in issues number 50, 59, 94, 105, 114. Gattegno has also offered complementary 'metaphoric' approaches to number using Cuisenaire rods. These are discussed in the books mentioned above. See, also, his textbooks for pupils (*Mathematics with Numbers in Colour*, books 1–7) and C. Gattegno (1963) *For the Teaching of Mathematics*, volume 3, Educational Explorers.

[26] D. Hume (1739) *A Treatise on Human Nature*, Book 1, paragraph 3, section 1.

[27] Georg Cantor (1845–1918) created a theory of infinite sets and transfinite numbers. Noting that two *finite* sets have the same number of elements when their elements can be paired in one–one correspondence, he extended this definition to infinite sets.

[28] Gottlob Frege (1848–1925) and Bertrand Russell (1872–1970) were both involved in the development of a philosophical foundation of mathematics that has been very influential in mathematics and in mathematics education.

[29] The developmental psychology of Jean Piaget (1896–1980) has dominated mathematics education for the last fifty years. His investigation of early number concepts was carried out in terms of sets and one–one correspondence (matching). Thus, 'conservation of number' was a manifestation of the unique ordinality of a finite set.

[30] C. Gattegno (1970) *The Common Sense of Teaching Mathematics*, Educational Solutions, chapter 2.

[31] This story is quoted and ascribed to the philosopher A. N. Whitehead in D. Hawkins (1964) *The Language of Nature*, Freeman, p. 23.

[32] M. Hughes (1984) 'Learning about number', *ESRC Newsletter*, no. 52, p. 9. The author adds that Patrick does not seem to be daunted by his failure: 'his manner expresses a certain contempt for the adult for asking such a bizarre question'.

[33] J. Jaynes (1982) *The Origin of Consciousness in the Breakdown of the Bicameral Mind*, Pelican, p. 52.

[34] Compare the similar 'teacher-lusts' discussed by Mary Boole; see *A Boolean Anthology*, ATM, 1972, p. 11.

[35] This is quoted in V. Walkerdine (1988) *The Mastery of Reason*, Routledge, p. 187. This book is also the source of the other brief quotations in this and the following paragraph.

[36] S. Turkle (1979) *Psychoanalytical Politics*, Burnett Books, p. 247. The passage in question concludes as follows: 'Lacan's ideas powerfully suggest that … we need not feel we are faced with a choice between poetic warmth and the cold, dry fruits of the Pythagorean tree'. The last phrase is echoed in my final paragraph. [*Added in proof*: My concluding optimistic paragraphs were written in the summer of 1990, before the terrible events of winter in the Gulf which emphasized how cold and dry the fruits of mathematics can be.]

[37] The following lines, and the ones at the end of the chapter, are from Rainer Maria Rilke's *Sonnets to Orpheus*, translated by J. B. Leishman (Hogarth Press, 1949). The first extract is from part 1, sonnet XII, and the second is from part 2, sonnet XX.

[38] H. Weyl (1949) *Philosophy of Mathematics and Natural Science*, Princeton, p. 284.

Acknowledgements

I am very grateful to John Mason and David Wheeler for their helpful comments on earlier versions of this chapter; and also to John Fauvel who brought the contemporary version of the Reisch picture to my attention. I owe a very special debt to David Pimm for his sympathetic and constructive suggestions and for the thoroughness of his editing.

20 From the concrete to the abstract

John Dewey

What is the concrete?

The maxim enjoined upon teachers, 'proceed from the concrete to the abstract', is familiar rather than wholly intelligible. Few who read and hear it gain a clear conception of the starting point, the concrete; of the nature of the goal, the abstract; and of the exact nature of the path to be traversed in going from one to the other. At times, the injunction is positively misunderstood, being taken to mean that education should advance from things to thought – as if any dealing with things in which thinking is not involved could possibly be educative. So understood, the maxim encourages mechanical, routine or sensuous excitation at one end of the educational scale – the lower – and academic and unapplied learning at the upper end.

Actually, all dealing with things, even the child's, is immersed in inference; things are clothed with the suggestions they arouse. They are significant as challenges to interpretation or as evidences to substantiate a belief. Nothing could be more unnatural than instruction in things without thought, in sense-perceptions without judgements connected with them. And if the abstract to which we are to proceed denotes thought apart from things, the goal is formal and empty, for effective thought always refers, more or less directly, to things.

Relation to direct and indirect meaning

Yet the maxim has a meaning which, understood and supplemented, states the direction of logical development. What is this meaning? 'Concrete' denotes a meaning definitely marked off from other meanings so that it is readily apprehended by itself. When we hear the words, *table, chair, stove, coat*, we do not have to reflect in order to grasp what is meant. The terms convey meaning so directly that no effort at translation is needed. The meaning of some terms and things, however, is grasped only by first calling to mind more familiar things and then tracing out connections between them and what we do not understand. Roughly speaking, the former kind of meaning is concrete; the latter is abstract.

Dependence on the intellectual status of the individual

To one who is thoroughly at home in physics and chemistry, the notions of *atom* and *molecule* are fairly concrete. They are constantly used without involving any labour of thought in apprehending what they mean. But the layman and the beginner in science have to remind themselves of things with which they already are well acquainted, and then go through a process of slow translation. Moreover, the terms *atom* and *molecule* lose their hard-won meaning only too easily if familiar things and the line of transition from them to the strange drop out of mind. The same difference is illustrated by any technical terms: *coefficient* and *exponent* in algebra, *triangle* and *square* in their geometric as distinct from their popular meanings; *capital* and *value* in political economy, and so on.

The difference as noted is purely relative to the intellectual progress of an individual; what is abstract at one period of growth is concrete at another; or even the contrary, as one finds that things supposed to be thoroughly familiar involve strange factors and unsolved problems. There is, nevertheless, a general line of cleavage that decides upon the whole what things fall within, and what fall without, the limits of familiar acquaintance. This line accordingly marks off the concrete and the abstract in a fairly permanent way. *The limits are fixed mainly by the demands of practical life.* Things such as sticks and stones, meat and potatoes, houses and trees, are constant features of the environment of which we have to take account in order to live. Hence, their important meanings are soon learned and are indissolubly associated with objects. We are acquainted with a thing (or it is familiar to us) when we have so much to do with it that its strange and troublesome corners are rubbed off. The necessities of social intercourse convey to adults a like concreteness upon such terms as *taxes, elections, wages, the law,* and so on. Things the meanings of which I personally do not take in directly, appliances of cook, carpenter, or weaver, for example, are nevertheless unhesitatingly classed as concrete, since they are directly connected with our common social life.

Relation to thinking as a means and as an end

By contrast, the abstract is the *theoretical*, that not intimately associated with practical concerns. The abstract thinker (the 'man of pure science', as he is sometimes called) deliberately abstracts from application in life; that is, he leaves practical uses out of account. This, however, is a merely negative statement. What remains when connections with use and application are excluded? *Evidently only what has to do with knowing considered as an end in itself.* Many notions in science are abstract, not only because they cannot be understood without a long apprenticeship in the science (which is equally true of technical matters in the arts), but also because the whole content of their meaning has been framed for the sole purpose of facilitating further knowledge, inquiry, and speculation. *When thinking is used as a means to some end, good, or value beyond itself, it is concrete; when it is employed simply as a means to more thinking, it is abstract.* To a theorist an idea is adequate and self-contained just because it engages and rewards thought; to a medical practitioner, an engineer, an artist, a merchant, a politician, it is complete only when employed in the furthering of some interest in life – health, wealth, beauty, goodness, success, or what you will.

Depreciation of 'mere theory'

The great majority of men under ordinary circumstances find the practical exigencies of life almost, if not quite, coercive. Their main business is the proper conduct of their affairs. Whatever is of significance only as affording scope for thinking is pallid and remote – almost artificial. Hence the contempt felt by the practical and successful executive for the 'mere theorist'; hence his conviction that certain things may be all very well in theory, but that they will not do in practice; hence, in general, the deprecia-tory way in which he uses the terms *abstract*, *theoretical*, and *intellectual*.

This attitude is justified, of course, under certain conditions. But deprecia-tion of theory does not contain the whole truth, as common or practical sense recognizes. There is such a thing, even from the common-sense standpoint, as being 'too practical', as being so intent upon the immediately practical as not to see beyond the end of one's nose or as to cut off the limb upon which one is sitting. The question is one of limits, of degrees and adjustments, rather than one of absolute separation. Truly practical men give their minds free play about a subject without asking too closely at every point for any advantage to be gained. Exclusive preoccupation with matters of use and application narrows the horizon and in the long run defeats itself. It does not pay to tether one's thoughts to the post of use with too short a rope. Power in action requires largeness of vision, which can be had only through the use of imagination. Men must at least have enough interest in thinking for the sake of thinking to escape the limitations of routine and custom. Interest in knowledge for the sake of knowledge, in thinking for the sake of the free play of thought, is necessary to the *emancipation* of practical life – to making it rich and progressive.

We now recur to the pedagogic maxim of going from the concrete to the abstract and call attention to three aspects of the process.

Beginning with practical manipulations

Since the *concrete* denotes thinking applied to activities for the sake of dealing with difficulties that present themselves practically, 'begin with the concrete' signifies that we should, at the outset of any new experience in learning, make much of what is already familiar, and if possible connect the new topics and principles with the pursuit of an end in some active occupation. We do not 'follow the order of nature' when we multiply mere sensations or accumulate physical objects. Instruction in number is not concrete merely because splints or beans or dots are employed. Whenever the use and bearing of number relations are clearly perceived, a number idea is concrete even if figures alone are used. Just what sort of symbol it is best to use at a given time – whether blocks, or lines, or figures – is entirely a matter of adjustment to the given case. If the physical things used in teaching number or geography or anything else do not leave the mind illuminated with recognition of a *meaning* beyond themselves, the instruc-tion that uses them is as abstruse as that which doles out ready-made definitions and rules, for it distracts attention from ideas or mere physical excitations.

The notion that we have only to put physical objects before the senses in order to impress upon the mind amounts almost to a superstition. The introduction of object lessons and sense-training scored a distinct advance over the prior method of linguistic symbols, but this advance tended to blind educators to the fact that only a half-way step had been taken. Things and sensations develop the child, indeed, but only when he *uses* them in mastering his body and coordinating his actions. Continuous occupations involve the use of natural materials, tools, modes of energy, and do it in a way that compels thinking as to how they are related to one another and to the realization of ends. But the mere isolated presentation of things to sense remains barren and dead. A few generations ago the great obstacle in the way of reform of primary education was belief in the almost magical efficacy of the symbols of language (including number) to produce mental training; at present, belief in the efficacy of objects just as objects blocks the way. As frequently happens, the better is an enemy of the best.

Transferring interest to intellectual matters

The interest in results, in the successful carrying on of an activity, should be gradually transferred to the *study* of objects – their properties, conse-quences, structures, causes, and effects. The adult when at work in his life calling is rarely free to devote time or energy – beyond the necessities of his immediate action – to the study of what he deals with. The educative activities of childhood should be so arranged that the activity creates a demand for attention to matters that have only an indirect and an intellec-tual connection with the original activity. To take an instance to which reference has already been made, the direct interest in carpentering or shop work should gradually pass into an interest in geometric and mechanical problems. The interest in cooking should grow into an interest in chemical experimentation and the physiology and hygiene of bodily growth. The original casual making of pictures should pass to an interest in the technique of representation of perspective, the handling of brush, pigments, etc. This development is what the term 'go' signifies in the maxim '*go* from the concrete to the abstract'; it represents the dynamic and educative phase of the process.

Developing delight in thinking

The outcome, the *abstract* to which education is to proceed, is an interest in intellectual matters for their own sake, a delight in thinking for the sake of thinking. It is an old story that acts and processes that at the outset are incidental to something else develop and maintain an absorbing value of their own. So it is with thinking and with knowledge; at first incidental to results and adjustments beyond themselves, they attract more and more attention to themselves till they become ends, not means. Children engage, unconstrainedly and continually, in reflective inspection and testing for the sake of what they are interested in doing. Habits of thinking thus generated may increase in amount till they become of importance on their own account. It is part of the business of a teacher to lead students to extricate and dwell upon the distinctively intellectual side of what they do until there develops a spontaneous interest in ideas and their relations with one another – that is, a genuine power of abstraction, of rising from engrossment in the present to the plane of ideas.

What is the abstract?

[...]

Abstract thinking not the whole end and not congenial to most persons

Abstract thinking, it should be noted, represents *an* end, not *the* end. The power of sustained thinking on matters remote from direct use is an outgrowth of thinking on practical and immediate matters, but not a substitute for it. The educational end is not the destruction of power to think practically in overcoming obstacles, utilizing resources, and achieving ends; it is not its replacement by abstract reflection. Nor is theoretical thinking a higher type of thinking than practical. A person who has at command both types of thinking is of a higher order than he who possesses only one. Methods that, in developing abstract intellectual abilities, weaken habits of practical or concrete thinking fall as much short of the educational ideal as do the methods that, in cultivating ability to plan, to invent, to arrange, to forecast, fail to secure some delight in thinking, irrespective of practical consequences.

Educators should also note the very great individual differences that exist; they should not try to force one pattern and model upon all. In many (probably the majority) the executive tendency, the habit of mind that thinks for purposes of conduct and achievement, not for the sake of knowing, remains dominant to the end. Engineers, lawyers, doctors, merchants, are much more numerous in adult life than scientists and philosophers. While education should strive to make men who, however prominent their professional interests and aims, partake of the spirit of the scholar, philosopher, and scientist, no good reason appears why education should esteem the one mental habit inherently superior to the other and deliberately try to transform the type from concrete to abstract. Have not our schools been one-sidedly devoted to the more abstract type of thinking, thus doing injustice to the majority of pupils? Has not the idea of a 'liberal' and 'humane' education tended too often in practice to the production of technical, because overspecialized, thinkers?

Education should aim to secure a working balance

The aim of education should be to secure a balanced interaction of the two types of mental attitude, having sufficient regard to the disposition of the individual not to hamper and cripple whatever powers are naturally strong to him. The narrowness of individuals of strong concrete bent needs to be liberalized. Every opportunity that occurs within practical activities for developing curiosity and susceptibility to intellectual problems should be seized. Violence is not done to natural disposition; rather the latter is broadened. Otherwise, the concrete becomes narrowing and deadening. As regards the smaller number of those who have a taste for abstract, purely intellectual topics, pains should be taken to multiply opportunities for the application of ideas, for translating symbolic truths into terms of everyday and social life. Every human being has both capabilities, and every individual will be more effective and happier if both powers are developed in easy and close interaction with each other. Otherwise the abstract becomes identical with the academic and pedantic.

21 Reflections on some words used in mathematics education

Eric Love and Dick Tahta

Many of the words used in mathematics, such as *similar, set, space, tangent*, or *normal*, have ordinary everyday meanings which may or may not be related in some way to their special technical meanings. Like all words, they change meaning as people use them in new and different ways. These layers of meaning may sometimes seem a hindrance to learners, but they could also be seen more positively as an enrichment. It is possible to imagine the everyday resonances and contexts of a word like *similar* enriching a learner's understanding, rather than having them denied in favour of a supposedly correct mathematical usage. According to Spencer-Brown, 'there seems to be no mathematical idea of any importance or profundity that is not mirrored, with an almost uncanny accuracy, in the common use of words, and this appears especially true when we consider words in their original, and sometimes long forgotten, senses'.[1] These issues relate to the ways in which teachers mediate the vocabulary of mathematicians to learners.

The vocabulary of mathematics education – the language used by teachers or other mathematical educators when talking about what they do – is more complicated. Words and expressions are taken both from mathematics and from more general educational discourse (which itself includes words that have already been appropriated from psychology and philosophy), and then acquire new senses, contexts and uses. Mathematicians are in the business of producing mathematics, and do not need to give attention to how mathematics is produced – something which *is* very much the concern of the mathematics educator. Hence, words from mathematics will acquire distinctive meanings when used in the context of mathematics in schools. For example, as Paul Dowling[2] has pointed out, whereas for mathematicians 'a fraction is a piece of cake' is a metaphor (and perhaps a rather dubious one), in the context of school mathematics, 'a piece of cake' is part of the sense of what a fraction is.

Words that are widely used by educational thinkers also take on specialized meanings (*process* is one such, discussed below). Within mathematics education, some words become influential jargon with a persuasive rhetoric of their own. The ways in which teachers think of what they are doing will affect what they do. Even teachers who do not hold with 'theorizing' cannot escape the history and contexts of the words they use. Keynes said: 'Practical men, who believe themselves to be quite exempt from any intellectual influences, are usually the slaves of some defunct economist.'[3] Teachers who feel that the acquisition of 'number bonds' is important, or that 'structured tasks' are desirable, are thinking in categories created by others. Through the use of the words, these categories will be reflected in the choices and stressings made in the classroom. But the experiences and phenomena that are invoked by the words will not be constant; the words tend to shift their meaning according to context. It often takes some time for practitioners to become aware of the ways in which these shifts in meaning occur, even when it is these practitioners themselves who are initiating the changes.

Raymond Williams, in his influential book *Keywords*,[4] traced the development of meaning for a range of words frequently used in discussions of culture and society – words as diverse as *creative, idealist, objective, management* and *romantic*. Although not specifically concerned with educational matters, he touched upon them in his account of a word such as *standards*, where he pointed out that 'standards' is used in two contradictory senses – that of being both arbitrary but fixed ('the standard metre') and that of changing ('standards have fallen'). The tension between these senses carries over into the ways that standards are defended or attacked. By means of such close readings, Williams aimed to explore the ideologies hidden behind his chosen words and to see how the meanings of the words have changed as they have been used to different ends (especially political ones). It would be valuable and illuminating to have a similar dictionary of words used in mathematics education that illustrated the interconnections between various technical terms, their etymological roots and their usages by teachers and others. We have only to think of the rise and fall of a word such as *structure*, widely used in the 1960s, but which is now almost absent from writings in mathematical education.

Preparing such a dictionary would be a major enterprise that would need the cooperative effort of large numbers of people. As a stimulus to such a task, we have taken a few significant words in mathematics education and offer an exploratory account of them. Although we hope that the chosen words are both indicative and illuminating, we could easily have chosen others. In making our selection, we have tried to give a sense of the range of ways in which we might gain insights about thinking in mathematical education by studying the use of words.

The words we examine are: *concept, numeracy, count* (with *tally* and *number*), *image, pattern, practical, structure, problem solving, understanding* and *process*. We give some incomplete notes and observations on each of these and conclude by discussing some of the possibilities and problems of such an approach.[5]

Some mathematics education words

'Concept'

There was only one reference to **concept** ('concepts such as division') in the 1958 Ministry of Education handbook on the teaching of mathematics in secondary schools, and only a few instances in the 1956 Mathematical Association report on primary school mathematics. Prior to this, various reports on teaching mathematics had given nods to the longstanding use of *concept* by philosophers and psychologists ('the fundamental concepts of the subject'). This was mainly as a variation on the phrase 'the idea of'. (So, Carson, in 1913: 'Although there is not much difficulty in imparting the idea of a fraction, it is vital that this, as any other mathematical concept, should acquire living reality for the student.')

Even in 1962, Richard Skemp felt the need to explain in some detail to mathematics teachers the difference between *facts* and *concepts*. But the word soon became commonplace – indeed, a cliché. People were said to have (or lack) *the concept of* place value or of area; young children were helped to 'form the concept' of three, or of angle, or of 'betweenness'. By the 1980s, its use had become so widespread that, according to Tony Orton:

> Mathematics learning consists very largely of building understanding of new concepts onto previously understood concepts. Examples of concepts are so widespread that it is almost unnecessary to quote any … here are a few: triangularity, percentage, relation, similarity, limit … Strangely, however, it is not easy to explain what a 'concept' is.

This dramatic spread of the use of the word in mathematical education was significantly due to the influence of the psychologist Jean Piaget, who was seen as studying the growth and development of *concepts* in young children's thinking. But it is curious to note that the word *concept* does not occur at all in Piaget's book, *The Child's Conception of Number*. The title was an ambiguous translation of the original *La genèse du nombre chez l'enfant*: the French emphasizes the metaphor of giving birth more clearly. The active notion of a **conception** – a conceiving and a growing – is left even more behind in phrases like 'concept of number' that soon became common in mathematics education. The gradual acceptance of *conception* and *concept* in discussions of Piaget's work meant that a later book called *La representation de l'espace chez l'enfant* was translated as *The Child's Conception of Space*.

The use of the noun carries with it a tendency to think of a *concept* as something which can be formed, made concrete, embodied in objects. Such difficulties in the use of this word were recognized in the nineteenth century and have remained problematic. Thus, according to William James:

> The word 'concept' is often used as if it stood for the object of discourse itself; and this looseness feeds such evasiveness in discussion that I shall avoid the use of the expression concept altogether … The word 'conception' is unambiguous. It properly denotes neither the mental state nor what the mental state signifies, but the relation between the two, namely the function of the mental state in signifying just that particular thing.

When one thinks of *concepts* as fixed, universal notions it then seems that 'understanding' amounts to 'acquiring' certain concepts which would therefore have to be put before you in some way. It is, thus, commonly thought that theories are 'built up' out of *concepts*. But, as Wittgenstein observed, all *concepts* are 'theory laden'. We pour our understanding into our *conceptions* and these belong to us in personal and individual ways. To say that a child has *a conception* of X, rather than *a concept* of X, is not merely a change of words, but it represents a shift towards thinking of what the child *conceives* as belonging to the child as an individual, in a way that 'having a concept' does not.

Hans Freudenthal has drawn attention to the way in which attempts at assisting **concept formation** in children are misguided, because they assume that in order to have X *conceived by* a child, one tries to teach the *concept* X. Because *the concept* cannot be taught directly, teachers turn to 'experiences' through which the child will acquire the concept. To predetermine a concept to be learned and to offer some material which supposedly 'embodies' it is, according to Freudenthal, 'to put the cart before the horse: teaching abstractions by concretizing them'.

'Numeracy'

Although **numeracy**, and its associated adjectives, **numerate** and **innumerate**, first appeared only in 1959, these terms shifted meaning so decisively in the following twenty years that the 1982 Cockcroft report devoted several sections to this change (paras 35–39). The first occurrence of these words was in the 1959 Crowther report on the education of (academic) sixth formers.

> Little is done to make science specialists more 'literate' than they were when they left the Fifth Form and nothing to make arts specialists more 'numerate', if we may coin a word to represent the mirror image of literacy.

> When we say that a scientist is 'illiterate', we mean that he is not well enough read to be able to communicate effectively with those who have had a literary education. When we say that a historian or a linguist is 'innumerate' we mean that he cannot even begin to understand what scientists and mathematicians are talking about … It is perhaps possible to distinguish two different aspects of numeracy that should concern the sixth former.

The emphasis here was on something much wider than mathematics, but within ten years there were advocates for introducing pre-school children to 'reading, writing and numeracy'. There was a progression from the original meaning of numeracy, via an idea of **basic numeracy** – then shortened to *numeracy*. (The use of the qualifier 'basic', as in *basic numeracy* or basic literacy, never seems, as David Fielker has pointed out, to include the things that virtually everybody can do (for example, counting), but is only applied to aspects that at least some people have difficulty with.)

By 1980, tests and examinations in *numeracy* were being devised and the new use of the term was so widespread that Cockcroft felt the need to point out:

> [The definition] 'to be able to perform basic arithmetical operations' … reflects the meaning which seems to be intended by most of those who have used the word in submissions to us.

This shift in use occurred at a time when mathematics was replacing arithmetic in the curriculum for all children, and 'mere arithmetic' was discredited. It is likely that *numeracy* was adopted to retain a hold on the traditional arithmetic which was felt to be under threat. **Numeracy skills** is still frequently used outside of mathematical educational circles as a synonym for arithmetical techniques.

There has been a considerable amount of reaction to this drift of meaning, with mathematics educators in particular fighting against the narrowing scope of the word. Michael Girling, being deliberately provocative, offered, in 1982: 'Basic numeracy is the ability to use a four-function electronic calculator *sensibly.*'

It could be that the problem lies with the word *numeracy*. It is striking that although 'illiterate' and 'illiteracy' were, together with 'literate', in use by the early 1600s (in a wide sense referring to knowledge of literature, rather than being able to read), it was a further 250 years before the word 'literacy' was coined; moreover, this use was in a school context. There is perhaps a need in educational circles to devise words which refer, not merely to positive attributes which can be learned, but to aspects that can be taught. Because it is much easier to teach techniques than more tenuous aspects ('understanding', 'appreciation'), the word becomes attached to the straightforward-seeming skills.

'Count', 'tally' and 'number'

The various uses of these and associated words are legion. Here, rather than looking at contemporary uses, we indicate some of the strands and how they arose from other languages.

count: Latin *computare* = to calculate, to compute → French *conter* → English *count* = to tell over one by one, to number; also, to repeat the numerals 'one, two, three', and so on. Hence, **counter,** a person who counts, but also a reckoning device as well as the shop counter on which calculations were made. In Othello, Cassio is described as 'a great arithmetician, this counter-caster' – the equivalent to our insult of a 'dessicated calculating machine'. Another insult is to say that somebody doesn't count. As a character in Russell Hoban's novel *Riddley Walker* observes: 'them as counts counts moren them as dont count'.

tally: Latin *talea* = cutting, rod, stick → Germanic *talo* = notch carved in stick for counting → English *tally*, *tell*, as in 'all told' (i.e. all counted), to tell (i.e. count heads), teller (bank cashier, or counter of votes), 'he telleth the number of the stars, he calleth them all by their names', and *tale* = story; also, numerical statement, list, account (e.g. by tale – as opposed to by weight).

number: Greek *nem* = to count, order, arrange → Latin *numerus* → English *number* – e.g. 'Oh teach us to number our days that we may apply our hearts to wisdom': moreover, Indo-European root *rei* = to arrange in order; so Greek *a-ri-thmos* = number → Latin *ritus* = ceremony → Old Saxon *rim* = series, number → German *reim* → English *rhyme* and *rite* (= holy order). Hence (ordinal) counting = (?) telling numbers with (according to James Joyce) 'rite words in rote order' and (with Shakespeare) 'favour infinite ... out of all count'. But *number* as a noun is a sum or aggregate of any collection of individual things or persons and a symbol or figure or collection of these, which represents graphically an arithmetical value, by which a person or a thing has a place assigned to it in a series. Also from *number* we have

numeral as adjective, expressing or denoting number; and as noun, word or figure(s) denoting number.

'Image'

Inevitably, **image** is now a word that is used in very many different ways and in very many different contexts. It is doubtful that these will have some essential component in common, though all usages echo in some way an original sense of a likeness, semblance or similarity. However, there are at least five distinct areas in which *images* are considered, and these have tended to develop quite different accompanying meanings and contexts.

Thus, **graphic images** now apply to pictures and computer screens, but also contain elements from the world of advertising and packaging; for example, a recent Royal Society subcommittee was concerned with the image of mathematics in society today. There is a technical use of **optical imagery**; mathematically, this is generalized from the notion of a reflected image into that of the image of any transformation. Our own images may be distinguished between those that are **perceptual**; that is, they correspond to actual sensuous inputs – appearances of actual reality. Otherwise, they are held to be **mental**, these being either based on memories from the past or dreams of the future. Finally, images are sometimes invoked as being **verbal**, namely descriptions or metaphors, especially where these may be held to conjure up a particularly vivid experience.

There is some confusion in present writing in mathematical education on the development of imagery about whether it is intended that children are to be helped to see what is there on a computer screen or in a photograph; or whether their own internal mental imagery is being fostered. (Or indeed, whether these amount to the same.) The idea of *mental images* – pictures in one's head – has been a highly problematic one for a very long time. The central, difficult issue has always been whether image can be separated from thought; and, indeed, whether either of these can be separated from word. For Aristotle, thought is impossible without an image; and according to Kant, thought without content is empty.

The trouble was that although many people were generally agreed that thoughts were representable by images, it was difficult to know how such images were generated. For Blake:

> If the Spectator could enter into three Images in his Imagination, approaching them on the fiery Chariot of his Contemplative Thought, if he could enter into Noah's Rainbow, or into his bosom, or could make a Friend and Companion of one of these Images of Wonder ... then would he arise from his Grave, then would he meet the Lord's Air, and then he would be happy.

For Kant, this was 'an art concealed in the depths of the human soul whose real modes of activity nature is hardly likely to allow us to discover, and to have open to our gaze'. It was perhaps inevitable that the new science of psychology would reject the subjectivity with which earlier accounts of imagery had been presented and the behaviourists banished consideration of mental imagery altogether.

On the other hand, there were different traditions in which imagery continued to be discussed and explored. Piaget carried out investigations into mental imagery which were related to his interest in the nature of so-called 'geometric intuition'. Before it is formalized, geometrical thought is accompanied by some form of imagery. For example, Piaget considered images had a symbolic function and that they represented, in some sense, concepts.

> The particular link between concept and image means that the image can be said to be symbolic, since even in a graphic copy the mental image constitutes not so much an attempt to produce a totally adequate representation of the thing 'seen', as an idea used by the subject to express the characteristic of what he 'sees'.

If images are symbols of geometrical thought, they are also intriguingly self-reflexive, in the sense that the symbol for a circle is itself a circle. Piaget emphasized that geometry was 'the only field in which the imagined form and content are homogeneous'. This point of view seems to suggest that a geometrical image is simultaneously an actual object *and* its representation, that the image is both signified and signifier. But it may be preferable to take up an earlier suggestion – originally made by C. S. Peirce – that image is the third term of a ternary relationship, mediating between signifier and signified.

Most investigators have differentiated between the images that are produced in response to actual external experience – what you actually see with your eyes or feel with your fingers – and those that you can conjure up for yourself, be these from the past, or from some 'imagined' future. It is the latter kind that the Mathematical Association's primary report was thinking of in 1955: 'A teacher's life would be a great deal simpler … if all children formed mental images of the same kind in the same way and at the same speed.'

In any case, it is the vividness of imagery that enables us to think of an image as a concrete object that may be said to be the actual content of geometry. This vividness is often associated with visual imagery, but of course, for very many people, it may be associated with auditory, or kinaesthetic, experience.

This sense of an image as a real object has often led mathematicians to agree with Plato in his construction of a world of ideal forms. Others have taken their experience as confirming their view of mathematics as a human construction. Meanwhile, many mathematics educators have become critical of the Piagetian emphasis on 'concepts' and have been more struck by the sense of an image as an object. Indeed, Caleb Gattegno proposed that mental imagery should be taken to be the 'stuff' of geometry, the actual material that geometry deals with. He suggested that it could be useful to think of the various other issues that tend to be raised about imagery as being part of a subsequent 'algebracization' of the primitive geometrical material.

Commenting on Paul Valéry's dictum that there is no geometry without language, a contemporary mathematician, René Thom, has asserted:

It is no less true ... that there is no intelligible language without a geometry, an underlying dynamic whose structurally stable states are formalized by the language.

If imagery can provide an entry into this 'underlying dynamic', then it is certainly true that computers now offer a very powerful method of working directly with images. As Gattegno emphasized, they also offer entry into controlled transformations of images, a dynamic which he characterized as algebraic. Certainly, it is likely that increased experience of working with computers, as well as increased digestion of the findings from the field of artificial intelligence, will change our understanding of imagery drastically in the next few years.

'Pattern'

Pattern has become a cliché of school mathematics – indeed, it is now so widely used as to be almost meaningless. Children are asked whether they can 'see the pattern' in hosts of numerical, algebraic, statistical and geometric contexts. The original meaning of the word (derived from *pater* – 'father' – and related to *patron*) may be found in Samuel Johnson's 'the original proposed to imitation; that which is to be copied', and of anything designed to serve as a model. This use survives in dress or knitting patterns; or in industrial processes, 'a pattern-shop'. Polya still used this sense in 1962 in his book *Mathematical Discovery*.

> A solution that you have obtained by your own effort or one that you have read or heard, but have followed with real interest and insight, may become a *pattern* for you, a model that you can imitate with advantage in solving similar problems.

The word came to be used for a decorative design created from a mechanical repetition of the *pattern* on pottery, fabrics, wallpaper, etc.; subsequently, *pattern* tended to be used for a regularly repeating design, including *tiling patterns*. Even here, there are difficulties about its use. Grünbaum and Shepherd, in their comprehensive work *Tilings and Patterns*, say:

> The vagueness ... extends even to the very definition of 'pattern' in the literature. In the works of some crystallographers, designers and art historians there are attempts at formulating a suitable definition, but always in a completely informal way that is irrelevant to subsequent developments. There seems to be not a single definition in the literature of 'pattern' that is, in any sense, useful.

They go on to give a precise mathematical definition which depends on a 'motif' which is copied elsewhere under strict rules.

In the nineteenth century, the word was applied to natural phenomena, both locally, where the visual connection with surfaces was retained – 'The broken frames cast patterns on the ground' (Dickens, *Edwin Drood*); and globally – seeing the overall phenomenon. Writers soon moved to a more metaphoric usage invoking the 'pattern of life' or the 'pattern of nature', and this has been retained over the years in 'patterns of child-care' or 'patterns of culture'. Whitehead, writing in 1925, saw the whole of mathematics as a *pattern* in this sense. Mathematics was formed from a 'key' (which was a version of the model or mould – the original meaning of *pattern*).

> The discovery of mathematics is the discovery that the totality of these general abstract conditions, which are concurrently applicable to the relationships among the entities of any one concrete occasion, are themselves interconnected in the manner of a pattern with a key to it. … The key to the patterns means this fact: that from a select set of those general conditions, exemplified on any one and the same occasion, a pattern involving an infinite variety of other such conditions … can be developed.

Thus, the key was the 'general conditions', the axioms from which the whole of mathematics could be derived (as Whitehead believed).

The other movement was to see more local phenomena as being similar to textile patterns – the essential link here was always with visual designs. In mathematics, *pattern* has come to be used for a very wide class of aspects. Sawyer (in *Prelude to Mathematics*, 1956) suggested that:

> For the purposes of this book we may say, 'Mathematics is the classification and study of all possible patterns'. Pattern is here used in a way that not everybody may agree with. It is to be understood in a very wide sense, to cover almost any kind of regularity that can be recognized by the mind. Life, and certainly intellectual life, is only possible because there are certain regularities in the world.

The visual sense of *pattern* has often been retained: psychologists speak of 'pattern recognition', usually applied to shape; numbers on a hundred square lie in a *pattern*; mathematics lessons are devoted to tiling *patterns* (which have been widely called 'tessellations' – a usage that would repay investigation). But the extension to seeing a *pattern* in a number sequence – essentially, being able to generalize it – is more metaphoric, and seemingly of more recent origin. There is also perhaps an echo of the Pythagorean shape of numbers: square, rectangular, triangular, and so on.

Pattern and **design** were almost synonymous in their application to textiles and the like, but have diverged widely in school use. *Design* has become associated first with art and then with craft and technology. Although *design* has been applied to natural phenomena ('the grand design'), it is closely tied to notions of deliberate creation. The transformation into a verb shows this clearly: 'design a —' is unexceptionable; there is no similar word when we are asked to create a *pattern*. It is as if the primary meaning of *pattern* is that relating to natural phenomena – and mathematics is seen as such rather than as something created.

It is worth noting that in French, for example, the word *pattern* does not have the same range of meanings. A whole gamut of words – *forme, fonction, regularité* – convey aspects of the mathematical use, but none takes the wide sense of the English word. It has been suggested that no word exists in French because the notion is 'insufficiently Cartesian'.

'Practical'

The two main senses of **practical** are: (a) that which is used by 'practical people', what they find useful, mathematics that can be applied in practice (especially in contrast to 'merely theoretical' mathematics); (b) involving actions with equipment rather than just writing or diagrams or symbols on paper. These are frequently confused or conflated, and have usually both been present in the uses of this word over the last hundred years in mathematics education.

Around the turn of the century, John Perry, an engineering professor, devised new syllabuses and practices (!) for school mathematics which he called *Practical Mathematics*. With Perry's scheme:

> in arithmetic, the emphasis was placed on decimals rather than fractions, including approximations, and the use of both logarithmic tables and slide rules. In algebra, the use of formulae featured prominently as well as the study of functions and graphs, using squared paper ... [Geometry was] based on measurement and drawing mixed with arithmetic and algebraic methods.

The syllabus and teaching methods included both senses of *practical*, on the one hand, introducing methods and ideas employed by people who used mathematics in their **practice** (for example, trigonometry as used by engineers). And, on the other, using equipment such as squared paper and rulers. The first of these by and large refers to the kind of mathematics being studied and the second to the ways in which it is studied (i.e. 'a practical approach'), although the inclusion of the slide-rule, a piece of equipment used (at that time) by engineers, indicates the movement between the two senses.

The controversy surrounding Perry's approaches used what was then an increasingly important distinction between the theoretical and the practical (one which is taken up by Raymond Williams). Hitherto, geometry had been a theoretical subject which did not involve measuring, so that, for example, the protractor was unknown in schools. Geometry was not seen as a subject either for experimentation or speculation, but rather one in which reasoning would reveal truths. The ground on which Perry was attacked was that practical studies could not be a substitute for the systematic knowledge gained by theoretical study.

The *practical approach* to learning mathematics had as its justification that it helped learners grasp ideas more readily. This remains the main reason for its advocacy, but in this it is an aid to learning and not the whole thing. A further justification is that learners will be better motivated to learn mathematics which they can see to be useful. But useful to whom? What is seen as being useful ranges from sums involving money to 'real problem solving'. As Valerie Walkerdine has observed, apparently practical activities like shopping with money in the primary school frequently have features (such as the children's money always being renewed) that make it quite unrealistic.

An altogether-different strand identified **practice** with doing something repeatedly – exercises – with the aim of attaining proficiency. This was widely used outside of formal education, but has been usually applied to learning. As distinct from listening or watching or other less active states, the emphasis with practice is on doing. A commonly used classroom technique in mathematics lessons was called **sharp practice** – not a criminal activity, but one in which oral questions and answers were conducted rapidly. This was warned against in the 1959 MA report on the teaching of mathematics in secondary modern schools: 'indiscriminate use of sharp practice may shake confidence and hinder understanding'. **Arithmetic practice**, which was still being advocated in the MA report on arithmetic in 1964 (and recommended 'even if decimal coinage is introduced'), was a method of carrying out multiplications with compound units in imperial weights and measures; today, it is certainly not practical in any of the senses of the word.

'Structure'

Structure is a word with very complex uses (Williams devotes seven pages to it), many of which bear on its occurrences in mathematical education. Some of the more common uses are:

> algebraic *structure*, the *structure* of the number system, computation and *structure*, *structural* apparatus, conceptual *structures*, *structured* approaches.

The uses which are widespread in education generally – and not just in mathematics – and which talk of *the structure* of lessons or topics or the curriculum, exhibit the two main senses which Williams points to. These are *structure* as referring to 'the whole product of building, as in "a wooden structure"', or to the manner of construction where the relationship of the parts to each other structure the whole. This distinction continually exhibits itself as a source of difficulty. A group of people, examining the teaching of mathematics, *structures* its thinking and produces *a structure* for others to use (in the form of guidelines or a syllabus or programme of study). These users, however, have only *the structure* and not the experience nor even the process of structuring. They will then put their own structuring on the documents, and very often operate quite differently from the original group. *Structure* is seen as a good in itself – textbooks offer 'a structured approach to' coursework, or primary mathematics, or … It is difficult to imagine a book proclaiming itself as 'unstructured'. Teachers, however, frequently observe that a lesson plan or work scheme is 'too structured' and does not permit the flexibility that they require.

In mathematical education, several strands of use of *structure* and its associated words are interestingly intertwined. The movement called **structuralism**, although usually thought of as literary, linguistic and anthropological, has a scientific and, especially, mathematical aspect. This latter was the project of the group of French mathematicians known as Bourbaki, who endeavoured to build up mathematics in a structured way starting with primitive ideas of sets and certain basic **mother structures**.

One influence of this was on the modern mathematics in schools movement in the 1960s (see below); another was on the psychological foundations being investigated by Piaget.

Piaget attempted to build the notions of the Bourbaki project into his *structuring* of the thought of children. Thus, the development of children's geometrical thinking was thought to correspond to the basic outlines of Bourbaki (from topological notions to metrical ones); and the development of number was seen as *structural*, arising from notions in set theory. There is yet another sense in which Piaget, who called himself a genetic epistemologist, is connected to the notion of structure: the **structuralist theory** of mathematics learning. Howson, Keitel and Kilpatrick comment on this theory of building mathematics curricula, which has been strongly associated with Jerome Bruner and Z. P. Dienes.

> The structuralist approach is based on investigations conducted by genetic epistemology theorists into the process of concept formation ... the theory proceeds as follows: cognitive structures are combinations of acquired concepts and thinking abilities. Simple structures, made of a few concepts, are developed into more elaborate ones through the addition of new concepts. At their highest stage of development, cognitive structures correspond to the structure of the sciences, taken as the essence of all concepts and processes contained in them.

Piaget's work in both of these aspects fed directly into the Nuffield Mathematics Project of the 1960s (to which he was a consultant). The project based its rationale on the *structuralist* theory of mathematics learning and also took over some of the sense of mathematical structure. It distinguished two aspects of teaching number as 'computation' and '*structure*'; in this connection, *structure* was intended to refer to work with the *structure* of the number system (which was seen as the relationships among numbers). In much comment and practice over the last fifteen years, emphasis on *structure* has been displaced by concentration on 'numeracy'.

Algebraic structure was one of the key notions of the Bourbaki programme and a highly influential conference in 1960 at Royaumont in France helped provide the impetus for a string of projects in many countries to include ideas of algebraic structure in school curricula. In Britain, this influence was mainly at the secondary level and comparatively small: 'algebraic structures' came to mean mostly some notions of set theory and groups.

In quite a different development, Stern published a book in 1949 on the approach to teaching arithmetic that she had developed, called a **structural approach**, because it was intended to utilize and demonstrate the structure of arithmetic rather than being based upon counting. Much of her work involved special apparatus, which together with other physical materials for the teaching of arithmetic became known as **structured** or **structural apparatus**. The phrase was always loosely applied, although J. D. Williams, who examined claims being made for teaching using such apparatus, said: 'They consist of concrete models which can be used to parallel mathematical operations.'

Gattegno, in 1962, asserted that Cuisenaire rods were *not* structural apparatus, because they were not created to teach number only but invoked algebraic relationships. His justification brings in yet another aspect of *structure*.

> Because pupils meet the less structured and move steadily towards more and more structured entities, we can expect that they behave mathematically in an entirely different way from the way we do and all who have their knowledge based upon counting.

A current use is a form of proof by reference to the *structure* of the problem as opposed to pattern spotting. The sequence 1, 2, 4, 8, … may or may not continue 16, 32, … But if the sequence arises from folding a piece of paper in half repeatedly, then from the *structure* of the problem, the numbers will continue to double, and the generalization is valid.

'Problem solving'

Problem has been used in specifically mathematical contexts for a long time, but there have been important distinctions in its use. The primary one is of something opposed to the mechanical aspects of mathematics. Arithmetic was divided in nineteenth-century texts into mechanical arithmetic and arithmetic problems. These were 'word' problems, where a sum was more or less dressed up. But *problem* was also used in a wider sense of a question that could not be answered by straight reproduction of a learned method. In one use, it became associated with a question that involved a tricky use of known procedures or some unexpected insight; in another, as the *research problems* undertaken by a professional mathematician.

The belief that problems are at the heart of mathematics, and that solving problems – and learning how to solve problems – is an essential component of learning mathematics, has been strongly to the forefront of much work in mathematical education over the last thirty years. The term **problem solving** has been used both for an activity – actually solving problems – and for a set of approaches to solving problems that can (perhaps) be taught. Many of the reformers sought to separate the kinds of problems that they wanted learners to work on by describing other kinds as **closed problems**, and more desirable ones as **open problems**, **problem situations**, **starting points** and **investigations**.

This batch of words has been used to convey the idea of children working on their own mathematics, rather than working at pre-determined exercises in an imitative way. There are two strands which are worth separating:

- the notion of children discovering aspects of mathematics for themselves, rather than being instructed by the teacher;
- the notion of children engaging in the act of mathematization – generalizing, abstracting, and so on.

This attractive idea, that children could learn mathematics by their own explorations, started to be widely written about in the late 1950s and early 1960s. Children were thought to be both exploring and finding things out:

the words **investigating** and **discovering** were used. Thus, according to Madeleine Goutard writing in 1963:

> As soon as the child's right to make mistakes is recognized, and as soon as the importance of personal investigation over the mere production of answers is realized, the move towards a new organization of activities ... is made possible ... The time that is devoted to individual investigations and discoveries should be, for the teacher, moments of near total withdrawal from the classroom.

Discovery learning was a widely-used phrase – and much ink was spilt over it: was it intended that children would discover all past mathematics? Several variants including **guided discovery** were coined, each indicating that children would need help in this task. But also present was a sense that children needed to – indeed, would inevitably – 'make the mathematics their own', by exploring and constructing their own versions of mathematical ideas.

In addition to children discovering parts of mathematics for themselves, they were also being helped to develop their problem-solving abilities: firstly, by solving problems, and then by having their focus directed to problem-solving techniques. The writings of Polya on **heuristic** are relevant here. Solving mathematical problems needed not merely a grasp of previously ready-made results and ideas, but also the ability to create classifications and relationships, and to test and criticize these both internally and against other social constructions. Attention shifted to the learning of these strategies, and this became an additional justification for children's investigative work.

In these recent developments, children were seen as working on something similar to *research problems*, where defining the problem that they were to work on was seen as essential and the actual mathematics worked on was, to a degree, irrelevant. The vocabulary of **open problems**, **starting-points**, **problem situations**, was devised to meet this distinction. **Real problem solving** originated in the US in the 1970s to convey a sense of working on very loosely-defined problems arising from the actual world of pupils – organizing dining arrangements, planning and running a trip or an event such as a jumble sale.

In writings on mathematical activity in the early 1960s, there is no mention of **investigation** in the sense of 'doing an investigation'. This construction developed from descriptions of pupils as 'investigating such-and-such', or 'carrying out an investigation into such-and-such'. By 1966, in the ATM Problems Document, we read: 'This is a list of situations which may form the starting points of mathematical investigations. Each one should be investigated as thoroughly as possible.'

In the 1980s, 'investigations' become institutionalized – part of the formal requirements for assessment of courses, for example in the Mathematical Association Diploma, the Open University Mathematics Foundation course, and in GCSE. They also appeared in the official recommendations of Cockcroft and HMI. With this, they have appeared in textbooks and teachers' guides; there are hints on how to do 'investigations', notes on what might be discovered from a particular starting point. Books with titles like *Structured Investigations* have appeared.

Such a development is a typical one in education – originally liberating ways of working become formalized and codified, losing their purpose as they become adapted for different ends or by those who have no personal commitment to the underlying intentions. In this case, those who *were* committed to the original intentions, strove to keep a distinctive vocabulary that would show their commitment to the process rather than the product by using active forms of the word: **investigatory, investigative**.

'Understanding'

The difficulty with **understanding**[6] and other words which try to grapple with similar ideas (such as **insight, comprehension**) is indicated by the ways in which they continually summon up metaphors – why should we think of ourselves as *standing under* something? *Understanding* is treated as a main aim of teaching – to be contrasted with skill acquisition through practice or with **rote learning**. The essential idea here seems to be that understanding is acquired through experience.

In 1955, the Mathematical Association's primary report claimed:

> No amount of practice and rote-learning will take the place of ... experience; unless practice and rote-learning are concerned with the ideas that have become part of a child they will never lead to real understanding.

> Those who are taught skills ... without a foundation of sufficiently wide practical experience will acquire spurious and superficial techniques which may mislead the teacher into supposing there is understanding where in fact none exists.

Experience is one of Williams' keywords, and his entry would be worth using as a starting point for explorations on its uses in education and, especially, mathematics education. One of the main distinctions in use is between the past ('being experienced') and the present ('having experiences'). Writing on mathematical education frequently slides from children having experiences to them becoming experienced. As the quotations show, understanding is often felt to arise from a range of experiences. The 1960s Nuffield project popularized the slogan 'I do and I understand'.

The word *understanding* has German roots and is related to *verstehen*, which, however, has the sense of standing before, i.e. in front of rather than below or under. The Latin equivalents tend to invoke possession – **comprehend, apprehend** – which then introduce metaphoric usages such as getting and having, grasping and holding, and so on. This leads to the idea that there is something relatively stable and explicit that has been seized and acquired: so the notion of a having an unchanging, once-and-for-all 'concept'. There are also metaphors of perception – **seeing**, recognizing, discerning, which give rise to insight and foresight. Here there is perhaps a sense of impermanence – 'now you see it, now you don't'.

But what is *understanding*? Even slight adjustments to the way the word is used indicate some of the problems involved. A shift occurs when one talks of having *an* understanding of something – does this imply it is only partial, perhaps in contrast to **real understanding**? In the phrase 'teaching for understanding', it is often unclear whether the pupils' own understanding is meant, or the pupils' acquisition of *the* understanding. Valerie Walkerdine has suggested that the quest for *real understanding* is a fantasy; in particular, that it is a male-orientated fantasy. According to her, *real understanding* is associated with activity, with typically male virtues of mastery and control. It is then contrasted with passivity, 'merely' getting the answers, rote learning, and so on.

Again, *understanding* is often spoken of as a once-and-for-all affair – you did not understand: now you do. Teachers often link this to the idea of 'a breakthrough' – their language for this has been explored by Martin Cortazzi (in *Primary Teaching How It Is*), who records many uses of metaphoric remarks in which 'it just clicked', 'it fitted together', 'he saw the light', 'she just took off'. Cortazzi notes that these ideas rarely involve any psychological theories of learning – indeed, the teacher appears to have a rather passive role in such events.

The notion of **rote learning** is often contrasted with *understanding*. The origin of this word is obscure: its meanings include custom, habit, mechanical performance, regular procedure, 'mere' routine 'especially by the exercise of memory without proper understanding of, or reflection upon, the matter in question'. Milton wrote of *rote lessons*; the term 'rote learning' dates from 1847, 'rote knowledge' from 1862.

Examples of negative use occur in early writers on mathematics teaching. Robert Record (in 1543) suggests: 'You must prove yourself to do some things that you were never taught, or else you shall not be able to do any more than you were taught, and were rather to learn by rote (as they call it) than by reason.'

This contrast between *rote learning* and *understanding* is echoed in the assumed conflict between facility (whether arithmetical or algebraic) and understanding. Godfrey claimed, in 1911, that:

> [Teachers] want boys to understand in order to manipulate correctly, whereas their ideal should be just reversed. The ultimate aim should be, not manipulation, but understanding and outlook.

Theories concerning what *understanding* mathematics might consist of have proliferated in recent years (thus, from von Glasersfeld, 'the consistent organization of conceptual structures'); most of these do not shed much light on what teachers and learners need to *do* if learners are to acquire understanding. Stieg Mellin-Olsen made an often-quoted distinction between **relational** and **instrumental understanding** – the former involving knowing what to do and why, the latter comprising knowing rules and how to apply them. Relational understanding is often seen as *real understanding*, but there are many aspects of working mathematically – algebraic manipulation is one – where *understanding* does not seem to be involved. This does not prevent there being a two-fold demand on students to 'get hold of' the concept, as well as to be able to practise the craft.

'Process'

This is a complicated word that has shifted its meaning in mathematics education dramatically over the last twenty years. It can, of course, be applied to any series of actions carried on in a definite manner. Until the 1960s (and even more recently), it was common to talk of 'the processes of arithmetic', or 'the processes of algebra'.

> The ability to perform the standard arithmetical processes correctly is of major importance, but it is of little value if it is not accompanied by an ability to recognize the situations in which the processes are needed.

(Ministry of Education, 1958)

> ... much of the teaching of mathematics has consisted of the teacher demonstrating a method, process, routine or algorithm to be used in particular circumstances, followed by the class carrying out an exercise consisting of routine questions which can all be solved using the given process.

(Orton, Learning Mathematics, 1987)

Process in this sense has been used interchangeably with *method*, *routine*, *technique*, *skill* and, more recently, *algorithm*. The use of **procedure** to describe a self-contained sequence of commands in writing about Logo seems to indicate a *process* of this kind; there is, perhaps, an implication that such sequences are not authoritative in the manner of a standard algorithm.

A more recent meaning of *process* has arisen from trying to describe the activity of doing mathematics. Attention has been focused on problem-solving abilities, on general strategies for mathematizing. Such strategies have been called mathematical or problem-solving processes. With this, came discussion of the 'process of doing mathematics', which both arose from and paralleled developments in other curriculum areas. Thus, Bruner, reacting to the 'curriculum by objectives' approach, emphasized the knowledge-getting *process*.

> A theory of instruction seeks to take account of the fact that the curriculum reflects not only the nature of knowledge itself ... but also the nature of the knower and the knowledge-getting process ... To instruct someone in [a discipline] is not a matter of getting him to commit results to mind. Rather it is to teach him to participate in the process that makes possible the establishment of knowledge. We teach a subject not to produce little living libraries on that subject, but rather to get the student to think mathematically for himself ... to take part in the process of knowledge-getting. Knowing is a process, not a product.

This *process/product* distinction was not as readily taken up in mathematics education as it was in the humanities and science. This may have been because the *products* of mathematical education were already being described as *processes* – things that pupils could do, rather than know as they would facts; or it might have been due to the difficulty of seeing mathematics in terms of this distinction.

In writing about teaching and learning mathematics, these distinctions have been expressed through the words *content* (the pre-existing conceptual structures) and *process* (the activity of making mathematics). According to Alan Bell:

> Content represents particular ideas and skills like rectangles, highest common factor, solution of equations. On the other side there is the mathematical process, or mathematical activity, that deserves its own syllabus to go alongside a syllabus of mathematical ideas; I would express it as consisting of abstraction, representation, generalization and proof.

Content is an essentially static notion (as the metaphor indicates), whereas *process* has dynamic implications. This static/dynamic contrast creates difficulties for what is being coded by each of the words. Any accurate description of learning mathematics needs to take account of the dynamic of learning new ideas. Although a syllabus or a curriculum is described as having content, learners understand and incorporate new ideas in their own way.

Equally pointedly, *process* – and especially the *processes* of problem solving – can be turned into a static content with various aspects being treated as identifiable things that can be acquired by a learner (for example, particular strategies). In the quotation from Bell above, this shift can already be seen happening in the assertion that 'it deserves its own syllabus to go alongside a syllabus of mathematical ideas'. One result of specifying *process* aspects in GCSE and in the English national curriculum has been that national assessment bodies and schools have started to formalize these – i.e. the *processes* are becoming additional *content* to be learned and tested. It is almost as if the act of naming aspects of mathematical activity was sufficient to cause them to vanish.

Some remarks in conclusion

In a trenchant critique of Raymond Williams' account of 'keywords', Quentin Skinner[7] has suggested that a study such as his needs to concentrate not on the internal structure of the words, but their role in upholding complete social philosophies. Changes in the social and cultural attitudes to words may be more significant than changes of meaning.

This may be illustrated by the use of the word *negotiation* in educational contexts. This yields a confused metaphor which has a least three common uses elsewhere: negotiating an obstacle or hazard; negotiating a loan at a bank; negotiating a wage settlement or agreement about work practices (as such, it is predominantly used about trade-union activities). Some teachers refer to their work in the classroom as involving a negotiating of meaning, in the sense that the teacher has to find a way of taking into account the learner's existing knowledge.[8] Teachers deal with children whose personal needs cannot be left out of the situation, so that for many of them there is always an element of classroom negotiation, in the positive sense of over-coming obstacles to a mutually satisfactory agreement.

But such notions have often been seized upon by recent critics of teacher education. Those who are ideologically opposed to the classroom methods implied by teachers who talk of negotiation tend to interpret the word in the sense used in trade-union contexts. Teachers are then seen as permitting – if not encouraging – children to become like 'selfish workers'. There are different, conflicting interpretations about what constitutes good manage-ment in industry; and these are reflected in conflicting attitudes to 'class-room management' – itself a phrase of relatively recent origin.

Similar conflicting attitudes may be found in the different ways people respond to words like *standards* or *basics*, or – indeed – most of the current educational catchwords. In some cases, the conflict remains hidden and there may be some resistance to having it made explicit. For example, those who prefer 'individual work' in their classroom (with children 'working at their own pace') often invoke notions of autonomy and self-reliance to support their preference over 'class teaching' which is seen as *formal*, *traditional* – and ineffective. As various critics have pointed out, this is to emphasize differences between children. But it would be a perfectly viable alternative to emphasize what children have in common, in which class teaching would be more valued, and 'working on your own' might be considered to be rather selfish.

Individual work suggests independence and self-reliance: 'I did it on my own'. There is a sense of something original, creative: 'It was all my own idea'. There is also the possible suggestion that mathematics is an activity that you should aim to do on your own, that it is a solo activity: 'doing your own algebra rather than another's'.[9] There is a sense that it is mine, rather than another's; so I can do what I want with it. This merges into the relatively recent metaphor of *owning* mathematics; this usage became acceptable in the 1980s when there was an emphasis on owning your own house rather than renting it. Such ownership does also sometimes contain an echo that *you* can't own it as well – because it is mine.

Behind all words there are hidden agendas. These are often hard to disentangle and attributions may be speculative. Does, for example, *child-centred education* sometimes also imply a middle-class bias? Ambiguities may also be found in apparently straightforward, technical examples. For instance, is there any significant difference between referring to *finding the derivative* and *differentiating*? Why are certain numbers said to be *irrational*? Why do people speak of *number bonds*? Such questions can involve quite complicated historical issues, though the last one is easily unravelled. Bonds were the invention of the psychologist, Edward Thorndike, who asserted in the 1920s that 2 + 3 and 5 become 'bonded' together in the memory. His theory of bonding has been discredited for half a century, but teachers still use *number bonds* in talking of what they wish children to learn. It is not clear whether people are invoking remnants of the psychological theory or simply using a shorthand for another idea.

One indication that there may be important, underlying ideologies is when educational issues are split into opposing notions: a teaching method may be described as *informal* or *formal*, a curriculum may be *modern* or *traditional*. It seems that there is always an Other lurking behind any one theme. Valerie Walkerdine[10] has drawn attention to the binary opposition of *work* and *play* in educational discourse. When one of these is particularly valued, the other tends to be denigrated. To take an example that we have already discussed, *real understanding* may be opposed to *rote learning*. It is also interesting to note that splitting may produce a pair of opposites from a single notion: 'authority' may become *authoritarian* or *authoritative*.

Skinner claimed that a proper study of the uses of words might give us 'insights into changing social beliefs and theories; changing social percep-tions and awarenesses; and into changing social values and attitudes'.[11] In our case, we are trying to be more modest: we hope that teachers and others concerned with mathematics education might pause for thought when they find themselves using some of the words we have explored. Some may even find that they can explore the uses of other words.[12] We offer suggestions below; some of these come from mathematics (but which have distinct connotations in school mathematics), some are taken from more general educational discourse, and some seem to have arisen within mathematics education itself.

Finally, it is worth mentioning that there appears to be a drift in the words that are used in mathematical education to nouns that label things – *investigations, experiences, patterns* – perhaps because it is felt that such things can be taught and evidence produced that they have been learned. Against this is a contrary motion to retain the dynamic aspects by using gerunds – *investigating, conceiving, imaging*. The adoption of active forms can be quite striking. The psychologist Bartlett insisted on using 'remembering' rather than referring to 'memory', because he wished to emphasize the act rather than the supposed 'faculty'. We suggest that it would be useful to do the same in mathematical education – although we retain the more familiar noun forms in the following list.

> abstract, achievement, activity, algorithm, anti-racist, applied, assessment, attainment, awareness, chalk and talk, concrete, context, curriculum, decimal, drill, equation, ethnomathematics, example, exercise, experience, exposition, fraction, game, in-struction, lesson, manipulation, modern, multicultural, number bond, proof, project, pure, puzzle, real, recreation, relevant, routine, set, sign, skill, space, sums, symbol, techniques, test, theorem, training, workshop.

Notes and references

1   Gordon Spencer-Brown (1979) *Laws of Form*, E. P. Dutton, p. 91.

2   Paul Dowling (1990) 'The Shogun's and other curriculum voices' in
    P. Dowling and R. Noss (eds), *Mathematics* versus *the National Curriculum*,
    Falmer Press, p. 47.

3   John Maynard Keynes (1936) *The General Theory of Employment, Interest and
    Money*, Macmillan, ch. 24, p. v.

4   Raymond Williams (1982) *Keywords*, Fontana, 2nd edn.

5   To avoid this chapter becoming burdened with notes, we have not given full
    references to the many quotations cited in this central section.

6   A further discussion of this word occurs in the chapter 'Understanding and
    desire' on pp. 220–46.

7   Quentin Skinner (1980) 'Language and social change' in L. Michael and
    C. Ricks (eds), *The State of the Language*, California University Press, p. 574.

8   Alan Bishop and Fred Goffree (1987) 'Classroom organisation and dynamics'
    in B. Christiansen, A. G. Howson and M. Otte (eds), *Perspectives on
    Mathematics Education*, Reidel.

9   John Mason *et al.* (1985) *Routes to/Roots of Algebra*, Open University.

10 Valerie Walkerdine (1988) *The Mastery of Reason*, Routledge.

11 Quentin Skinner, *op cit*.

12 The words *abstract* and *concrete* are discussed in a passage by John Dewey
    (reprinted on pp. 247–51), which sets out to uncover some confusions in the
    use of those words. Inevitably, it does so within the ideological assumptions
    of American progressive education in the 1930s.

Acknowledgements

Our thanks are due to many others for suggestions and comments on
various versions of our accounts of particular words. In particular, we wish
to acknowledge the help of Christine Hopkins, Geoffrey Howson, David
Pimm, Mike Price and David Wheeler.